Illustrative Mathematics®
LEARN MATH FOR LIFE

ACCELERATED
7

Units

4 5 6

STUDENT WORKBOOK
Book 2

KendallHunt |

Proportional Relationships

Representing Linear Relationships

Finding Slopes and Linear Equations

Systems of Linear Equations

Associations in Numerical Data

Illustrative Mathematics®
LEARN MATH FOR LIFE

ACCELERATED

7

Unit

4

STUDENT WORKBOOK
Book 2

Kendall Hunt |

Lesson 1: Writing and Graphing Inequalities

Let's write inequalities.

1.1: Estimate Heights of People

1. Here is a picture of a man.

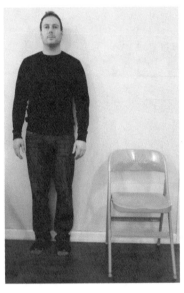

a. Name a number, in feet, that is clearly too high for this man's height.

b. Name a number, in feet, that is clearly too low for his height.

c. Make an estimate of his height.

Pause here for a class discussion.

2. Here is a picture of the same man standing next to a child.

If the man's actual height is 5 feet 10 inches, what can you say about the height of the child in this picture?

Be prepared to explain your reasoning.

1.2: Stories about 9

1. Your teacher will give you a set of paper slips with four stories and questions involving the number 9. Match each question to three representations of the solution: a description or a list, a number line, or an inequality statement.

2. Compare your matching decisions with another group's. If there are disagreements, discuss until both groups come to an agreement. Then, record your final matching decisions here.

   a. A fishing boat can hold fewer than 9 people. How many people (x) can it hold?

      ■ Description or list:

      ■ Number line:

      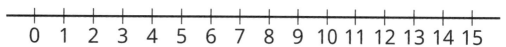

      ■ Inequality:

   b. Lin needs more than 9 ounces of butter to make cookies for her party. How many ounces of butter (x) would be enough?

      ■ Description or list:

      ■ Number line:

      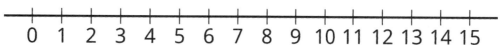

      ■ Inequality:

   c. A magician will perform her magic tricks only if there are at least 9 people in the audience. For how many people (x) will she perform her magic tricks?

      ■ Description or list:

      ■ Number line:

      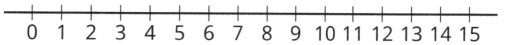

      ■ Inequality:

d. A food scale can measure up to 9 kilograms of weight. What weights (*x*) can the scale measure?

 ■ Description or list:

 ■ Number line:

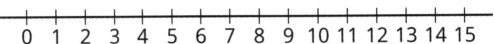

 ■ Inequality:

1.3: How High and How Low Can It Be?

Here is a picture of a person and a basketball hoop. Based on the picture, what do you think are reasonable estimates for the maximum and minimum heights of the basketball hoop?

1. Complete the first blank in each sentence with an estimate, and the second blank with "taller" or "shorter."

 a. I estimate the *minimum* height of the basketball hoop to be _____ feet; this means the hoop cannot be _____ than this height.

 b. I estimate the *maximum* height of the basketball hoop to be _____ feet; this means the hoop cannot be _____ than this height.

2. Write two inequalities—one to show your estimate for the *minimum* height of the basketball hoop, and another for the *maximum* height. Use an inequality symbol and the variable *h* to represent the unknown height.

3. Plot each estimate for minimum or maximum value on a number line.

  ○ Minimum:

  ○ Maximum:

4. Suppose a classmate estimated the value of h to be 19 feet. Does this estimate agree with your inequality for the maximum height? Does it agree with your inequality for the minimum height? Explain or show how you know.

5. Ask a partner for an estimate of h. Record the estimate and check if it agrees with your inequalities for maximum and minimum heights.

Are you ready for more?

1. Find 3 different numbers that a could be if $|a| < 5$. Plot these points on the number line. Then plot as many other possibilities for a as you can.

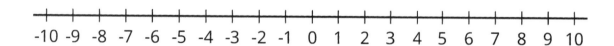

2. Find 3 different numbers that b could be if $|b| > 3$. Plot these points on the number line. Then plot as many other possibilities for b as you can.

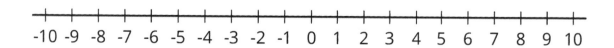

Lesson 1 Summary

An inequality tells us that one value is *less than* or *greater than* another value.

Suppose we knew the temperature is *less than* 3°F, but we don't know exactly what it is. To represent what we know about the temperature t in °F we can write the inequality:

$$t < 3$$

The temperature can also be graphed on a number line. Any point to the left of 3 is a possible value for t. The open circle at 3 means that t cannot be *equal* to 3, because the temperature is *less than* 3.

Here is another example. Suppose a young traveler has to be at least 16 years old to fly on an airplane without an accompanying adult.

If a represents the age of the traveler, any number greater than 16 is a possible value for a, and 16 itself is also a possible value of a. We can show this on a number line by drawing a closed circle at 16 to show that it meets the requirement (a 16-year-old person can travel alone). From there, we draw a line that points to the right.

We can also write an inequality and equation to show possible values for a:

$$a > 16$$
$$a = 16$$

iM KH

Lesson 1 Practice Problems

1. At the book sale, all books cost less than $5.

    a. What is the most expensive a book could be?

    b. Write an inequality to represent costs of books at the sale.

    c. Draw a number line to represent the inequality.

2. Kiran started his homework *before* 7:00 p.m. and finished his homework *after* 8:00 p.m. Let h represent the number of hours Kiran worked on his homework.

    Decide if each statement it is definitely true, definitely not true, or possibly true. Explain your reasoning.

    a. $h > 1$

    b. $h > 2$

    c. $h < 1$

    d. $h < 2$

3. a. Show that the two triangles are congruent.

    b. Find the side lengths of DEF and the angle measures of ABC.

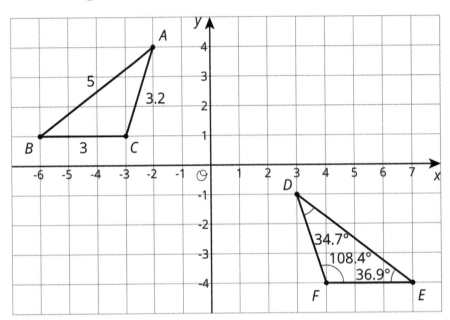

(From Unit 1, Lesson 11.)

4. Here is a polygon on a grid.

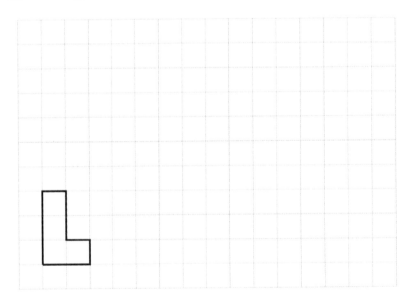

Draw a scaled copy of this polygon that has a perimeter of 30 units. What is the scale factor? Explain how you know.

(From Unit 2, Lesson 2.)

Lesson 2: Solutions of Inequalities

Let's think about the solutions to inequalities.

2.1: Unknowns on a Number Line

The number line shows several points, each labeled with a letter.

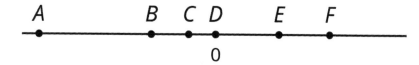

1. Fill in each blank with a letter so that the inequality statements are true.

   a. _____ > _____

   b. _____ < _____

2. Jada says that she found three different ways to complete the first question correctly. Do you think this is possible? Explain your reasoning.

3. List a possible value for each letter on the number line based on its location.

2.2: Amusement Park Rides

Priya finds these height requirements for some of the rides at an amusement park.

To ride the . . .	you must be . . .
High Bounce	between 55 and 72 inches tall
Climb-A-Thon	under 60 inches tall
Twirl-O-Coaster	58 inches minimum

1. Write an inequality for each of the the three height requirements. Use h for the unknown height. Then, represent each height requirement on a number line.

   ○ High Bounce

   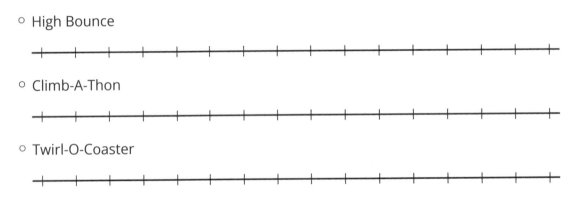

   ○ Climb-A-Thon

   ○ Twirl-O-Coaster

   Pause here for additional instructions from your teacher.

2. Han's cousin is 55 inches tall. Han doesn't think she is tall enough to ride the High Bounce, but Kiran believes that she is tall enough. Do you agree with Han or Kiran? Be prepared to explain your reasoning.

3. Priya can ride the Climb-A-Thon, but she cannot ride the High Bounce or the Twirl-O-Coaster. Which, if any, of the following could be Priya's height? Be prepared to explain your reasoning.

   ○ 59 inches
   ○ 53 inches
   ○ 56 inches

4. Jada is 56 inches tall. Which rides can she go on?

5. Kiran is 60 inches tall. Which rides can he go on?

6. The inequalities $h < 75$ and $h > 64$ represent the height restrictions, in inches, of another ride. Write three values that are **solutions** to both of these inequalities.

Are you ready for more?

1. Represent the height restrictions for all three rides on a single number line, using a different color for each ride.

2. Which part of the number line is shaded with all 3 colors?

3. Name one possible height a person could be in order to go on all three rides.

2.3: What Number Am I?

Your teacher will give your group two sets of cards—one set shows inequalities and the other shows numbers. Place the inequality cards face up where everyone can see them. Shuffle the number cards and stack them face down.

To play:

- One person in your group is the detective. The other people will give clues.
- Pick one number card from the stack and show it to everyone except the detective.
- The people giving clues each choose an inequality that will help the detective identify the unknown number.
- The detective studies the inequalities and makes three guesses.

  ○ If the detective does not guess the right number, each person chooses another inequality to help.

  ○ When the detective does guess the right number, a new person becomes the detective.

- Repeat the game until everyone has had a turn being the detective.

Lesson 2 Summary

Let's say a movie ticket costs less than $10. If c represents the cost of a movie ticket, we can use $c < 10$ to express what we know about the cost of a ticket.

Any value of c that makes the inequality true is called a **solution to the inequality**.

For example, 5 is a solution to the inequality $c < 10$ because $5 < 10$ (or "5 is less than 10") is a true statement, but 12 is not a solution because $12 < 10$ ("12 is less than 10") is *not* a true statement.

If a situation involves more than one boundary or limit, we will need more than one inequality to express it.

For example, if we knew that it rained for *more* than 10 minutes but *less* than 30 minutes, we can describe the number of minutes that it rained (r) with the following inequalities and number lines.

$$r > 10$$

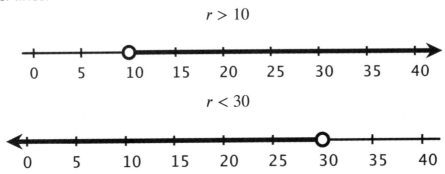

$$r < 30$$

Any number of minutes greater than 10 is a solution to $r > 10$, and any number less than 30 is a solution to $r < 30$. But to meet the condition of "more than 10 but less than 30," the solutions are limited to the numbers between 10 and 30 minutes, *not* including 10 and 30.

We can show the solutions visually by graphing the two inequalities on one number line.

Glossary

- solution to an inequality

iM KH

Lesson 2 Practice Problems

1. a. Select **all** numbers that are solutions to the inequality $k > 5$.

    4   5   6   5.2   5.01   0.5

    b. Draw a number line to represent this inequality.

2. A sign on the road says: "Speed limit, 60 miles per hour."

    a. Let s be the speed of a car. Write an inequality that matches the information on the sign.

    b. Draw a number line to represent the solutions to the inequality.

    c. Could 60 be a value of s? Explain your reasoning.

3. One day in Boston, MA, the high temperature was 60 degrees Fahrenheit, and the low temperature was 52 degrees.

    a. Write one or more inequalities to describe the temperatures T that are between the high and low temperature on that day.

    b. Show the possible temperatures on a number line.

4. Describe a rigid transformation that you could use to show the polygons are congruent.

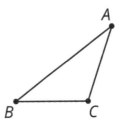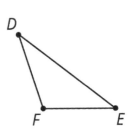

(From Unit 1, Lesson 11.)

5. a. Jada is taller than Diego. Diego is 54 inches tall (4 feet, 6 inches). Write an inequality that compares Jada's height in inches, j, to Diego's height.

   b. Jada is shorter than Elena. Elena is 5 feet tall. Write an inequality that compares Jada's height in inches, j, to Elena's height.

(From Unit 4, Lesson 1.)

iM KH

Lesson 3: Interpreting Inequalities

Let's examine what inequalities can tell us.

3.1: True or False: Fractions and Decimals

Is each equation true or false? Be prepared to explain your reasoning.

1. $3(12 + 5) = (3 \cdot 12) \cdot (3 \cdot 5)$

2. $\frac{1}{3} \cdot \frac{3}{4} = \frac{3}{4} \cdot \frac{2}{6}$

3. $2 \cdot (1.5) \cdot 12 = 4 \cdot (0.75) \cdot 6$

3.2: Basketball Game

Noah scored n points in a basketball game.

1. What does $15 < n$ mean in the context of the basketball game?

2. What does $n < 25$ mean in the context of the basketball game?

3. Draw two number lines to represent the solutions to the two inequalities.

4. Name a possible value for n that is a solution to both inequalities.

5. Name a possible value for n that is a solution to $15 < n$, but not a solution to $n < 25$.

6. Can -8 be a solution to n in this context? Explain your reasoning.

3.3: Unbalanced Hangers

1. Here is a diagram of an unbalanced hanger.

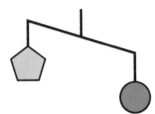

   a. Jada says that the weight of one circle is greater than the weight of one pentagon. Write an inequality to represent her statement. Let p be the weight of one pentagon and c be the weight of one circle.

   b. A circle weighs 12 ounces. Use this information to write another inequality to represent the relationship of the weights. Then, describe what this inequality means in this context.

2. Here is another diagram of an unbalanced hanger.

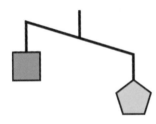

   a. Write an inequality to represent the relationship of the weights. Let p be the weight of one pentagon and s be the weight of one square.

   b. One pentagon weighs 8 ounces. Use this information to write another inequality to represent the relationship of the weights. Then, describe what this inequality means in this context.

   c. Graph the solutions to this inequality on a number line.

3. Based on your work so far, can you tell the relationship between the weight of a square and the weight of a circle? If so, write an inequality to represent that relationship. If not, explain your reasoning.

iM KH

4. This is another diagram of an unbalanced hanger.

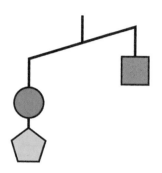

Andre writes the following inequality: $c + p < s$. Do you agree with his inequality? Explain your reasoning.

5. Jada looks at another diagram of an unbalanced hangar and writes: $s + c > 2t$, where t represents the weight of one triangle. Draw a sketch of the diagram.

Are you ready for more?

Here is a picture of a balanced hanger. It shows that the total weight of the three triangles is the same as the total weight of the four squares.

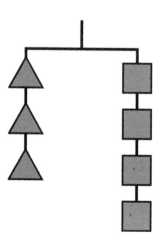

1. What does this tell you about the weight of one square when compared to one triangle? Explain how you know.

2. Write an equation or an inequality to describe the relationship between the weight of a square and that of a triangle. Let s be the weight of a square and t be the weight of a triangle.

Lesson 3 Summary

When we find the solutions to an inequality, we should think about its context carefully. A number may be a solution to an inequality outside of a context, but may not make sense when considered in context.

- Suppose a basketball player scored more than 11 points in a game, and we represent the number of points she scored, s, with the inequality $s > 11$. By looking only at $s > 11$, we can say that numbers such as 12, $14\frac{1}{2}$, and 130.25 are all solutions to the inequality because they each make the inequality true.

$$12 > 11 \qquad\qquad 14\frac{1}{2} > 11 \qquad\qquad 130.25 > 11$$

In a basketball game, however, it is only possible to score a whole number of points, so fractional and decimal scores are not possible. It is also highly unlikely that one person would score more than 130 points in a single game.

In other words, the context of an inequality may limit its solutions.

Here is another example:

- The solutions to $r < 30$ can include numbers such as $27\frac{3}{4}$, 18.5, 0, and -7. But if r represents the number of minutes of rain yesterday (and it did rain), then our solutions are limited to positive numbers. Zero or negative number of minutes would not make sense in this context.

To show the upper and lower boundaries, we can write two inequalities:

$$0 < r \qquad\qquad\qquad\qquad r < 30$$

Inequalities can also represent comparison of two unknown numbers.

- Let's say we knew that a puppy weighs more than a kitten, but we did not know the weight of either animal. We can represent the weight of the puppy, in pounds, with p and the weight of the kitten, in pounds, with k, and write this inequality:

$$p > k$$

Lesson 3 Practice Problems

1. There is a closed carton of eggs in Mai's refrigerator. The carton contains e eggs and it can hold 12 eggs.

    a. What does the inequality $e < 12$ mean in this context?

    b. What does the inequality $e > 0$ mean in this context?

    c. What are some possible values of e that will make both $e < 12$ and $e > 0$ true?

2. Here is a diagram of an unbalanced hanger.

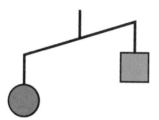

    a. Write an inequality to represent the relationship of the weights. Use s to represent the weight of the square in grams and c to represent the weight of the circle in grams.

    b. One red circle weighs 12 grams. Write an inequality to represent the weight of one blue square.

    c. Could 0 be a value of s? Explain your reasoning.

3. Here is an inequality: $-3x > 18$.

    a. List some values for x that would make this inequality true.

    b. How are the solutions to the inequality $-3x \geq 18$ different from the solutions to $-3x > 18$? Explain your reasoning.

4. Tyler has more than $10. Elena has more money than Tyler. Mai has more money than Elena. Let t be the amount of money that Tyler has, let e be the amount of money that Elena has, and let m be the amount of money that Mai has. Select **all** statements that are true:

   A. $t < j$

   B. $m > 10$

   C. $e > 10$

   D. $t > 10$

   E. $e > m$

   F. $t < e$

5. For each inequality, find two values for x that make the inequality true and two values that make it false.

   a. $x + 3 > 70$

   b. $x + 3 < 70$

   c. $-5x < 2$

   d. $5x < 2$

Lesson 4: Finding Solutions to Inequalities in Context

Let's solve more complicated inequalities.

4.1: Solutions to Equations and Solutions to Inequalities

1. Solve $-x = 10$

2. Find 2 solutions to $-x > 10$

3. Solve $2x = -20$

4. Find 2 solutions to $2x > -20$

4.2: Earning Money for Soccer Stuff

1. Andre has a summer job selling magazine subscriptions. He earns $25 per week plus $3 for every subscription he sells. Andre hopes to make at least enough money this week to buy a new pair of soccer cleats.

    a. Let n represent the number of magazine subscriptions Andre sells this week. Write an expression for the amount of money he makes this week.

    b. The least expensive pair of cleats Andre wants costs $68. Write and solve an equation to find out how many magazine subscriptions Andre needs to sell to buy the cleats.

c. If Andre sold 16 magazine subscriptions this week, would he reach his goal? Explain your reasoning.

d. What are some other numbers of magazine subscriptions Andre could have sold and still reached his goal?

e. Write an *inequality* expressing that Andre wants to make at least $68.

f. Write an inequality to describe the number of subscriptions Andre must sell to reach his goal.

2. Diego has budgeted $35 from his summer job earnings to buy shorts and socks for soccer. He needs 5 pairs of socks and a pair of shorts. The socks cost different amounts in different stores. The shorts he wants cost $19.95.

a. Let x represent the price of one pair of socks. Write an expression for the total cost of the socks and shorts.

b. Write and solve an equation that says that Diego spent exactly $35 on the socks and shorts.

c. List some other possible prices for the socks that would still allow Diego to stay within his budget.

d. Write an inequality to represent the amount Diego can spend on a single pair of socks.

4.3: Granola Bars and Savings

1. Kiran has $100 saved in a bank account. (The account doesn't earn interest.) He asked Clare to help him figure out how much he could take out each month if he needs to have at least $25 in the account a year from now.

    a. Clare wrote the inequality $-12x + 100 \geq 25$, where x represents the amount Kiran takes out each month. What does $-12x$ represent?

    b. Find some values of x that would work for Kiran.

    c. We could express *all* the values that would work using either $x \leq$ __ or $x \geq$ __. Which one should we use?

    d. Write the answer to Kiran's question using mathematical notation.

2. A teacher wants to buy 9 boxes of granola bars for a school trip. Each box usually costs $7, but many grocery stores are having a sale on granola bars this week. Different stores are selling boxes of granola bars at different discounts.

    a. If x represents the dollar amount of the discount, then the amount the teacher will pay can be expressed as $9(7 - x)$. In this expression, what does the quantity $7 - x$ represent?

    b. The teacher has $36 to spend on the granola bars. The equation $9(7 - x) = 36$ represents a situation where she spends all $36. Solve this equation.

    c. What does the solution mean in this situation?

d. The teacher does not have to spend all $36. Write an inequality relating 36 and $9(7 - x)$ representing this situation.

e. The solution to this inequality must either look like $x \geq 3$ or $x \leq 3$. Which do you think it is? Explain your reasoning.

Are you ready for more?

Jada and Diego baked a large batch of cookies.

- They selected $\frac{1}{4}$ of the cookies to give to their teachers.
- Next, they threw away one burnt cookie.
- They delivered $\frac{2}{5}$ of the remaining cookies to a local nursing home.
- Next, they gave 3 cookies to some neighborhood kids.
- They wrapped up $\frac{2}{3}$ of the remaining cookies to save for their friends.

After all this, they had 15 cookies left. How many cookies did they bake?

Lesson 4 Summary

We use inequalities to describe a range of numbers. In many places, you are allowed to get a driver's license when you are at least 16 years old. When checking if someone is old enough to get a license, we want to know if their age is at least 16. If h is the age of a person, then we can check if they are allowed to get a driver's license by checking if their age makes the inequality $h > 16$ (they are older than 16) or the equation $h = 16$ (they are 16) true. The symbol $\geq$, pronounced "greater than or equal to," combines these two cases and we can just check if $h \geq 16$ (their age is greater than or equal to 16). The inequality $h \geq 16$ can be represented on a number line:

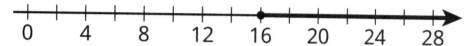

To compare $=$, $>$, and $\geq$, let's consider a situation three ways. Suppose Elena has $5 and sells pens for $1.50 each. Her goal is to save $20. We could solve the equation $1.5x + 5 = 20$ to find the number of pens, x, that Elena needs to sell in order to save exactly $20. Adding -5 to each side of the equation gives us $1.5x = 15$, and then dividing each side by 1.5 gives the solution $x = 10$ pens.

What if Elena wanted to save more than $20? The inequality $1.5x + 5 > 20$ tells us that the amount of money Elena makes needs to be greater than $20. The solution to the previous equation will help us understand what the solutions to the inequality will be. We know that if she sells 10 pens, she will make $20. Since each pen gives her more money, she needs to sell more than 10 pens to make more than $20. So the solution to the inequality is $x > 10$.

What if Elena wanted to save at least $20? The inequality $1.5x + 5 \geq 20$ tells us that the amount of money Elena makes needs to be at least $20. The solution to this inequality is $x \geq 10$.

Lesson 4 Practice Problems

1. The solution to $5 - 3x > 35$ is either $x > -10$ or $-10 > x$. Which solution is correct? Explain how you know.

2. The school band director determined from past experience that if they charge t dollars for a ticket to the concert, they can expect attendance of $1000 - 50t$. The director used this model to figure out that the ticket price needs to be $8 or greater in order for at least 600 to attend. Do you agree with this claim? Why or why not?

3. Which inequality is true when the value of x is -3?

    A. $-x - 6 < -3.5$

    B. $-x - 6 > 3.5$

    C. $-x - 6 > -3.5$

    D. $x - 6 > -3.5$

    (From Unit 4, Lesson 3.)

4. Draw the solution set for each of the following inequalities.

    a. $x \leq 5$

    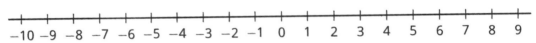

    b. $x < \frac{5}{2}$

    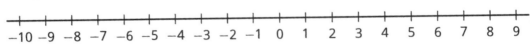

    (From Unit 4, Lesson 3.)

iM KH

5. Write three different equations that match the tape diagram.

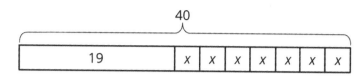

(From Unit 3, Lesson 3.)

6. A baker wants to reduce the amount of sugar in his cake recipes. He decides to reduce the amount used in 1 cake by $\frac{1}{2}$ cup. He then uses $4\frac{1}{2}$ cups of sugar to bake 6 cakes.

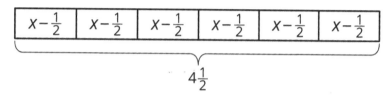

a. Describe how the tape diagram represents the story.

b. How much sugar was originally in each cake recipe?

(From Unit 3, Lesson 2.)

Lesson 5: Efficiently Solving Inequalities

Let's solve more complicated inequalities.

5.1: Lots of Negatives

Here is an inequality: $-x \geq -4$.

1. Predict what you think the solutions on the number line will look like.

2. Select **all** the values that are solutions to $-x \geq -4$:
    a. 3
    b. -3
    c. 4
    d. -4
    e. 4.001
    f. -4.001

3. Graph the solutions to the inequality on the number line:

5.2: Inequalities with Tables

1. Let's investigate the inequality $x - 3 > -2$.

x	-4	-3	-2	-1	0	1	2	3	4
$x - 3$	-7		-5				-1		1

a. Complete the table.
b. For which values of x is it true that $x - 3 = -2$?
c. For which values of x is it true that $x - 3 > -2$?
d. Graph the solutions to $x - 3 > -2$ on the number line:

iM KH

2. Here is an inequality: $2x < 6$.

   a. Predict which values of x will make the inequality $2x < 6$ true.

   b. Complete the table. Does it match your prediction?

x	-4	-3	-2	-1	0	1	2	3	4
$2x$									

   c. Graph the solutions to $2x < 6$ on the number line:

3. Here is an inequality: $-2x < 6$.

   a. Predict which values of x will make the inequality $-2x < 6$ true.

   b. Complete the table. Does it match your prediction?

x	-4	-3	-2	-1	0	1	2	3	4
$-2x$									

   c. Graph the solutions to $-2x < 6$ on the number line:

   d. How are the solutions to $2x < 6$ different from the solutions to $-2x < 6$?

5.3: Which Side are the Solutions?

1. Let's investigate $-4x + 5 \geq 25$.

   a. Solve $-4x + 5 = 25$.

   b. Is $-4x + 5 \geq 25$ true when x is 0? What about when x is 7? What about when x is -7?

   c. Graph the solutions to $-4x + 5 \geq 25$ on the number line.

2. Let's investigate $\frac{4}{3}x + 3 < \frac{23}{3}$.

   a. Solve $\frac{4}{3}x + 3 = \frac{23}{3}$.

   b. Is $\frac{4}{3}x + 3 < \frac{23}{3}$ true when x is 0?

   c. Graph the solutions to $\frac{4}{3}x + 3 < \frac{23}{3}$ on the number line.

3. Solve the inequality $3(x + 4) > 17.4$ and graph the solutions on the number line.

iM KH

4. Solve the inequality $-3\left(x - \frac{4}{3}\right) \leq 6$ and graph the solutions on the number line.

Are you ready for more?

Write at least three different inequalities whose solution is $x > -10$. Find one with x on the left side that uses a $<$.

Lesson 5 Summary

Here is an inequality: $3(10 - 2x) < 18$. The solution to this inequality is all the values you could use in place of x to make the inequality true.

In order to solve this, we can first solve the related equation $3(10 - 2x) = 18$ to get the solution $x = 2$. That means 2 is the boundary between values of x that make the inequality true and values that make the inequality false.

To solve the inequality, we can check numbers greater than 2 and less than 2 and see which ones make the inequality true.

Let's check a number that is greater than 2: $x = 5$. Replacing x with 5 in the inequality, we get $3(10 - 2 \cdot 5) < 18$ or just $0 < 18$. This is true, so $x = 5$ is a solution. This means that all values greater than 2 make the inequality true. We can write the solutions as $x > 2$ and also represent the solutions on a number line:

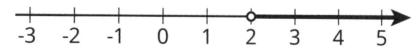

Notice that 2 itself is not a solution because it's the value of x that makes $3(10 - 2x)$ *equal* to 18, and so it does not make $3(10 - 2x) < 18$ true.

For confirmation that we found the correct solution, we can also test a value that is less than 2. If we test $x = 0$, we get $3(10 - 2 \cdot 0) < 18$ or just $30 < 18$. This is false, so $x = 0$ and all values of x that are less than 2 are not solutions.

Lesson 5 Practice Problems

1. a. Consider the inequality $-1 \leq \frac{x}{2}$.

   i. Predict which values of x will make the inequality true.

   ii. Complete the table to check your prediction.

x	-4	-3	-2	-1	0	1	2	3	4
$\frac{x}{2}$									

   b. Consider the inequality $1 \leq \frac{-x}{2}$.

   i. Predict which values of x will make it true.

   ii. Complete the table to check your prediction.

x	-4	-3	-2	-1	0	1	2	3	4
$-\frac{x}{2}$									

2. Diego is solving the inequality $100 - 3x \geq -50$. He solves the equation $100 - 3x = -50$ and gets $x = 50$. What is the solution to the inequality?

   A. $x < 50$

   B. $x \leq 50$

   C. $x > 50$

   D. $x \geq 50$

3. Solve the inequality $-5(x - 1) > -40$, and graph the solution on a number line.

4. Select **all** values of x that make the inequality $-x + 6 \geq 10$ true.

    A. -3.9

    B. 4

    C. -4.01

    D. -4

    E. 4.01

    F. 3.9

    G. 0

    H. -7

(From Unit 4, Lesson 3.)

5. Draw the solution set for each of the following inequalities.

    a. $x > 7$

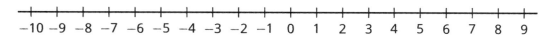

    b. $x \geq -4.2$

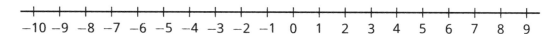

(From Unit 4, Lesson 3.)

Lesson 6: Modeling with Inequalities

Let's look at solutions to inequalities.

6.1: Possible Values

The stage manager of the school musical is trying to figure out how many sandwiches he can order with the $83 he collected from the cast and crew. Sandwiches cost $5.99 each, so he lets x represent the number of sandwiches he will order and writes $5.99x \leq 83$. He solves this to 2 decimal places, getting $x \leq 13.86$.

Which of these are valid statements about this situation? (Select **all** that apply.)

1. He can call the sandwich shop and order exactly 13.86 sandwiches.

2. He can round up and order 14 sandwiches.

3. He can order 12 sandwiches.

4. He can order 9.5 sandwiches.

5. He can order 2 sandwiches.

6. He can order -4 sandwiches.

6.2: Elevator

A mover is loading an elevator with many identical 48-pound boxes.
The mover weighs 185 pounds. The elevator can carry at most 2000 pounds.

1. Write an inequality that says that the mover will not overload the elevator on a particular ride. Check your inequality with your partner.

2. Solve your inequality and explain what the solution means.

3. Graph the solution to your inequality on a number line.

4. If the mover asked, "How many boxes can I load on this elevator at a time?" what would you tell them?

6.3: Info Gap: Giving Advice

Your teacher will give you either a *problem card* or a *data card*. Do not show or read your card to your partner.

If your teacher gives you the *problem card*:

1. Silently read your card and think about what information you need to be able to answer the question.

2. Ask your partner for the specific information that you need.

3. Explain how you are using the information to solve the problem.

   Continue to ask questions until you have enough information to solve the problem.

4. Share the *problem card* and solve the problem independently.

5. Read the *data card* and discuss your reasoning.

If your teacher gives you the *data card*:

1. Silently read your card.

2. Ask your partner *"What specific information do you need?"* and wait for them to *ask* for information.

   If your partner asks for information that is not on the card, do not do the calculations for them. Tell them you don't have that information.

3. Before sharing the information, ask *"Why do you need that information?"*

   Listen to your partner's reasoning and ask clarifying questions.

4. Read the *problem card* and solve the problem independently.

5. Share the *data card* and discuss your reasoning.

Pause here so your teacher can review your work. Ask your teacher for a new set of cards and repeat the activity, trading roles with your partner.

Are you ready for more?

In a day care group, nine babies are five months old and 12 babies are seven months old. How many full months from now will the average age of the 21 babies first surpass 20 months old?

Lesson 6 Summary

We can represent and solve many real-world problems with inequalities. Whenever we write an inequality, it is important to decide what quantity we are representing with a variable. After we make that decision, we can connect the quantities in the situation to write an expression, and finally, the whole inequality.

As we are solving the inequality or equation to answer a question, it is important to keep the meaning of each quantity in mind. This helps us to decide if the final answer makes sense in the context of the situation.

For example: Han has 50 centimeters of wire and wants to make a square picture frame with a loop to hang it that uses 3 centimeters for the loop. This situation can be represented by $3 + 4s = 50$, where s is the length of each side (if we want to use all the wire). We can also use $3 + 4s \leq 50$ if we want to allow for solutions that don't use all the wire. In this case, any positive number that is less or equal to 11.75 cm is a solution to the inequality. Each solution represents a possible side length for the picture frame since Han can bend the wire at any point. In other situations, the variable may represent a quantity that increases by whole numbers, such as with numbers of magazines, loads of laundry, or students. In those cases, only whole-number solutions make sense.

Lesson 6 Practice Problems

1. 28 students travel on a field trip. They bring a van that can seat 12 students. Elena and Kiran's teacher asks other adults to drive cars that seat 3 children each to transport the rest of the students.

   Elena wonders if she should use the inequality $12 + 3n > 28$ or $12 + 3n \geq 28$ to figure out how many cars are needed. Kiran doesn't think it matters in this case. Do you agree with Kiran? Explain your reasoning.

2.   a. In the cafeteria, there is one large 10-seat table and many smaller 4-seat tables. There are enough tables to fit 200 students. Write an inequality whose solution is the possible number of 4-seat tables in the cafeteria.

      b. 5 barrels catch rainwater in the schoolyard. Four barrels are the same size, and the fifth barrel holds 10 liters of water. Combined, the 5 barrels can hold at least 200 liters of water. Write an inequality whose solution is the possible size of each of the 4 barrels.

      c. How are these two problems similar? How are they different?

3. Priya looks at the inequality $12 - x > 5$ and says "I subtract a number from 12 and want a result that is bigger than 5. That means that the solutions should be values of x that are smaller than something."

   Do you agree with Priya? Explain your reasoning and include solutions to the inequality in your explanation.

4. When a store had sold $\frac{2}{5}$ of the shirts that were on display, they brought out another 30 from the stockroom. The store likes to keep at least 150 shirts on display. The manager wrote the inequality $\frac{3}{5}x + 30 \geq 150$ to describe the situation.

   a. Explain what $\frac{3}{5}$ means in the inequality.

   b. Solve the inequality.

   c. Explain what the solution means in the situation.

5. Select **all** the inequalities that have the same graph as $x < 4$.

   A. $x < 2$

   B. $x + 6 < 10$

   C. $5x < 20$

   D. $x - 2 > 2$

   E. $x < 8$

   (From Unit 4, Lesson 3.)

iM KH

Lesson 7: Subtraction in Equivalent Expressions

Let's find ways to work with subtraction in expressions.

7.1: Number Talk: Additive Inverses

Find each sum or difference mentally.

$-30 + -10$

$-10 + -30$

$-30 - 10$

$10 - -30$

7.2: A Helpful Observation

Lin and Kiran are trying to calculate $7\frac{3}{4} + 3\frac{5}{6} - 1\frac{3}{4}$. Here is their conversation:

Lin: "I plan to first add $7\frac{3}{4}$ and $3\frac{5}{6}$, so I will have to start by finding equivalent fractions with a common denominator."

Kiran: "It would be a lot easier if we could start by working with the $1\frac{3}{4}$ and $7\frac{3}{4}$. Can we rewrite it like $7\frac{3}{4} + 1\frac{3}{4} - 3\frac{5}{6}$?"

Lin: "You can't switch the order of numbers in a subtraction problem like you can with addition; $2 - 3$ is not equal to $3 - 2$."

Kiran: "That's true, but do you remember what we learned about rewriting subtraction expressions using addition? $2 - 3$ is equal to $2 + (-3)$."

1. Write an expression that is equivalent to $7\frac{3}{4} + 3\frac{5}{6} - 1\frac{3}{4}$ that uses addition instead of subtraction.

2. If you wrote the **terms** of your new expression in a different order, would it still be equivalent? Explain your reasoning.

7.3: Organizing Work

1. Write two expressions for the area of the big rectangle.

	8y	x	12
$\frac{1}{2}$			

2. Use the distributive property to write an expression that is equivalent to $\frac{1}{2}(8y + \text{-}x + \text{-}12)$. The boxes can help you organize your work.

	8y	-x	-12
$\frac{1}{2}$			

3. Use the distributive property to write an expression that is equivalent to $\frac{1}{2}(8y - x - 12)$.

Are you ready for more?

Here is a calendar for April 2017.

April 2017

Sunday	Monday	Tuesday	Wednesday	Thursday	Friday	Saturday
						1
2	3	4	5	6	7	8
9	10	11	12	13	14	15
16	17	18	19	20	21	22
23	24	25	26	27	28	29
30						

Let's choose a date: the 10th. Look at the numbers above, below, and to either side of the 10th: 3, 17, 9, 11.

1. Average these four numbers. What do you notice?

2. Choose a different date that is in a location where it has a date above, below, and to either side. Average these four numbers. What do you notice?

3. Explain why the same thing will happen for any date in a location where it has a date above, below, and to either side.

Lesson 7 Summary

Working with subtraction and signed numbers can sometimes get tricky. We can apply what we know about the relationship between addition and subtraction—that subtracting a number gives the same result as adding its opposite—to our work with expressions. Then, we can make use of the properties of addition that allow us to add and group in any order. This can make calculations simpler. For example:

$$\frac{5}{8} - \frac{2}{3} - \frac{1}{8}$$

$$\frac{5}{8} + \text{-}\frac{2}{3} + \text{-}\frac{1}{8}$$

$$\frac{5}{8} + \text{-}\frac{1}{8} + \text{-}\frac{2}{3}$$

$$\frac{4}{8} + \text{-}\frac{2}{3}$$

We can also organize the work of multiplying signed numbers in expressions. The product $\frac{3}{2}(6y - 2x - 8)$ can be found by drawing a rectangle with the first factor, $\frac{3}{2}$, on one side, and the three terms inside the parentheses on the other side:

	6y	-2x	-8
$\frac{3}{2}$			

Multiply $\frac{3}{2}$ by each term across the top and perform the multiplications:

	6y	-2x	-8
$\frac{3}{2}$	$\frac{3}{2} \cdot 6y$	$\frac{3}{2} \cdot \text{-}2x$	$\frac{3}{2} \cdot \text{-}8$

	6y	-2x	-8
$\frac{3}{2}$	9y	-3x	-12

Reassemble the parts to get the expanded version of the original expression:

$$\frac{3}{2}(6y - 2x - 8) = 9y - 3x - 12$$

Glossary

- term

Lesson 7 Practice Problems

1. For each expression, write an equivalent expression that uses only addition.

    a. $20 - 9 + 8 - 7$

    b. $4x - 7y - 5z + 6$

    c. $-3x - 8y - 4 - \frac{8}{7}z$

2. Use the distributive property to write an expression that is equivalent to each expression. If you get stuck, consider drawing boxes to help organize your work.

    a. $9(4x - 3y - \frac{2}{3})$

    b. $-2(-6x + 3y - 1)$

    c. $\frac{1}{5}(20y - 4x - 13)$

    d. $8(-x - \frac{1}{2})$

    e. $-8(-x - \frac{3}{4}y + \frac{7}{2})$

3. Kiran wrote the expression $x - 10$ for this number puzzle: "Pick a number, add -2, and multiply by 5."

    Lin thinks Kiran made a mistake.

    a. How can she convince Kiran he made a mistake?

    b. What would be a correct expression for this number puzzle?

4. Solve each equation.

  a. $5(n - 4) = -60$

  b. $-3t + -8 = 25$

  c. $7p - 8 = -22$

  d. $\frac{2}{5}(j + 40) = -4$

  e. $4(w + 1) = -6$

(From Unit 3, Lesson 9.)

5. A map of a rectangular park has a length of 4 inches and a width of 6 inches. It uses a scale of 1 inch for every 30 miles.

  a. What is the actual area of the park? Show how you know.

  b. The map needs to be reproduced at a different scale so that it has an area of 6 square inches and can fit in a brochure. At what scale should the map be reproduced so that it fits on the brochure? Show your reasoning.

(From Unit 2, Lesson 7.)

Lesson 8: Expanding and Factoring

Let's use the distributive property to write expressions in different ways.

8.1: Number Talk: Parentheses

Find the value of each expression mentally.

$2 + 3 \cdot 4$

$(2 + 3)(4)$

$2 - 3 \cdot 4$

$2 - (3 + 4)$

8.2: Factoring and Expanding with Negative Numbers

In each row, write the equivalent expression. If you get stuck, use a diagram to organize your work. The first row is provided as an example. Diagrams are provided for the first three rows.

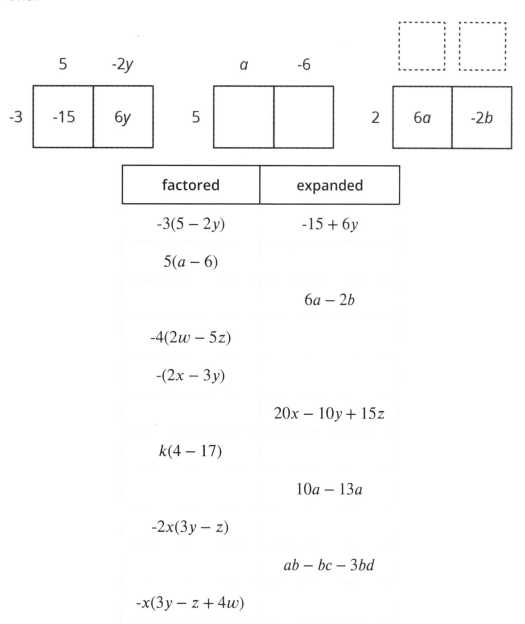

factored	expanded
$-3(5 - 2y)$	$-15 + 6y$
$5(a - 6)$	
	$6a - 2b$
$-4(2w - 5z)$	
$-(2x - 3y)$	
	$20x - 10y + 15z$
$k(4 - 17)$	
	$10a - 13a$
$-2x(3y - z)$	
	$ab - bc - 3bd$
$-x(3y - z + 4w)$	

Are you ready for more?

Expand to create an equivalent expression that uses the fewest number of terms: $\left(\left(\left(\left(x+1\right)\frac{1}{2}\right)+1\right)\frac{1}{2}\right)+1$. If we wrote a new expression following the same pattern so that there were 20 sets of parentheses, how could it be expanded into an equivalent expression that uses the fewest number of terms?

Lesson 8 Summary

We can use properties of operations in different ways to rewrite expressions and create equivalent expressions. We have already seen that we can use the distributive property to **expand** an expression, for example $3(x+5) = 3x + 15$. We can also use the distributive property in the other direction and **factor** an expression, for example $8x + 12 = 4(2x + 3)$.

We can organize the work of using distributive property to rewrite the expression $12x - 8$. In this case we know the product and need to find the factors.

The terms of the product go inside:

We look at the expressions and think about a factor they have in common. $12x$ and -8 each have a factor of 4. We place the common factor on one side of the large rectangle:

Now we think: "4 times *what* is 12x?" "4 times *what* is -8?" and write the other factors on the other side of the rectangle:

So, $12x - 8$ is equivalent to $4(3x - 2)$.

Glossary

- expand
- factor (an expression)

Lesson 8 Practice Problems

1.   a. Expand to write an equivalent expression: $\frac{-1}{4}(-8x + 12y)$

        b. Factor to write an equivalent expression: $36a - 16$

2. Lin missed math class on the day they worked on expanding and factoring. Kiran is helping Lin catch up.

    a. Lin understands that expanding is using the distributive property, but she doesn't understand what factoring is or why it works. How can Kiran explain factoring to Lin?

    b. Lin asks Kiran how the diagrams with boxes help with factoring. What should Kiran tell Lin about the boxes?

    c. Lin asks Kiran to help her factor the expression $-4xy - 12xz + 20xw$. How can Kiran use this example to Lin understand factoring?

3. Complete the equation with numbers that makes the expression on the right side of the equal sign equivalent to the expression on the left side.

$$75a + 25b = \underline{}(\underline{}a + b)$$

4. Solve each equation.

   a. $\frac{-1}{8}d - 4 = \frac{-3}{8}$

   b. $\frac{-1}{4}m + 5 = 16$

   c. $10b + \text{-}45 = \text{-}43$

   d. $\text{-}8(y - 1.25) = 4$

   e. $3.2(s + 10) = 32$

   (From Unit 3, Lesson 9.)

5. For each inequality, decide whether the solution is represented by $x < 4.5$ or $x > 4.5$.

   a. $\text{-}24 > \text{-}6(x - 0.5)$

   b. $\text{-}8x + 6 > \text{-}30$

   c. $\text{-}2(x + 3.2) < \text{-}15.4$

   (From Unit 4, Lesson 5.)

iM KH

Lesson 9: Combining Like Terms (Part 1)

Let's see how we can tell that expressions are equivalent.

9.1: Why is it True?

Explain why each statement is true.

1. $5 + 2 + 3 = 5 + (2 + 3)$

2. $9a$ is equivalent to $11a - 2a$.

3. $7a + 4 - 2a$ is equivalent to $7a + \text{-}2a + 4$.

4. $8a - (8a - 8)$ is equivalent to 8.

9.2: A's and B's

Diego and Jada are both trying to write an expression with fewer terms that is equivalent to

$$7a + 5b - 3a + 4b$$

- Jada thinks $10a + 1b$ is equivalent to the original expression.

- Diego thinks $4a + 9b$ is equivalent to the original expression.

1. We can show expressions are equivalent by writing out all the variables. Explain why the expression on each row (after the first row) is equivalent to the expression on the row before it.

$$7a + 5b - 3a + 4b$$
$$(a + a + a + a + a + a + a) + (b + b + b + b + b) - (a + a + a) + (b + b + b + b)$$
$$(a + a + a + a) + (a + a + a) + (b + b + b + b + b) - (a + a + a) + (b + b + b + b)$$
$$(a + a + a + a) + (b + b + b + b + b) + (a + a + a) - (a + a + a) + (b + b + b + b)$$
$$(a + a + a + a) + (b + b + b + b + b) + (b + b + b + b)$$
$$(a + a + a + a) + (b + b + b + b + b + b + b + b + b)$$
$$4a + 9b$$

2. Here is another way we can rewrite the expressions. Explain why the expression on each row (after the first row) is equivalent to the expression on the row before it.

$$7a + 5b - 3a + 4b$$
$$7a + 5b + (\text{-}3a) + 4b$$
$$7a + (\text{-}3a) + 5b + 4b$$
$$(7 + \text{-}3)a + (5 + 4)b$$
$$4a + 9b$$

Are you ready for more?

Follow the instructions for a number puzzle:

- Take the number formed by the first 3 digits of your phone number and multiply it by 40
- Add 1 to the result
- Multiply by 500
- Add the number formed by the last 4 digits of your phone number, and then add it again
- Subtract 500
- Multiply by $\frac{1}{2}$

1. What is the final number?

2. How does this number puzzle work?

3. Can you invent a new number puzzle that gives a surprising result?

9.3: Making Sides Equal

Replace each ? with an expression that will make the left side of the equation equivalent to the right side.

Set A

1. $6x + ? = 10x$

2. $6x + ? = 2x$

3. $6x + ? = -10x$

4. $6x + ? = 0$

5. $6x + ? = 10$

Check your results with your partner and resolve any disagreements. Next move on to Set B.

Set B

1. $6x - ? = 2x$

2. $6x - ? = 10x$

3. $6x - ? = x$

4. $6x - ? = 6$

5. $6x - ? = 4x - 10$

Lesson 9 Summary

There are many ways to write equivalent expressions that may look very different from each other. We have several tools to find out if two expressions are equivalent.

- Two expressions are definitely not equivalent if they have different values when we substitute the same number for the variable. For example, $2(-3 + x) + 8$ and $2x + 5$ are not equivalent because when x is 1, the first expression equals 4 and the second expression equals 7.

- If two expressions are equal for many different values we substitute for the variable, then the expressions *may* be equivalent, but we don't know for sure. It is impossible to compare the two expressions for all values. To know for sure, we use properties of operations. For example, $2(-3 + x) + 8$ is equivalent to $2x + 2$ because:

$2(-3 + x) + 8$
$\quad$-6 + 2x + 8$ $\quad$ by the distributive property
$\quad$2x + $-6 + 8$ $\quad$ by the commutative property
$2x + (-6 + 8)$ $\quad$ by the associative property
$\qquad 2x + 2$

iM KH

Lesson 9 Practice Problems

1. Andre says that $10x + 6$ and $5x + 11$ are equivalent because they both equal 16 when x is 1. Do you agree with Andre? Explain your reasoning.

2. Select **all** expressions that can be subtracted from $9x$ to result in the expression $3x + 5$.

   A. $-5 + 6x$

   B. $5 - 6x$

   C. $6x + 5$

   D. $6x - 5$

   E. $-6x + 5$

3. Select **all** the statements that are true for any value of x.

   A. $7x + (2x + 7) = 9x + 7$

   B. $7x + (2x - 1) = 9x + 1$

   C. $\frac{1}{2}x + (3 - \frac{1}{2}x) = 3$

   D. $5x - (8 - 6x) = \text{-}x - 8$

   E. $0.4x - (0.2x + 8) = 0.2x - 8$

   F. $6x - (2x - 4) = 4x + 4$

4. For each situation, would you describe it with $x < 25$, $x > 25$, $x \leq 25$, or $x \geq 25$?

   a. The library is having a party for any student who read at least 25 books over the summer. Priya read x books and was invited to the party.

   b. Kiran read x books over the summer but was not invited to the party.

   c.

   d.

   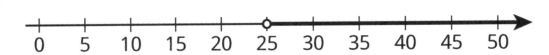

(From Unit 4, Lesson 3.)

5. A line is represented by the equation $\frac{y}{x-2} = \frac{3}{11}$. What are the coordinates of some points that lie on the line? Graph the line on graph paper.

(From Unit 2, Lesson 17.)

iM KH

6. Select **all** the statements that must be true for *any* scaled copy Q of Polygon P.

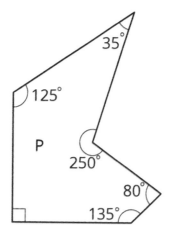

A. The side lengths are all whole numbers.

B. The angle measures are all whole numbers.

C. Q has exactly 1 right angle.

D. If the scale factor between P and Q is $\frac{1}{5}$, then each side length of P is multiplied by $\frac{1}{5}$ to get the corresponding side length of Q.

E. If the scale factor is 2, each angle in P is multiplied by 2 to get the corresponding angle in Q.

F. Q has 2 acute angles and 3 obtuse angles.

(From Unit 2, Lesson 3.)

Lesson 10: Combining Like Terms (Part 2)

Let's see how to use properties correctly to write equivalent expressions.

10.1: True or False?

Select **all** the statements that are true. Be prepared to explain your reasoning.

1. $4 - 2(3 + 7) = 4 - 2 \cdot 3 - 2 \cdot 7$

2. $4 - 2(3 + 7) = 4 + \text{-}2 \cdot 3 + \text{-}2 \cdot 7$

3. $4 - 2(3 + 7) = 4 - 2 \cdot 3 + 2 \cdot 7$

4. $4 - 2(3 + 7) = 4 - (2 \cdot 3 + 2 \cdot 7)$

10.2: Seeing it Differently

Some students are trying to write an expression with fewer terms that is equivalent to $8 - 3(4 - 9x)$.

Noah says, "I worked the problem from left to right and ended up with $20 - 45x$."

$$8 - 3(4 - 9x)$$

$$5(4 - 9x)$$

$$20 - 45x$$

Lin says, "I started inside the parentheses and ended up with $23x$."

$$8 - 3(4 - 9x)$$

$$8 - 3(\text{-}5x)$$

$$8 + 15x$$

$$23x$$

Jada says, "I used the distributive property and ended up with $27x - 4$."

$$8 - 3(4 - 9x)$$

$$8 - (12 - 27x)$$

$$8 - 12 - (\text{-}27x)$$

$$27x - 4$$

Andre says, "I also used the distributive property, but I ended up with $\text{-}4 - 27x$."

$$8 - 3(4 - 9x)$$

$$8 - 12 - 27x$$

$$\text{-}4 - 27x$$

iM KH

1. Do you agree with any of them? Explain your reasoning.

2. For each strategy that you disagree with, find and describe the errors.

Are you ready for more?

1. Jada's neighbor said, "My age is the difference between twice my age in 4 years and twice my age 4 years ago." How old is Jada's neighbor?

2. Another neighbor said, "My age is the difference between twice my age in 5 years and and twice my age 5 years ago." How old is this neighbor?

3. A third neighbor had the same claim for 17 years from now and 17 years ago, and a fourth for 21 years. Determine those neighbors' ages.

10.3: Grouping Differently

Diego was taking a math quiz. There was a question on the quiz that had the expression $8x - 9 - 12x + 5$. Diego's teacher told the class there was a typo and the expression was supposed to have one set of parentheses in it.

1. Where could you put parentheses in $8x - 9 - 12x + 5$ to make a new expression that is still equivalent to the original expression? How do you know that your new expression is equivalent?

2. Where could you put parentheses in $8x - 9 - 12x + 5$ to make a new expression that is not equivalent to the original expression? List as many different answers as you can.

Lesson 10 Summary

Combining like terms allows us to write expressions more simply with fewer terms. But it can sometimes be tricky with long expressions, parentheses, and negatives. It is helpful to think about some common errors that we can be aware of and try to avoid:

- $6x - x$ is not equivalent to 6. While it might be tempting to think that subtracting x makes the x disappear, the expression is really saying take 1 x away from 6 x's, and the distributive property tells us that $6x - x$ is equivalent to $(6 - 1)x$.

- $7 - 2x$ is not equivalent to $5x$. The expression $7 - 2x$ tells us to double an unknown amount and subtract it from 7. This is not always the same as taking 5 copies of the unknown.

- $7 - 4(x + 2)$ is not equivalent to $3(x + 2)$. The expression tells us to subtract 4 copies of an amount from 7, not to take $(7 - 4)$ copies of the amount.

If we think about the meaning and properties of operations when we take steps to rewrite expressions, we can be sure we are getting equivalent expressions and are not changing their value in the process.

Lesson 10 Practice Problems

1. ○ Noah says that $9x - 2x + 4x$ is equivalent to $3x$, because the subtraction sign tells us to subtract everything that comes after $9x$.

    ○ Elena says that $9x - 2x + 4x$ is equivalent to $11x$, because the subtraction only applies to $2x$.

    Do you agree with either of them? Explain your reasoning.

2. Identify the error in generating an expression equivalent to $4 + 2x - \frac{1}{2}(10 - 4x)$. Then correct the error.

    $4 + 2x + \frac{-1}{2}(10 + \text{-}4x)$
    $4 + 2x + \text{-}5 + 2x$
    $4 + 2x - 5 + 2x$
    $\text{-}1$

3. Select **all** expressions that are equivalent to $5x - 15 - 20x + 10$.

    A. $5x - (15 + 20x) + 10$

    B. $5x + \text{-}15 + \text{-}20x + 10$

    C. $5(x - 3 - 4x + 2)$

    D. $\text{-}5(\text{-}x + 3 + 4x + \text{-}2)$

    E. $\text{-}15x - 5$

    F. $\text{-}5(3x + 1)$

    G. $\text{-}15(x - \frac{1}{3})$

4. The school marching band has a budget of up to $750 to cover 15 new uniforms and competition fees that total $300. How much can they spend for one uniform?

    a. Write an inequality to represent this situation.

    b. Solve the inequality and describe what it means in the situation.

(From Unit 4, Lesson 4.)

5. Solve the inequality that represents each story. Then interpret what the solution means in the story.

    a. For every $9 that Elena earns, she gives x dollars to charity. This happens 7 times this month. Elena wants to be sure she keeps at least $42 from this month's earnings. $7(9 - x) \geq 42$

    b. Lin buys a candle that is 9 inches tall and burns down x inches per minute. She wants to let the candle burn for 7 minutes until it is less than 6 inches tall. $9 - 7x < 6$

(From Unit 4, Lesson 6.)

iM KH

Lesson 11: Combining Like Terms (Part 3)

Let's see how we can combine terms in an expression to write it with less terms.

11.1: Are They Equal?

Select **all** expressions that are equal to $8 - 12 - (6 + 4)$.

1. $8 - 6 - 12 + 4$

2. $8 - 12 - 6 - 4$

3. $8 - 12 + (6 + 4)$

4. $8 - 12 - 6 + 4$

5. $8 - 4 - 12 - 6$

11.2: X's and Y's

Match each expression in column A with an equivalent expression from column B. Be prepared to explain your reasoning.

A

1. $(9x + 5y) + (3x + 7y)$

2. $(9x + 5y) - (3x + 7y)$

3. $(9x + 5y) - (3x - 7y)$

4. $9x - 7y + 3x + 5y$

5. $9x - 7y + 3x - 5y$

6. $9x - 7y - 3x - 5y$

B

1. $12(x + y)$

2. $12(x - y)$

3. $6(x - 2y)$

4. $9x + 5y + 3x - 7y$

5. $9x + 5y - 3x + 7y$

6. $9x - 3x + 5y - 7y$

11.3: Seeing Structure and Factoring

Write each expression with fewer terms. Show or explain your reasoning.

1. $3 \cdot 15 + 4 \cdot 15 - 5 \cdot 15$

2. $3x + 4x - 5x$

3. $3(x - 2) + 4(x - 2) - 5(x - 2)$

4. $3\left(\frac{5}{2}x + 6\frac{1}{2}\right) + 4\left(\frac{5}{2}x + 6\frac{1}{2}\right) - 5\left(\frac{5}{2}x + 6\frac{1}{2}\right)$

Lesson 11 Summary

Combining like terms is a useful strategy that we will see again and again in our future work with mathematical expressions. It is helpful to review the things we have learned about this important concept.

- Combining like terms is an application of the distributive property. For example:

$$2x + 9x$$
$$(2 + 9) \cdot x$$
$$11x$$

- It often also involves the commutative and associative properties to change the order or grouping of addition. For example:

$$2a + 3b + 4a + 5b$$
$$2a + 4a + 3b + 5b$$
$$(2a + 4a) + (3b + 5b)$$
$$6a + 8b$$

- We can't change order or grouping when subtracting; so in order to apply the commutative or associative properties to expressions with subtraction, we need to rewrite subtraction as addition. For example:

$$2a - 3b - 4a - 5b$$
$$2a + \text{-}3b + \text{-}4a + \text{-}5b$$
$$2a + \text{-}4a + \text{-}3b + \text{-}5b$$
$$\text{-}2a + \text{-}8b$$
$$\text{-}2a - 8b$$

- Since combining like terms uses properties of operations, it results in expressions that are equivalent.

- The like terms that are combined do not have to be a single number or variable; they may be longer expressions as well. Terms can be combined in any sum where there is a common factor in all the terms. For example, each term in the expression $5(x + 3) - 0.5(x + 3) + 2(x + 3)$ has a factor of $(x + 3)$. We can rewrite the expression with fewer terms by using the distributive property:

$$5(x + 3) - 0.5(x + 3) + 2(x + 3)$$
$$(5 - 0.5 + 2)(x + 3)$$
$$6.5(x + 3)$$

Lesson 11 Practice Problems

1. Jada says, "I can tell that $\frac{-2}{3}(x + 5) + 4(x + 5) - \frac{10}{3}(x + 5)$ equals 0 just by looking at it." Is Jada correct? Explain how you know.

2. In each row, decide whether the expression in column A is equivalent to the expression in column B. If they are not equivalent, show how to change one expression to make them equivalent.

A	B
a. $3x - 2x + 0.5x$	a. $1.5x$
b. $3(x + 4) - 2(x + 4)$	b. $x + 3$
c. $6(x + 4) - 2(x + 5)$	c. $2(2x + 7)$
d. $3(x + 4) - 2(x + 4) + 0.5(x + 4)$	d. 1.5
e. $20\left(\frac{2}{5}x + \frac{3}{4}y - \frac{1}{2}\right)$	e. $\frac{1}{2}(16x + 30y - 20)$

3. For each situation, write an expression for the new balance using as few terms as possible.

   a. A checking account has a balance of -$126.89. A customer makes two deposits, one $3\frac{1}{2}$ times the other, and then withdraws $25.

   b. A checking account has a balance of $350. A customer makes two withdrawals, one $50 more than the other. Then he makes a deposit of $75.

   (From Unit 4, Lesson 9.)

iM KH

4. Tyler is using the distributive property on the expression $9 - 4(5x - 6)$. Here is his work:

$9 - 4(5x - 6)$
$9 + (\text{-}4)(5x + \text{-}6)$
$9 + \text{-}20x + \text{-}6$
$3 - 20x$

Mai thinks Tyler's answer is incorrect. She says, "If expressions are equivalent then they are equal for any value of the variable. Why don't you try to substitute the same value for x in all the equations and see where they are not equal?"

a. Find the step where Tyler made an error.

b. Explain what he did wrong.

c. Correct Tyler's work.

(From Unit 4, Lesson 10.)

5. a. If $(11 + x)$ is positive, but $(4 + x)$ is negative, what is one number that x could be?

b. If $(\text{-}3 + y)$ is positive, but $(\text{-}9 + y)$ is negative, what is one number that y could be?

c. If $(\text{-}5 + z)$ is positive, but $(\text{-}6 + z)$ is negative, what is one number that z could be?

(From Unit 4, Lesson 3.)

Unit 4 Lesson 11 Practice Problems 69

Lesson 12: Balanced Moves

Let's rewrite equations while keeping the same solutions.

12.1: Matching Hangers

Figures A, B, C, and D show the result of simplifying the hanger in Figure A by removing equal weights from each side.

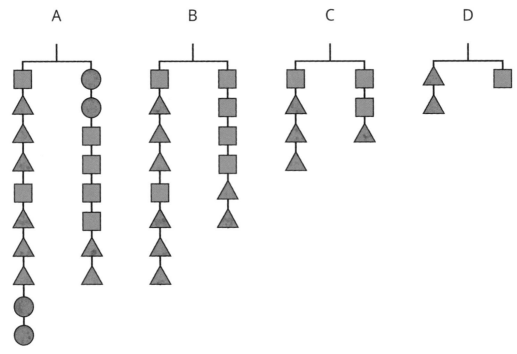

Here are some equations. Each equation represents one of the hanger diagrams.

$$2(x + 3y) = 4x + 2y$$
$$2y = x$$
$$2(x + 3y) + 2z = 2z + 4x + 2y$$
$$x + 3y = 2x + y$$

    1. Write the equation that goes with each figure:

      A:

      B:

      C:

      D:

iM KH

2. Each variable (x, y, and z) represents the weight of one shape. Which goes with which?

3. Explain what was done to each equation to create the next equation. If you get stuck, think about how the hangers changed.

12.2: Matching Equation Moves

Your teacher will give you some cards. Each of the cards 1 through 6 show two equations. Each of the cards A through E describe a move that turns one equation into another.

1. Match each number card with a letter card.

2. One of the letter cards will not have a match. For this card, write two equations showing the described move.

12.3: Keeping Equality

1. Noah and Lin both solved the equation $14a = 2(a - 3)$.
   Do you agree with either of them? Why?   Noah's solution: Lin's solution:

$$14a = 2(a - 3)$$
$$14a = 2a - 6$$
$$12a = \text{-}6$$
$$a = \text{-}\frac{1}{2}$$

$$14a = 2(a - 3)$$
$$7a = a - 3$$
$$6a = \text{-}3$$
$$a = \text{-}\frac{1}{2}$$

2. Elena is asked to solve $15 - 10x = 5(x + 9)$. What do you recommend she does to each side first?

3. Diego is asked to solve $3x - 8 = 4(x + 5)$. What do you recommend he does to each side first?

Are you ready for more?

In a cryptarithmetic puzzle, the digits 0–9 are represented with letters of the alphabet. Use your understanding of addition to find which digits go with the letters A, B, E, G, H, L, N, and R.

HANGER + HANGER + HANGER = ALGEBRA

Lesson 12 Summary

An equation tells us that two expressions have equal value. For example, if $4x + 9$ and $-2x - 3$ have equal value, we can write the equation

$$4x + 9 = -2x - 3$$

Earlier, we used hangers to understand that if we add the same positive number to each side of the equation, the sides will still have equal value. It also works if we add *negative numbers*! For example, we can add -9 to each side of the equation.

$$4x + 9 + -9 = -2x - 3 + -9 \qquad \text{add -9 to each side}$$
$$4x = -2x - 12 \qquad \text{combine like terms}$$

Since expressions represent numbers, we can also add *expressions* to each side of an equation. For example, we can add $2x$ to each side and still maintain equality.

$$4x + 2x = -2x - 12 + 2x \qquad \text{add } 2x \text{ to each side}$$
$$6x = -12 \qquad \text{combine like terms}$$

If we multiply or divide the expressions on each side of an equation by the same number, we will also maintain the equality (so long as we do not divide by zero).

$$6x \cdot \frac{1}{6} = -12 \cdot \frac{1}{6} \qquad \text{multiply each side by } \frac{1}{6}$$

or

$$6x \div 6 = -12 \div 6 \qquad \text{divide each side by 6}$$

Now we can see that $x = -2$ is the solution to our equation.

We will use these moves in systematic ways to solve equations in future lessons.

Lesson 12 Practice Problems

1. In this hanger, the weight of the triangle is x and the weight of the square is y.

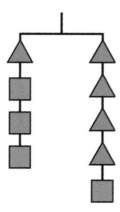

a. Write an equation using x and y to represent the hanger.

b. If x is 6, what is y?

2. Andre and Diego were each trying to solve $2x + 6 = 3x - 8$. Describe the first step they each make to the equation.

a. The result of Andre's first step was $-x + 6 = -8$.

b. The result of Diego's first step was $6 = x - 8$.

3. Match each set of equations with the move that turned the first equation into the second.

A. $6x + 9 = 4x - 3$
   $2x + 9 = -3$

B. $-4(5x - 7) = -18$
   $5x - 7 = 4.5$

C. $8 - 10x = 7 + 5x$
   $4 - 10x = 3 + 5x$

D. $\frac{-5x}{4} = 4$
   $5x = -16$

E. $12x + 4 = 20x + 24$
   $3x + 1 = 5x + 6$

1. Multiply both sides by $\frac{-1}{4}$

2. Multiply both sides by -4

3. Multiply both sides by $\frac{1}{4}$

4. Add -4x to both sides

5. Add -4 to both sides

4. What is the weight of a square if a triangle weighs 4 grams?

Explain your reasoning.

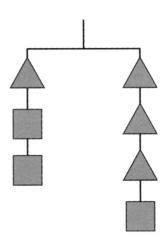

iꟾ KH

5. Here is a balanced hanger diagram.

Each triangle weighs 2.5 pounds, each circle weighs 3 pounds, and x represents the weight of each square. Select *all* equations that represent the hanger.

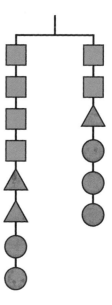

A. $x + x + x + x + 11 = x + 11.5$

B. $2x = 0.5$

C. $4x + 5 + 6 = 2x + 2.5 + 6$

D. $2x + 2.5 = 3$

E. $4x + 2.5 + 2.5 + 3 + 3 = 2x + 2.5 + 3 + 3 + 3$

Lesson 13: More Balanced Moves

Let's rewrite some more equations while keeping the same solutions.

13.1: Different Equations?

Equation 1

$$x - 3 = 2 - 4x$$

Which of these have the same solution as Equation 1? Be prepared to explain your reasoning.

Equation A	Equation B	Equation C	Equation D
$2x - 6 = 4 - 8x$	$x - 5 = \text{-}4x$	$2(1 - 2x) = x - 3$	$\text{-}3 = 2 - 5x$

13.2: Step by Step by Step by Step

Here is an equation, and then all the steps Clare wrote to solve it:

$$14x - 2x + 3 = 3(5x + 9)$$
$$12x + 3 = 3(5x + 9)$$
$$3(4x + 1) = 3(5x + 9)$$
$$4x + 1 = 5x + 9$$
$$1 = x + 9$$
$$\text{-}8 = x$$

Here is the same equation, and the steps Lin wrote to solve it:

$$14x - 2x + 3 = 3(5x + 9)$$
$$12x + 3 = 3(5x + 9)$$
$$12x + 3 = 15x + 27$$
$$12x = 15x + 24$$
$$\text{-}3x = 24$$
$$x = \text{-}8$$

1. Are both of their *solutions* correct? Explain your reasoning.

2. Describe some ways the steps they took are alike and different.

iM KH

3. Mai and Noah also solved the equation, but some of their steps have errors. Find the incorrect step in each solution and explain why it is incorrect.

Mai:

$$14x - 2x + 3 = 3(5x + 9)$$
$$12x + 3 = 3(5x + 9)$$
$$7x + 3 = 3(9)$$
$$7x + 3 = 27$$
$$7x = 24$$
$$x = \frac{24}{7}$$

Noah:

$$14x - 2x + 3 = 3(5x + 9)$$
$$12x + 3 = 15x + 27$$
$$27x + 3 = 27$$
$$27x = 24$$
$$x = \frac{24}{27}$$

13.3: Make Your Own Steps

Solve these equations for x.

1. $\frac{12 + 6x}{3} = \frac{5 - 9}{2}$

2. $x - 4 = \frac{1}{3}(6x - 54)$

3. $-(3x - 12) = 9x - 4$

Are you ready for more?

I have 24 pencils and 3 cups. The second cup holds one more pencil than the first. The third holds one more than the second. How many pencils does each cup contain?

13.4: Trading Moves

Your teacher will give you 4 cards, each with an equation.

1. With your partner, select a card and choose who will take the first turn.

2. During your turn, decide what the next move to solve the equation should be, explain your choice to your partner, and then write it down once you both agree. Switch roles for the next move. This continues until the equation is solved.

3. Choose a second equation to solve in the same way, trading the card back and forth after each move.

4. For the last two equations, choose one each to solve and then trade with your partner when you finish to check one another's work.

Lesson 13 Summary

How do we make sure the solution we find for an equation is correct? Accidentally adding when we meant to subtract, missing a negative when we distribute, forgetting to write an x from one line to the next–there are many possible mistakes to watch out for!

Fortunately, each step we take solving an equation results in a new equation with the same solution as the original. This means we can check our work by substituting the value of the solution into the original equation. For example, say we solve the following equation:

$$2x = -3(x + 5)$$
$$2x = -3x + 15$$
$$5x = 15$$
$$x = 3$$

Substituting 3 in place of x into the original equation,

$$2(3) = -3(3 + 5)$$
$$6 = -3(8)$$
$$6 = -24$$

we get a statement that isn't true! This tells us we must have made a mistake somewhere. Checking our original steps carefully, we made a mistake when distributing -3. Fixing it, we now have

$$2x = -3(x + 5)$$
$$2x = -3x - 15$$
$$5x = -15$$
$$x = -3$$

Substituting -3 in place of x into the original equation to make sure we didn't make another mistake:

$$2(-3) = -3(-3 + 5)$$
$$-6 = -3(2)$$
$$-6 = -6$$

This equation is true, so $x = -3$ is the solution.

Lesson 13 Practice Problems

1. Mai and Tyler work on the equation $\frac{2}{5}b + 1 = -11$ together. Mai's solution is $b = -25$ and Tyler's is $b = -28$. Here is their work. Do you agree with their solutions? Explain or show your reasoning.

Mai:

$\frac{2}{5}b + 1 = -11$

$\frac{2}{5}b = -10$

$b = -10 \cdot \frac{5}{2}$

$b = -25$

Tyler:

$\frac{2}{5}b + 1 = -11$

$2b + 1 = -55$

$2b = -56$

$b = -28$

2. Solve $3(x - 4) = 12x$

iM KH

3. Describe what is being done in each step while solving the equation.

    a. $2(\text{-}3x + 4) = 5x + 2$

    b. $\text{-}6x + 8 = 5x + 2$

    c. $8 = 11x + 2$

    d. $6 = 11x$

    e. $x = \frac{6}{11}$

4. Andre solved an equation, but when he checked his answer he saw his solution was incorrect. He knows he made a mistake, but he can't find it. Where is Andre's mistake and what is the solution to the equation?

$$\text{-}2(3x - 5) = 4(x + 3) + 8$$
$$\text{-}6x + 10 = 4x + 12 + 8$$
$$\text{-}6x + 10 = 4x + 20$$
$$10 = \text{-}2x + 20$$
$$\text{-}10 = \text{-}2x$$
$$5 = x$$

Lesson 14: Strategic Solving

Let's solve linear equations like a boss.

14.1: Equal Perimeters

The triangle and the square have equal perimeters.

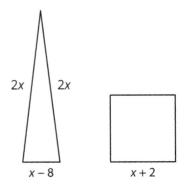

1. Find the value of x.

2. What is the perimeter of each of the figures?

14.2: Predicting Solutions

Without solving, identify whether these equations have a solution that is positive, negative, or zero.

1. $\frac{x}{6} = \frac{3x}{4}$

2. $7x = 3.25$

3. $7x = 32.5$

4. $3x + 11 = 11$

5. $9 - 4x = 4$

6. $-8 + 5x = -20$

7. $-\frac{1}{2}(-8 + 5x) = -20$

iM KH

14.3: Which Would You Rather Solve?

Here are a lot of equations:

A. $-\frac{5}{6}(8 + 5b) = 75 + \frac{5}{3}b$

B. $-\frac{1}{2}(t + 3) - 10 = -6.5$

C. $\frac{10-v}{4} = 2(v + 17)$

D. $2(4k + 3) - 13 = 2(18 - k) - 13$

E. $\frac{n}{7} - 12 = 5n + 5$

F. $3(c - 1) + 2(3c + 1) = -(3c + 1)$

G. $\frac{4m-3}{4} = -\frac{9+4m}{8}$

H. $p - 5(p + 4) = p - (8 - p)$

I. $2(2q + 1.5) = 18 - q$

J. $2r + 49 = -8(-r - 5)$

1. Without solving, identify 3 equations that you think would be least difficult to solve and 3 equations you think would be most difficult to solve. Be prepared to explain your reasoning.

2. Choose 3 equations to solve. At least one should be from your "least difficult" list and one should be from your "most difficult" list.

Are you ready for more?

Mai gave half of her brownies, and then half a brownie more, to Kiran. Then she gave half of what was left, and half a brownie more, to Tyler. That left her with one remaining brownie. How many brownies did she have to start with?

Lesson 14 Summary

Sometimes we are asked to solve equations with a lot of things going on on each side. For example,

$$x - 2(x + 5) = \frac{3(2x - 20)}{6}$$

This equation has variables on each side, parentheses, and even a fraction to think about. Before we start distributing, let's take a closer look at the fraction on the right side. The expression $2x - 20$ is being multiplied by 3 and divided by 6, which is the same as just dividing by 2, so we can re-write the equation as

$$x - 2(x + 5) = \frac{2x - 20}{2}$$

But now it's easier to see that all the terms on the numerator of right side are divisible by 2, which means we can re-write the right side again as

$$x - 2(x + 5) = x - 10$$

At this point, we could do some distribution and then collect like terms on each side of the equation. Another choice would be to use the structure of the equation. Both the left and the right side have something being subtracted from x. But, if the two sides are equal, that means the "something" being subtracted on each side must also be equal. Thinking this way, the equation can now be re-written with less terms as

$$2(x + 5) = 10$$

Only a few steps left! But what can we tell about the solution to this problem right now? Is it positive? Negative? Zero? Well, the 2 and the 5 multiplied together are 10, so that means the 2 and the x multiplied together cannot have a positive or a negative value. Finishing the steps we have:

$$\begin{aligned}
2(x + 5) &= 10 \\
x + 5 &= 5 \qquad \text{Divide each side by 2} \\
x &= 0 \qquad \text{Subtract 5 from each side}
\end{aligned}$$

Neither positive nor negative. Just as predicted.

Lesson 14 Practice Problems

1. Solve each of these equations. Explain or show your reasoning.

$2b + 8 - 5b + 3 = \text{-}13 + 8b - 5$ $\qquad\qquad$ $2x + 7 - 5x + 8 = 3(5 + 6x) - 12x$

$2c - 3 = 2(6 - c) + 7c$

2. Solve each equation and check your solution.

$\text{-}3w - 4 = w + 3$ $\qquad\qquad$ $3(3 - 3x) = 2(x + 3) - 30$

$\frac{1}{3}(z + 4) - 6 = \frac{2}{3}(5 - z)$

3. Elena said the equation $9x + 15 = 3x + 15$ has no solutions because $9x$ is greater than $3x$. Do you agree with Elena? Explain your reasoning.

4. Which of the changes would keep the hanger in balance?

Select all that apply.

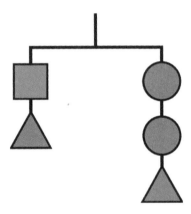

A. Adding two circles on the left and a square on the right

B. Adding 2 triangles to each side

C. Adding two circles on the right and a square on the left

D. Adding a circle on the left and a square on the right

E. Adding a triangle on the left and a square on the right

(From Unit 4, Lesson 12.)

Lesson 15: All, Some, or No Solutions

Let's think about how many solutions an equation can have.

15.1: Which One Doesn't Belong: Equations

Which one doesn't belong?

1. $5 + 7 = 7 + 5$

2. $5 \cdot 7 = 7 \cdot 5$

3. $2 = 7 - 5$

4. $5 - 7 = 7 - 5$

15.2: Thinking About Solutions

$$n = n$$

$$5 - 9 + 3x = \text{-}10 + 6 + 3x$$

$$2t + 6 = 2(t + 3)$$

$$\frac{1}{2} + x = \frac{1}{3} + x$$

$$3(n + 1) = 3n + 1$$

$$y \cdot \text{-}6 \cdot \text{-}3 = 2 \cdot y \cdot 9$$

$$\frac{1}{4}(20d + 4) = 5d$$

$$v + 2 = v - 2$$

1. Sort these equations into the two types: true for all values and true for no values.

2. Write the other side of this equation so that this equation is true for all values of u.
$$6(u - 2) + 2 =$$

3. Write the other side of this equation so that this equation is true for no values of u.
$$6(u - 2) + 2 =$$

Are you ready for more?

Consecutive numbers follow one right after the other. An example of three consecutive numbers is 17, 18, and 19. Another example is -100, -99, -98.

How many sets of two or more consecutive positive integers can be added to obtain a sum of 100?

15.3: What's the Equation?

1. Complete each equation so that it is true for all values of x.

   a. $3x + 6 = 3(x + \underline{})$

   b. $x - 2 = \text{-}(\underline{} - x)$

   c. $\frac{15x - 10}{5} = \underline{} - 2$

2. Complete each equation so that it is true for no values of x.

   a. $3x + 6 = 3(x + \underline{})$

   b. $x - 2 = \text{-}(\underline{} - x)$

   c. $\frac{15x - 10}{5} = \underline{} - 2$

3. Describe how you know whether an equation will be true for all values of x or true for no values of x.

Lesson 15 Summary

An equation is a statement that two expressions have an equal value. The equation

$$2x = 6$$

is a true statement if x is 3:

$$2 \cdot 3 = 6$$

It is a false statement if x is 4:

$$2 \cdot 4 = 6$$

The equation $2x = 6$ has *one and only one solution*, because there is only one number (3) that you can double to get 6.

Some equations are true no matter what the value of the variable is. For example:

$$2x = x + x$$

is always true, because if you double a number, that will always be the same as adding the number to itself. Equations like $2x = x + x$ have an *infinite number of solutions*. We say it is true for all values of x.

Some equations have *no solutions*. For example:

$$x = x + 1$$

has no solutions, because no matter what the value of x is, it can't equal one more than itself.

When we solve an equation, we are looking for the values of the variable that make the equation true. When we try to solve the equation, we make allowable moves assuming it *has* a solution. Sometimes we make allowable moves and get an equation like this:

$$8 = 7$$

This statement is false, so it must be that the original equation had no solution at all.

Lesson 15 Practice Problems

1. For each equation, decide if it is always true or never true.

   a. $x - 13 = x + 1$

   b. $x + \frac{1}{2} = x - \frac{1}{2}$

   c. $2(x + 3) = 5x + 6 - 3x$

   d. $x - 3 = 2x - 3 - x$

   e. $3(x - 5) = 2(x - 5) + x$

2. Mai says that the equation $2x + 2 = x + 1$ has no solution because the left hand side is double the right hand side. Do you agree with Mai? Explain your reasoning.

3. a. Write the other side of this equation so it's true for all values of x:
   $\frac{1}{2}(6x - 10) - x =$

   b. Write the other side of this equation so it's true for no values of x:
   $\frac{1}{2}(6x - 10) - x =$

iM KH

4. Here is an equation that is true for all values of x: $5(x + 2) = 5x + 10$. Elena saw this equation and says she can tell $20(x + 2) + 31 = 4(5x + 10) + 31$ is also true for any value of x. How can she tell? Explain your reasoning.

5. Elena and Lin are trying to solve $\frac{1}{2}x + 3 = \frac{7}{2}x + 5$. Describe the change they each make to each side of the equation.

   a. Elena's first step is to write $3 = \frac{7}{2}x - \frac{1}{2}x + 5$.

   b. Lin's first step is to write $x + 6 = 7x + 10$.

   (From Unit 4, Lesson 13.)

6. Solve each equation and check your solution.

   $$3x - 6 = 4(2 - 3x) - 8x \qquad \frac{1}{2}z + 6 = \frac{3}{2}(z + 6) \qquad 9 - 7w = 8w + 8$$

   (From Unit 4, Lesson 14.)

Lesson 16: How Many Solutions?

Let's solve equations with different numbers of solutions.

16.1: Matching Solutions

Consider the unfinished equation $12(x - 3) + 18 = $ _____. Match the following expressions with the number of solutions the equation would have with that expression on the right hand side.

1. $6(2x - 3)$
2. $4(3x - 3)$
3. $4(2x - 3)$

- one solution
- no solutions
- all solutions

16.2: Thinking About Solutions Some More

Your teacher will give you some cards.

1. With your partner, solve each equation.

2. Then, sort them into categories.

3. Describe the defining characteristics of those categories and be prepared to share your reasoning with the class.

16.3: Make Use of Structure

For each equation, determine whether it has no solutions, exactly one solution, or is true for all values of x (and has infinitely many solutions). If an equation has one solution, solve to find the value of x that makes the statement true.

1. a. $6x + 8 = 7x + 13$

    b. $6x + 8 = 2(3x + 4)$

    c. $6x + 8 = 6x + 13$

2.   a. $\frac{1}{4}(12 - 4x) = 3 - x$

     b. $x - 3 = 3 - x$

     c. $x - 3 = 3 + x$

3.   a. $-5x - 3x + 2 = -8x + 2$

     b. $-5x - 3x - 4 = -8x + 2$

     c. $-5x - 4x - 2 = -8x + 2$

4.   a. $4(2x - 2) + 2 = 4(x - 2)$

     b. $4x + 2(2x - 3) = 8(x - 1)$

     c. $4x + 2(2x - 3) = 4(2x - 2) + 2$

5.   a. $x - 3(2 - 3x) = 2(5x + 3)$

     b. $x - 3(2 + 3x) = 2(5x - 3)$

     c. $x - 3(2 - 3x) = 2(5x - 3)$

6. What do you notice about equations with one solution? How is this different from equations with no solutions and equations that are true for every x?

Are you ready for more?

Consecutive numbers follow one right after the other. An example of three consecutive numbers is 17, 18, and 19. Another example is -100, -99, -98.

1. Choose any set of three consecutive numbers. Find their average. What do you notice?

2. Find the average of another set of three consecutive numbers. What do you notice?

3. Explain why the thing you noticed must always work, or find a counterexample.

Lesson 16 Summary

Sometimes it's possible to look at the structure of an equation and tell if it has infinitely many solutions or no solutions. For example, look at

$$2(12x + 18) + 6 = 18x + 6(x + 7).$$

Using the distributive property on the left and right sides, we get

$$24x + 36 + 6 = 18x + 6x + 42.$$

From here, collecting like terms gives us

$$24x + 42 = 24x + 42.$$

Since the left and right sides of the equation are the same, we know that this equation is true for any value of x without doing any more moves!

Similarly, we can sometimes use structure to tell if an equation has no solutions. For example, look at

$$6(6x + 5) = 12(3x + 2) + 12.$$

If we think about each move as we go, we can stop when we realize there is no solution:

$$\frac{1}{6} \cdot 6(6x + 5) = \frac{1}{6} \cdot (12(3x + 2) + 12) \qquad \text{Multiply each side by } \frac{1}{6}.$$

$$6x + 5 = 2(3x + 2) + 2 \qquad \text{Distribute } \frac{1}{6} \text{ on the right side.}$$

$$6x + 5 = 6x + 4 + 2 \qquad \text{Distribute 2 on the right side.}$$

The last move makes it clear that the **constant terms** on each side, 5 and $4 + 2$, are not the same. Since adding 5 to an amount is always less than adding $4 + 2$ to that same amount, we know there are no solutions.

Doing moves to keep an equation balanced is a powerful part of solving equations, but thinking about what the structure of an equation tells us about the solutions is just as important.

Glossary

- coefficient
- constant term

Lesson 16 Practice Problems

1. Lin was looking at the equation $2x - 32 + 4(3x - 2462) = 14x$. She said, "I can tell right away there are no solutions, because on the left side, you will have $2x + 12x$ and a bunch of constants, but you have just $14x$ on the right side." Do you agree with Lin? Explain your reasoning.

2. Han was looking at the equation $6x - 4 + 2(5x + 2) = 16x$. He said, "I can tell right away there are no solutions, because on the left side, you will have $6x + 10x$ and a bunch of constants, but you have just $16x$ on the right side." Do you agree with Han? Explain your reasoning.

3. Decide whether each equation is true for all, one, or no values of x.

   a. $6x - 4 = -4 + 6x$

   b. $4x - 6 = 4x + 3$

   c. $-2x + 4 = -3x + 4$

4. Solve each of these equations. Explain or show your reasoning.

    a. $3(x - 5) = 6$

    b. $2\left(x - \frac{2}{3}\right) = 0$

    c. $4x - 5 = 2 - x$

(From Unit 4, Lesson 13.)

5. In the picture triangle $A'B'C'$ is an image of triangle ABC after a rotation. The center of rotation is E.

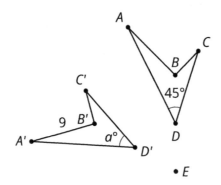

    a. What is the length of side AB? Explain how you know.

    b. What is the measure of angle D'? Explain how you know.

(From Unit 1, Lesson 6.)

6. Solve each of these equations. Explain or show your reasoning.

$$2(x + 5) = 3x + 1 \qquad 3y - 4 = 6 - 2y \qquad 3(n + 2) = 9(6 - n)$$

(From Unit 4, Lesson 13.)

Lesson 17: When Are They the Same?

Let's use equations to think about situations.

17.1: Which Would You Choose?

If you were babysitting, would you rather

- Charge $5 for the first hour and $8 for each additional hour?

Or

- Charge $15 for the first hour and $6 for each additional hour?

Explain your reasoning.

17.2: Water Tanks

The amount of water in two tanks every 5 minutes is shown in the table.

time (minutes)	tank 1 (liters)	tank 2 (liters)
0	25	1000
5	175	900
10	325	800
15	475	700
20	625	600
25	775	500
30	925	400
35	1075	300
40	1225	200
45	1375	100
50	1525	0

1. Describe what is happening in each tank. Either draw a picture, say it verbally, or write a few sentences.

2. Use the table to estimate when the tanks will have the same amount of water.

3. The amount of water (in liters) in tank 1 after t minutes is $30t + 25$. The amount of water (in liters) in tank 2 after t minutes is $-20t + 1000$. Find the time when the amount of water will be equal.

17.3: Elevators

A building has two elevators that both go above and below ground.

At a certain time of day, the travel time it takes elevator A to reach height h in meters is $0.8h + 16$ seconds.

The travel time it takes elevator B to reach height h in meters is $-0.8h + 12$ seconds.

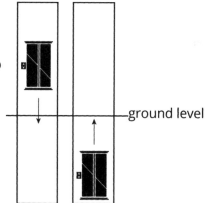

ground level

1. What is the height of each elevator at this time?

2. How long would it take each elevator to reach ground level at this time?

3. If the two elevators travel toward one another, at what height do they pass each other? How long would it take?

4. If you are on an underground parking level 14 meters below ground, which elevator would reach you first?

Are you ready for more?

1. In a two-digit number, the ones digit is twice the tens digit. If the digits are reversed, the new number is 36 more than the original number. Find the number.

2. The sum of the digits of a two-digit number is 11. If the digits are reversed, the new number is 45 less than the original number. Find the number.

3. The sum of the digits in a two-digit number is 8. The value of the number is 4 less than 5 times the ones digit. Find the number.

Lesson 17 Summary

Imagine a full 1,500 liter water tank that springs a leak, losing 2 liters per minute. We could represent the number of liters left in the tank with the expression $-2x + 1,500$, where x represents the number of minutes the tank has been leaking.

Now imagine at the same time, a second tank has 300 liters and is being filled at a rate of 6 liters per minute. We could represent the amount of water in liters in this second tank with the expression $6x + 300$, where x represents the number of minutes that have passed.

Since one tank is losing water and the other is gaining water, at some point they will have the same amount of water—but when? Asking when the two tanks have the same number of liters is the same as asking when $-2x + 1,500$ (the number of liters in the first tank after x minutes) is equal to $6x + 300$ (the number of liters in the second tank after x minutes),

$$-2x + 1,500 = 6x + 300.$$

Solving for x gives us $x = 150$ minutes. So after 150 minutes, the number of liters of the first tank is equal to the number of liters of the second tank. But how much water is actually in each tank at that time? Since both tanks have the same number of liters after 150 minutes, we could substitute $x = 150$ minutes into either expression.

Using the expression for the first tank, we get $-2(150) + 1,500$ which is equal to $-300 + 1,500$, or 1,200 liters.

If we use the expression for the second tank, we get $6(150) + 300$, or just $900 + 300$, which is also 1,200 liters. That means that after 150 minutes, each tank has 1,200 liters.

Lesson 17 Practice Problems

1. Cell phone Plan A costs $70 per month and comes with a free $500 phone. Cell phone Plan B costs $50 per month but does not come with a phone. If you buy the $500 phone and choose Plan B, how many months is it until your cost is the same as Plan A's?

2. Priya and Han are biking in the same direction on the same path.

   a. Han is riding at a constant speed of 16 miles per hour. Write an expression that shows how many miles Han has gone after t hours.

   b. Priya started riding a half hour before Han. If Han has been riding for t hours, how long has Priya been riding?

   c. Priya is riding at a constant speed of 12 miles per hour. Write an expression that shows how many miles Priya has gone after Han has been riding for t hours.

   d. Use your expressions to find when Han and Priya meet.

3. Which story matches the equation $-6 + 3x = 2 + 4x$?

    A. At 5 p.m., the temperatures recorded at two weather stations in Antarctica are -6 degrees and 2 degrees. The temperature changes at the same constant rate, x degrees per hour, throughout the night at both locations. The temperature at the first station 3 hours after this recording is the same as the temperature at the second station 4 hours after this recording.

    B. Elena and Kiran play a card game. Every time they collect a pair of matching cards, they earn x points. At one point in the game, Kiran has -6 points and Elena has 2 points. After Elena collects 3 pairs and Kiran collects 4 pairs, they have the same number of points.

4. For what value of x do the expressions $\frac{2}{3}x + 2$ and $\frac{4}{3}x - 6$ have the same value?

5. Decide whether each equation is true for all, one, or no values of x.

    a. $2x + 8 = -3.5x + 19$

    b. $9(x - 2) = 7x + 5$

    c. $3(3x + 2) - 2x = 7x + 6$

(From Unit 4, Lesson 16.)

iM KH

6. Solve each equation. Explain your reasoning.

$3d + 16 = -2(5 - 3d)$

$2k - 3(4 - k) = 3k + 4$

$\frac{3y-6}{9} = \frac{4-2y}{-3}$

(From Unit 4, Lesson 14.)

7. Describe a rigid transformation that takes Polygon A to Polygon B.

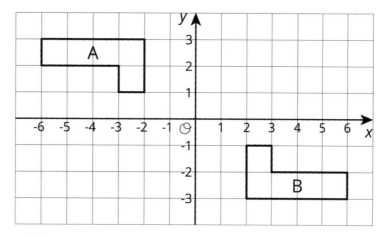

(From Unit 1, Lesson 6.)

Lesson 18: Applications of Expressions

- Let's use expressions to solve problems.

18.1: Algebra Talk: Equivalent to $0.75t - 21$

Decide whether each expression is equivalent to $0.75t - 21$. Be prepared to explain how you know.

$\frac{3}{4}t - 21$

$\frac{3}{4}(t - 21)$

$0.75(t - 28)$

$t - 0.25t - 21$

18.2: Two Ways to Calculate

Usually when you want to calculate something, there is more than one way to do it. For one or more of these situations, show how the two different ways of calculating are equivalent to each other.

1. Estimating the temperature in Fahrenheit when you know the temperature in Celsius
   a. Double the temperature in Celsius, then add 30.

   b. Add 15 to the temperature in Celsius, then double the result.

2. Calculating a 15% tip on a restaurant bill
   a. Take 10% of the bill amount, take 5% of the bill amount, and add those two values together.

   b. Multiply the bill amount by 3, divide the result by 2, and then take $\frac{1}{10}$ of that result.

iM KH

3. Changing a distance in miles to a distance in kilometers
   a. Take the number of miles, double it, then decrease the result by 20%.

   b. Divide the number of miles by 5, then multiply the result by 8.

18.3: Which Way?

You have two coupons to the same store: one for 20% off and one for $30 off. The cashier will let you use them both, and will let you decide in which order to use them.

- Mai says that it doesn't matter in which order you use them. You will get the same discount either way.

- Jada says that you should apply the 20% off coupon first, and then the $30 off coupon.

- Han says that you should apply the $30 off coupon first, and then the 20% off coupon.

- Kiran says that it depends on how much you are spending.

Do you agree with any of them? Explain your reasoning.

Learning Targets

Lesson 1: Writing and Graphing Inequalities

- I can graph inequalities on a number line.

- I can write an inequality to represent a situation.

Lesson 2: Solutions of Inequalities

- I can determine if a particular number is a solution to an inequality.

- I can explain what it means for a number to be a solution to an inequality.

- I can graph the solutions to an inequality on a number line.

Lesson 3: Interpreting Inequalities

- I can explain what the solution to an inequality means in a situation.

- I can write inequalities that involves more than one variable.

Lesson 4: Finding Solutions to Inequalities in Context

- I can describe the solutions to a inequality by solving a related equation and then reasoning about values that make the inequality true.

- I can write an inequality to represent a situation.

Lesson 5: Efficiently Solving Inequalities

- I can graph the solutions to an inequality on a number line.

- I can solve inequalities by solving a related equation and then checking which values are solutions to the original inequality.

Lesson 6: Modeling with Inequalities

- I can use what I know about inequalities to solve real-world problems.

Lesson 7: Subtraction in Equivalent Expressions

- I can organize my work when I use the distributive property.

- I can re-write subtraction as adding the opposite and then rearrange terms in an expression.

Lesson 8: Expanding and Factoring

- I can organize my work when I use the distributive property.

- I can use the distributive property to rewrite expressions with positive and negative numbers.

- I understand that factoring and expanding are words used to describe using the distributive property to write equivalent expressions.

Lesson 9: Combining Like Terms (Part 1)

- I can figure out whether two expressions are equivalent to each other.

- When possible, I can write an equivalent expression that has fewer terms.

Lesson 10: Combining Like Terms (Part 2)

- I am aware of some common pitfalls when writing equivalent expressions, and I can avoid them.

- When possible, I can write an equivalent expression that has fewer terms.

Lesson 11: Combining Like Terms (Part 3)

- Given an expression, I can use various strategies to write an equivalent expression.

- When I look at an expression, I can notice if some parts have common factors and make the expression shorter by combining those parts.

Lesson 12: Balanced Moves

- I can add, subtract, multiply, or divide each side of an equation by the same expression to get a new equation with the same solution.

Lesson 13: More Balanced Moves

- I can make sense of multiple ways to solve an equation.

Lesson 14: Strategic Solving

- I can solve linear equations in one variable.

Lesson 15: All, Some, or No Solutions

- I can determine whether an equation has no solutions, one solution, or infinitely many solutions.

Lesson 16: How Many Solutions?

- I can solve equations with different numbers of solutions.

Lesson 17: When Are They the Same?

- I can use an expression to find when two things, like height, are the same in a real-world situation.

Lesson 18: Applications of Expressions

- I can write algebraic expressions to understand and justify a choice between two options.

ACCELERATED

7

Unit

5

STUDENT WORKBOOK

Book 2

Lesson 1: Understanding Proportional Relationships

Let's study some graphs.

1.1: Notice and Wonder: Two Graphs

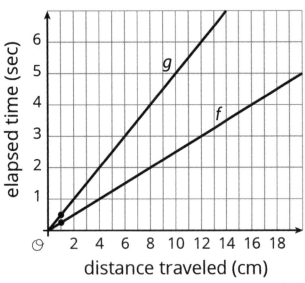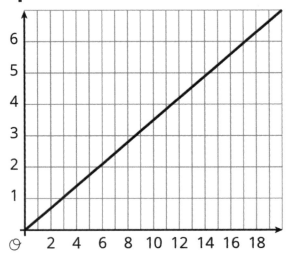

What do you notice? What do you wonder?

1.2: Moving Through Representations

A ladybug and ant move at constant speeds. The diagrams with tick marks show their positions at different times. Each tick mark represents 1 centimeter.

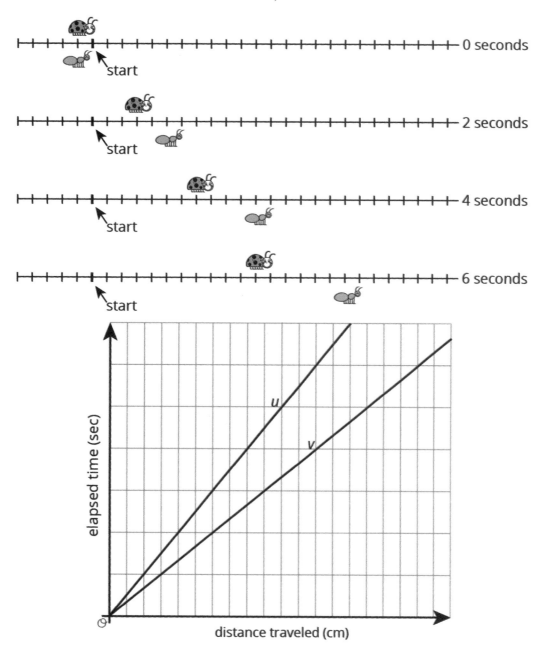

1. Lines u and v also show the positions of the two bugs. Which line shows the ladybug's movement? Which line shows the ant's movement? Explain your reasoning.

2. How long does it take the ladybug to travel 12 cm? The ant?

3. Scale the vertical and horizontal axes by labeling each grid line with a number. You will need to use the time and distance information shown in the tick-mark diagrams.

4. Mark and label the point on line u and the point on line v that represent the time and position of each bug after traveling 1 cm.

Are you ready for more?

1. How fast is each bug traveling?

2. Will there ever be a time when the ant is twice as far away from the start as the ladybug? Explain or show your reasoning.

1.3: Moving Twice as Fast

Refer to the tick-mark diagrams and graph in the earlier activity when needed.

1. Imagine a bug that is moving twice as fast as the ladybug. On each tick-mark diagram, mark the position of this bug.

2. Plot this bug's positions on the coordinate axes with lines u and v, and connect them with a line.

3. Write an equation for each of the three lines.

Lesson 1 Summary

Graphing is a way to help us make sense of relationships. But the graph of a line on a coordinate axes without scale or labels isn't very helpful. For example, let's say we know that on longer bike rides Kiran can ride 4 miles every 16 minutes and Mai can ride 4 miles every 12 minutes. Here are the graphs of these relationships:

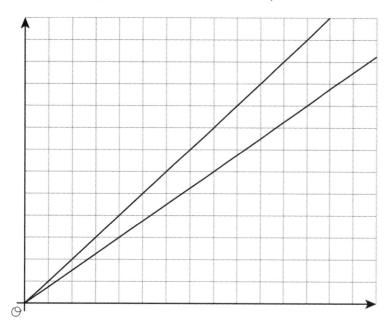

Without labels we can't even tell which line is Kiran and which is Mai! Without labels and a scale on the axes, we can't use these graphs to answer questions like:

1. Which graph goes with which rider?

2. Who rides faster?

3. If Kiran and Mai start a bike trip at the same time, how far are they after 24 minutes?

4. How long will it take each of them to reach the end of the 12 mile bike path?

Here are the same graphs, but now with labels and scale:

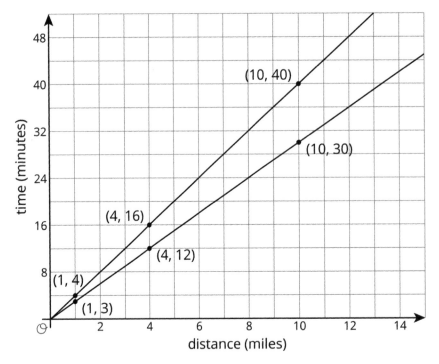

Revisiting the questions from earlier:

1. Which graph goes with each rider? If Kiran rides 4 miles in 16 minutes, then the point $(4, 16)$ is on his graph. If he rides for 1 mile, it will take 4 minutes. 10 miles will take 40 minutes. So the upper graph represents Kiran's ride. Mai's points for the same distances are $(1, 3)$, $(4, 12)$, and $(10, 30)$, so hers is the lower graph. (A letter next to each line would help us remember which is which!)

2. Who rides faster? Mai rides faster because she can ride the same distance as Kiran in a shorter time.

3. If Kiran and Mai start a bike trip at the same time, how far are they after 20 minutes? The points on the graphs at height 20 are 5 miles for Kiran and a little less than 7 miles for Mai.

4. How long will it take each of them to reach the end of the 12 mile bike path? The points on the graphs at a horizontal distance of 12 are 36 minutes for Mai and 48 minutes for Kiran. (Kiran's time after 12 miles is almost off the grid!)

Glossary

- constant of proportionality

iM KH

Lesson 1 Practice Problems

1. Priya jogs at a constant speed. The relationship between her distance and time is shown on the graph. Diego bikes at a constant speed twice as fast as Priya. Sketch a graph showing the relationship between Diego's distance and time.

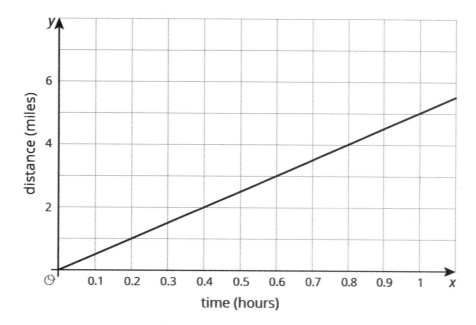

2. A you-pick blueberry farm offers 6 lbs of blueberries for $16.50.

Sketch a graph of the relationship between cost and pounds of blueberries.

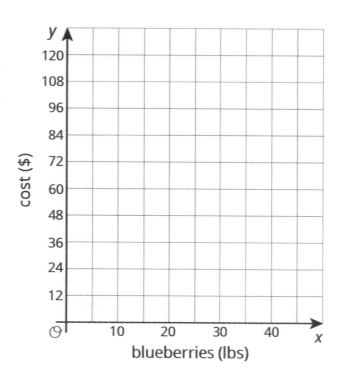

3. A line contains the points (-4, 1) and (4, 6). Decide whether or not each of these points is also on the line:

  a. $(0, 3.5)$

  b. $(12, 11)$

  c. $(80, 50)$

  d. $(-1, 2.875)$

(From Unit 2, Lesson 17.)

4. Select **all** the inequalities that have the same solutions as $-4x < 20$.

  A. $-x < 5$

  B. $4x > -20$

  C. $4x < -20$

  D. $x < -5$

  E. $x > 5$

  F. $x > -5$

(From Unit 4, Lesson 3.)

iM KH

Lesson 2: Representing Proportional Relationships

Let's graph proportional relationships.

2.1: An Unknown Situation

Here is a graph that could represent a variety of different situations.

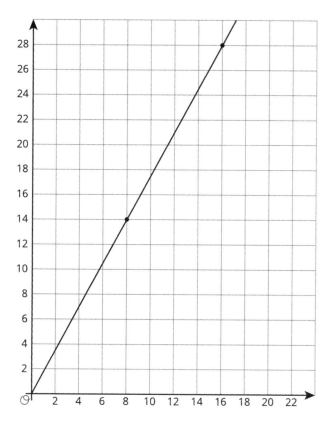

1. Write an equation for the graph.

2. Sketch a new graph of this relationship.

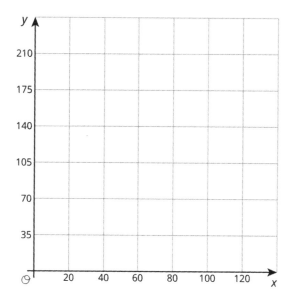

2.2: Card Sort: Proportional Relationships

Your teacher will give you 12 graphs of proportional relationships.

1. Sort the graphs into groups based on what proportional relationship they represent.

2. Write an equation for each *different* proportional relationship you find.

2.3: Different Scales

Two large water tanks are filling with water. Tank A is not filled at a constant rate, and the relationship between its volume of water and time is graphed on each set of axes. Tank B is filled at a constant rate of $\frac{1}{2}$ liters per minute. The relationship between its volume of water and time can be described by the equation $v = \frac{1}{2}t$, where t is the time in minutes and v is the total volume in liters of water in the tank.

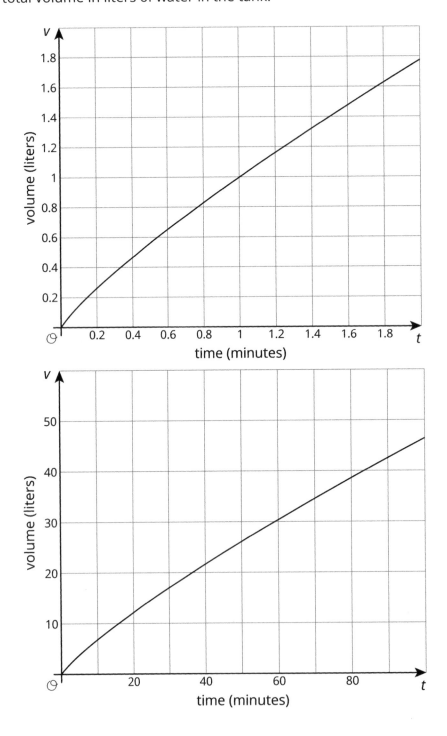

iM KH

1. Sketch and label a graph of the relationship between the volume of water v and time t for Tank B on each of the axes.

2. Answer the following questions and say which graph you used to find your answer.

   a. After 30 seconds, which tank has the most water?

   b. At approximately what times do both tanks have the same amount of water?

   c. At approximately what times do both tanks contain 1 liter of water? 20 liters?

Are you ready for more?

A giant tortoise travels at 0.17 miles per hour and an arctic hare travels at 37 miles per hour.

1. Draw separate graphs that show the relationship between time elapsed, in hours, and distance traveled, in miles, for both the tortoise and the hare.

2. Would it be helpful to try to put both graphs on the same pair of axes? Why or why not?

3. The tortoise and the hare start out together and after half an hour the hare stops to take a rest. How long does it take the tortoise to catch up?

2.4: Representations of Proportional Relationships

1. Here are two ways to represent a situation.

Description:

Jada and Noah counted the number of steps they took to walk a set distance. To walk the same distance, Jada took 8 steps while Noah took 10 steps. Then they found that when Noah took 15 steps, Jada took 12 steps.

Equation:

Let x represent the number of steps Jada takes and let y represent the number of steps Noah takes.

$$y = \frac{5}{4}x$$

a. Create a table that represents this situation with at least 3 pairs of values.

b. Graph this relationship and label the axes.

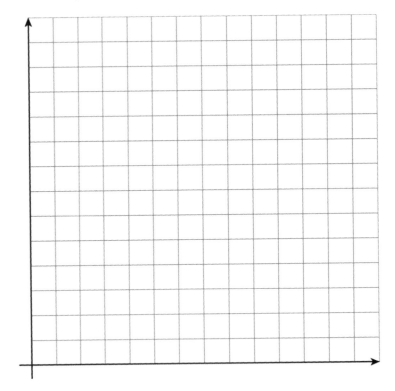

c. How can you see or calculate the constant of proportionality in each representation? What does it mean?

iM KH

d. Explain how you can tell that the equation, description, graph, and table all represent the same situation.

2. Here are two ways to represent a situation.

Description:

The Origami Club is doing a car wash fundraiser to raise money for a trip. They charge the same price for every car. After 11 cars, they raised a total of $93.50. After 23 cars, they raised a total of $195.50.

Table:

number of cars	amount raised in dollars
11	93.50
23	195.50

a. Write an equation that represents this situation. (Use c to represent number of cars and use m to represent amount raised in dollars.)

b. Create a graph that represents this situation.

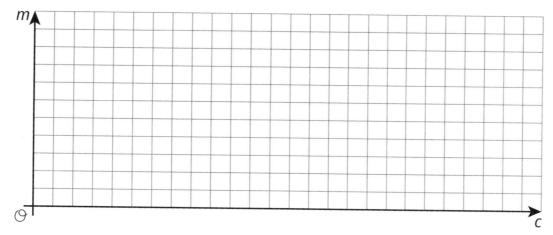

c. How can you see or calculate the constant of proportionality in each representation? What does it mean?

    d. Explain how you can tell that the equation, description, graph, and table all represent the same situation.

2.5: Info Gap: Proportional Relationships

Your teacher will give you either a *problem card* or a *data card*. Do not show or read your card to your partner.

If your teacher gives you the *problem card*:

1. Silently read your card and think about what information you need to be able to answer the question.

2. Ask your partner for the specific information that you need.

3. Explain how you are using the information to solve the problem.

    Continue to ask questions until you have enough information to solve the problem.

4. Share the *problem card* and solve the problem independently.

5. Read the *data card* and discuss your reasoning.

If your teacher gives you the *data card*:

1. Silently read your card.

2. Ask your partner *"What specific information do you need?"* and wait for them to *ask* for information.

    If your partner asks for information that is not on the card, do not do the calculations for them. Tell them you don't have that information.

3. Before sharing the information, ask *"Why do you need that information?"* Listen to your partner's reasoning and ask clarifying questions.

4. Read the *problem card* and solve the problem independently.

5. Share the *data card* and discuss your reasoning.

Pause here so your teacher can review your work. Ask your teacher for a new set of cards and repeat the activity, trading roles with your partner.

Are you ready for more?

Ten people can dig five holes in three hours. If n people digging at the same rate dig m holes in d hours:

    1. Is n proportional to m when $d = 3$?

    2. Is n proportional to d when $m = 5$?

    3. Is m proportional to d when $n = 10$?

Lesson 2 Summary

The scales we choose when graphing a relationship often depend on what information we want to know. For example, say two water tanks are filled at different constant rates. The relationship between time in minutes t and volume in liters v of tank A is given by $v = 2.2t$.

For tank B the relationship is $v = 2.75t$

These equations tell us that tank A is being filled at a constant rate of 2.2 liters per minute and tank B is being filled at a constant rate of 2.75 liters per minute.

If we want to use graphs to see at what times the two tanks will have 110 liters of water, then using an axis scale from 0 to 10, as shown here, isn't very helpful.

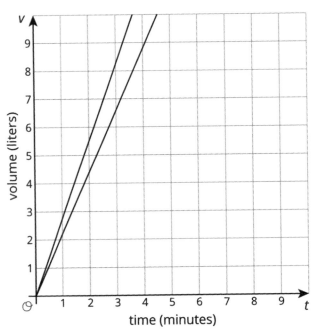

If we use a vertical scale that goes to 150 liters, a bit beyond the 110 we are looking for, and a horizontal scale that goes to 100 minutes, we get a much more useful set of axes for answering our question.

Now we can see that the two tanks will reach 110 liters 10 minutes apart—tank B after 40 minutes of filling and tank A after 50 minutes of filling.

It is important to note that both of these graphs are correct, but one uses a range of values that helps answer the question. In order to always pick a helpful scale, we should consider the situation and the questions asked about it.

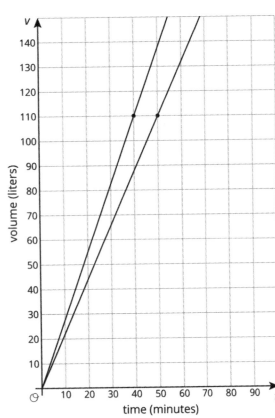

iM KH

What representation we choose for a proportional relationship also depends on our purpose. When we create representations we can choose helpful values by paying attention to the context. For example, if Tank C fills at a constant rate of 2.5 liters per minute, we could write the equation $v = 2.5t$. If we want to compare how long it takes Tanks A, B, and C to reach 110 liters, then we could graph them on the same axis. If we want to see the change in volume every 30 minutes, we could use a table:

minutes (t)	liters (v)
0	0
30	75
60	150
90	225

No matter the representation or the scale used, the constant of proportionality, 2.5, is evident in each. In the equation it is the number we multiply t by. In the graph it is the slope, and in the table it is the number by which we multiply values in the left column to get numbers in the right column. We can think of the constant of proportionality as a rate of change of v with respect to t. In this case the **rate of change** is 2.5 liters per minute.

Glossary

- rate of change

Lesson 2 Practice Problems

1. The tortoise and the hare are having a race. After the hare runs 16 miles the tortoise has only run 4 miles.

   The relationship between the distance x the tortoise "runs" in miles for every y miles the hare runs is $y = 4x$. Graph this relationship.

   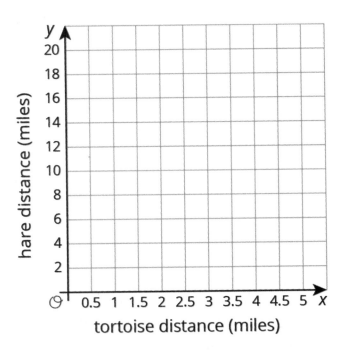

2. The table shows a proportional relationship between the weight on a spring scale and the distance the spring has stretched.

   a. Complete the table.

   b. Describe the scales you could use on the x and y axes of a coordinate grid that would show all the distances and weights in the table.

distance (cm)	weight (newtons)
20	28
55	
	140
1	

iM KH

3. Students are selling raffle tickets for a school fundraiser. They collect $24 for every 10 raffle tickets they sell.

   a. Suppose M is the amount of money the students collect for selling R raffle tickets. Write an equation that reflects the relationship between M and R.

   b. Label and scale the axes and graph this situation with M on the vertical axis and R on the horizontal axis. Make sure the scale is large enough to see how much they would raise if they sell 1000 tickets.

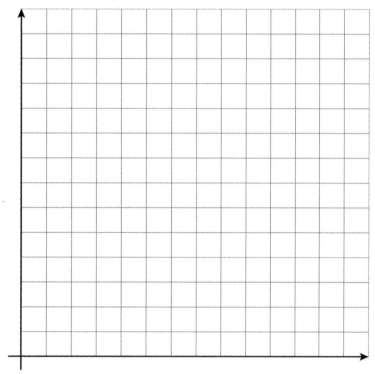

4. Describe how you can tell whether a line's slope is greater than 1, equal to 1, or less than 1.

(From Unit 2, Lesson 15.)

Lesson 3: Comparing Proportional Relationships

Let's compare proportional relationships.

3.1: What's the Relationship?

The equation $y = 4.2x$ could represent a variety of different situations.

1. Write a description of a situation represented by this equation. Decide what quantities x and y represent in your situation.

2. Make a table and a graph that represent the situation.

3.2: Comparing Two Different Representations

1. Elena babysits her neighbor's children. Her earnings are given by the equation $y = 8.40x$, where x represents the number of hours she worked and y represents the amount of money she earned.

   Jada earns $7 per hour mowing her neighbors' lawns.

   a. Who makes more money after working 12 hours? How much more do they make? Explain your reasoning by creating a graph or a table.

   b. What is the rate of change for each situation and what does it mean?

   c. Using your graph or table, determine how long it would take each person to earn $150.

2. Clare and Han have summer jobs stuffing envelopes for two different companies.

Han earns $15 for every 300 envelopes he finishes.

Clare's earnings can be seen in the table.

number of envelopes	money in dollars
400	40
900	90

a. By creating a graph, show how much money each person makes after stuffing 1,500 envelopes.

b. What is the rate of change for each situation and what does it mean?

c. Using your graph, determine how much more money one person makes relative to the other after stuffing 1,500 envelopes. Explain or show your reasoning.

3. Tyler plans to start a lemonade stand and is trying to perfect his recipe for lemonade. He wants to make sure the recipe doesn't use too much lemonade mix (lemon juice and sugar) but still tastes good.

Lemonade Recipe 1 is given by the equation $y = 4x$ where x represents the amount of lemonade mix in cups and y represents the amount of water in cups.

Lemonade Recipe 2 is given in the table.

lemonade mix (cups)	water (cups)
10	50
13	65
21	105

a. If Tyler had 16 cups of lemonade mix, how many cups of water would he need for each recipe? Explain your reasoning by creating a graph or a table.

b. What is the rate of change for each situation and what does it mean?

c. Tyler has a 5-gallon jug (which holds 80 cups) to use for his lemonade stand and 16 cups of lemonade mix. Which lemonade recipe should he use? Explain or show your reasoning.

Are you ready for more?

Han and Clare are still stuffing envelopes. Han can stuff 20 envelopes in a minute, and Clare can stuff 10 envelopes in a minute. They start working together on a pile of 1,000 envelopes.

   1. How long does it take them to finish the pile?

   2. Who earns more money?

Lesson 3 Summary

When two proportional relationships are represented in different ways, we compare them by finding a common piece of information.

For example, Clare's earnings are represented by the equation $y = 14.5x$, where y is her earnings in dollars for working x hours.

The table shows some information about Jada's pay.

time worked (hours)	earnings (dollars)
7	92.75
4.5	59.63
37	490.25

Who is paid at a higher rate per hour? How much more does that person have after 20 hours?

In Clare's equation we see that the rate of change (how many dollars she earns every hour) is 14.50.

We can calculate Jada's rate of change by dividing a value in the earnings column by the value in the same row in the time worked column. Using the last row, the rate of change for Jada is 13.25, since $490.25 \div 37 = 13.25$. An equation representing Jada's earnings is $y = 13.25x$. This means she earns $13.25 per hour.

So Clare is paid at a higher rate than Jada. Clare earns $1.25 more per hour than Jada. After 20 hours of work, she earns $25 more than Jada because $20 \cdot (1.25) = 25$.

Lesson 3 Practice Problems

1. A contractor must haul a large amount of dirt to a work site. She collected information from two hauling companies.

EZ Excavation gives its prices in a table.

dirt (cubic yards)	cost (dollars)
8	196
20	490
26	637

Happy Hauling Service gives its prices in a graph.

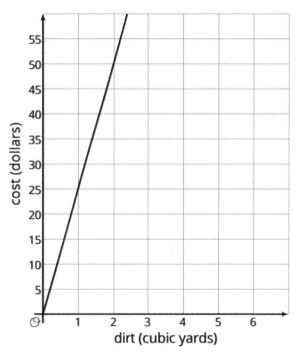

a. How much would each hauling company charge to haul 40 cubic yards of dirt? Explain or show your reasoning.

b. Calculate the rate of change for each relationship. What do they mean for each company?

c. If the contractor has 40 cubic yards of dirt to haul and a budget of $1000, which hauling company should she hire? Explain or show your reasoning.

2. Andre and Priya are tracking the number of steps they walk. Andre records that he can walk 6000 steps in 50 minutes. Priya writes the equation $y = 118x$, where y is the number of steps and x is the number of minutes she walks, to describe her step rate. This week, Andre and Priya each walk for a total of 5 hours. Who walks more steps? How many more?

3. Find the coordinates of point D in each diagram:

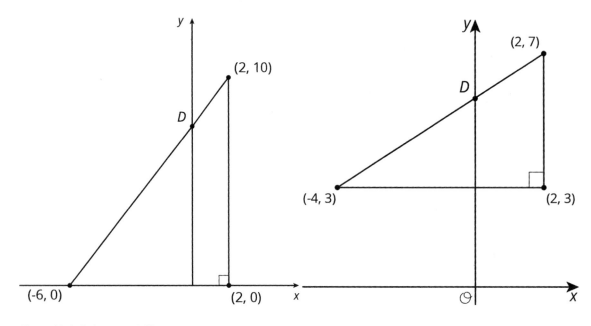

(From Unit 2, Lesson 16.)

4. Solve each equation.

$$\frac{1}{7}a + \frac{3}{4} = \frac{9}{8}$$
$$\frac{2}{3} + \frac{1}{5}b = \frac{5}{6}$$
$$\frac{3}{2} = \frac{4}{3}c + \frac{2}{3}$$

$$0.3d + 7.9 = 9.1$$
$$11.03 = 8.78 + 0.02e$$

(From Unit 3, Lesson 7.)

Lesson 4: Introduction to Linear Relationships

Let's explore some relationships between two variables.

4.1: Number Talk: Fraction Division

Find the value of $2\frac{5}{8} \div \frac{1}{2}$.

4.2: Stacking Cups

We have two stacks of styrofoam cups.

- One stack has 6 cups, and its height is 15 cm.
- The other stack has 12 cups, and its height is 23 cm.

How many cups are needed for a stack with a height of 50 cm?

iM KH

4.3: Connecting Slope to Rate of Change

1. If you didn't create your own graph of the situation before, do so now.

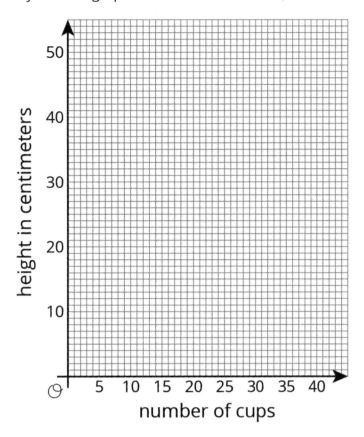

2. What are some ways you can tell that the number of cups is not proportional to the height of the stack?

3. What is the **slope** of the line in your graph? What does the slope mean in this situation?

4. At what point does your line intersect the vertical axis? What do the coordinates of this point tell you about the cups?

5. How much height does each cup after the first add to the stack?

Lesson 4 Summary

Andre starts babysitting and charges $10 for traveling to and from the job, and $15 per hour. For every additional hour he works he charges another $15. If we graph Andre's earnings based on how long he works, we have a line that starts at $10 on the vertical axis and then increases by $15 each hour. A **linear relationship** is any relationship between two quantities where one quantity has a constant **rate of change** with respect to the other.

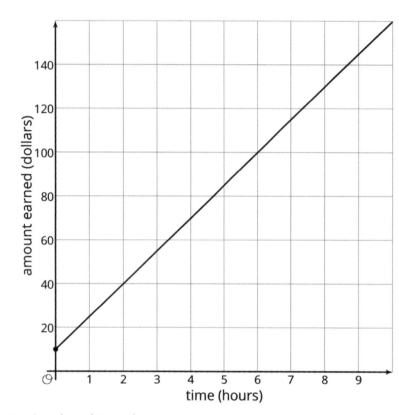

We can figure out the rate of change using the graph. Because the rate of change is constant, we can take any two points on the graph and divide the amount of vertical change by the amount of horizontal change. For example, take the points $(2, 40)$ and $(6, 100)$. They mean that Andre earns $40 for working 2 hours and $100 for working 6 hours. The rate of change is $\frac{100-40}{6-2} = 15$ dollars per hour. Andre's earnings go up $15 for each hour of babysitting.

Notice that this is the same way we calculate the **slope** of the line. That's why the graph is a line, and why we call this a linear relationship. The rate of change of a linear relationship is the same as the slope of its graph.

With proportional relationships we are used to graphs that contain the point $(0, 0)$. But proportional relationships are just one type of linear relationship. In the following lessons, we will continue to explore the other type of linear relationship where the quantities are not both 0 at the same time.

Glossary

- linear relationship

Lesson 4 Practice Problems

1. A restaurant offers delivery for their pizzas. The total cost is a delivery fee added to the price of the pizzas. One customer pays $25 to have 2 pizzas delivered. Another customer pays $58 for 5 pizzas. How many pizzas are delivered to a customer who pays $80?

2. To paint a house, a painting company charges a flat rate of $500 for supplies, plus $50 for each hour of labor.

   a. How much would the painting company charge to paint a house that needs 20 hours of labor? A house that needs 50 hours?

   b. Draw a line representing the relationship between x, the number of hours it takes the painting company to finish the house, and y, the total cost of painting the house. Label the two points from the earlier question on your graph.

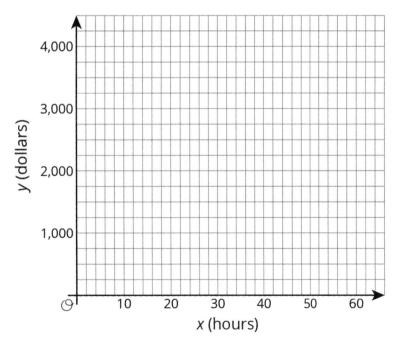

   c. Find the slope of the line. What is the meaning of the slope in this context?

3. Tyler and Elena are on the cross country team.

Tyler's distances and times for a training run are shown on the graph.

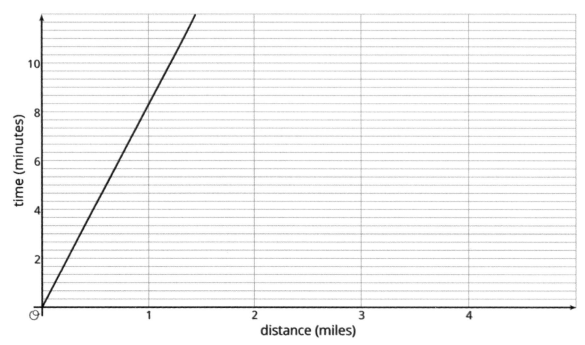

Elena's distances and times for a training run are given by the equation $y = 8.5x$, where x represents distance in miles and y represents time in minutes.

a. Who ran farther in 10 minutes? How much farther? Explain how you know.

b. Calculate each runner's pace in minutes per mile.

c. Who ran faster during the training run? Explain or show your reasoning.

(From Unit 5, Lesson 3.)

4. Write an equation for the line that passes through $(2, 5)$ and $(6, 7)$.

(From Unit 2, Lesson 17.)

iM KH

Lesson 5: More Linear Relationships

Let's explore some more relationships between two variables.

5.1: Growing

Look for a growing pattern. Describe the pattern you see.

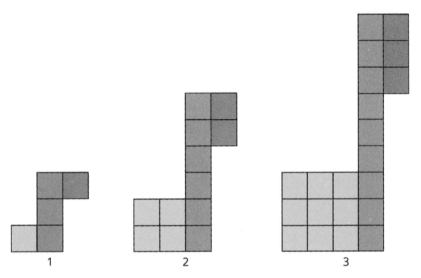

1. If your pattern continues growing in the same way, how many tiles of each color will be in the 4th and 5th diagram? The 10th diagram?

2. How many tiles of each color will be in the nth diagram? Be prepared to explain how your reasoning.

5.2: Slopes, Vertical Intercepts, and Graphs

Your teacher will give you 6 cards describing different situations and 6 cards with graphs.

1. Match each situation to a graph.

2. Pick one proportional relationship and one non-proportional relationship and answer the following questions about them.

   a. How can you find the slope from the graph? Explain or show your reasoning.

   b. Explain what the slope means in the situation.

   c. Find the point where the line crosses the vertical axis. What does that point tell you about the situation?

5.3: Summer Reading

Lin has a summer reading assignment. After reading the first 30 pages of the book, she plans to read 40 pages each day until she finishes. Lin makes the graph shown here to track how many total pages she'll read over the next few days.

After day 1, Lin reaches page 70, which matches the point $(1, 70)$ she made on her graph. After day 4, Lin reaches page 190, which does not match the point $(4, 160)$ she made on her graph. Lin is not sure what went wrong since she knows she followed her reading plan.

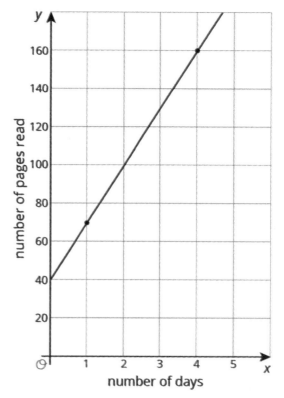

1. Sketch a line showing Lin's original plan on the axes.

2. What does the **vertical intercept** mean in this situation? How do the vertical intercepts of the two lines compare?

3. What does the slope mean in this situation? How do the slopes of the two lines compare?

Are you ready for more?

Jada's grandparents started a savings account for her in 2010. The table shows the amount in the account each year.

If this relationship is graphed with the year on the horizontal axis and the amount in dollars on the vertical axis, what is the vertical intercept? What does it mean in this context?

year	amount in dollars
2010	600
2012	750
2014	900
2016	1050

Lesson 5 Summary

At the start of summer break, Jada and Lin decide to save some of the money they earn helping out their neighbors to use during the school year. Jada starts by putting $20 into a savings jar in her room and plans to save $10 a week. Lin starts by putting $10 into a savings jar in her room plans to save $20 a week. Here are graphs of how much money they will save after 10 weeks if they each follow their plans:

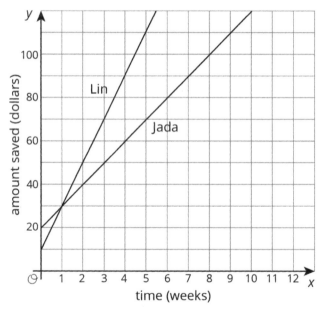

The value where a line intersects the vertical axis is called the **vertical intercept**. When the vertical axis is labeled with a variable like y, this value is also often called the *y-intercept*. Jada's graph has a vertical intercept of $20 while Lin's graph has a vertical intercept of $10. These values reflect the amount of money they each started with. At 1 week they will have saved the same amount, $30. But after week 1, Lin is saving more money per week (so she has a larger rate of change), so she will end up saving more money over the summer if they each follow their plans.

Glossary

- vertical intercept

Lesson 5 Practice Problems

1. Explain what the slope and intercept mean in each situation.

   a. A graph represents the perimeter, y, in units, for an equilateral triangle with side length x units. The slope of the line is 3 and the y-intercept is 0.

   b. The amount of money, y, in a cash box after x tickets are purchased for carnival games. The slope of the line is $\frac{1}{4}$ and the y-intercept is 8.

   c. The number of chapters read, y, after x days. The slope of the line is $\frac{5}{4}$ and the y-intercept is 2.

   d. The graph shows the cost in dollars, y, of a muffin delivery and the number of muffins, x, ordered. The slope of the line is 2 and the y-intercept is 3.

2. Customers at the gym pay a membership fee to join and then a fee for each class they attend. Here is a graph that represents the situation.

   a. What does the slope of the line shown by the points mean in this situation?

   b. What does the vertical intercept mean in this situation?

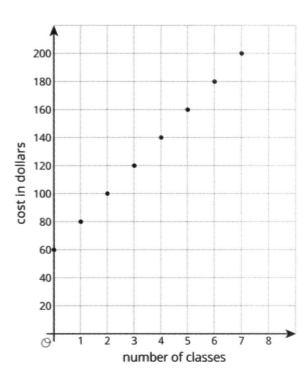

3. The graph shows the relationship between the number of cups of flour and the number of cups of sugar in Lin's favorite brownie recipe.

The table shows the amounts of flour and sugar needed for Noah's favorite brownie recipe.

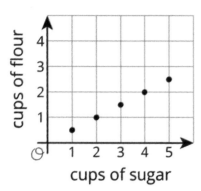

cups of sugar	cups of flour
$\frac{3}{2}$	1
3	2
$4\frac{1}{2}$	3

a. Noah and Lin buy a 12-cup bag of sugar and divide it evenly to make their recipes. If they each use all their sugar, how much flour do they each need?

b. Noah and Lin buy a 10-cup bag of flour and divide it evenly to make their recipes. If they each use all their flour, how much sugar do they each need?

(From Unit 5, Lesson 3.)

4. The diagram can be represented by the equation $25 = 2 + 6x$. Explain where you can see the 6 in the diagram.

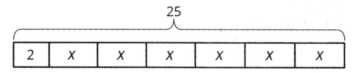

(From Unit 3, Lesson 3.)

iM KH

Lesson 6: Representations of Linear Relationships

Let's write equations from real situations.

6.1: Estimation: Which Holds More?

Which glass will hold the most water? The least?

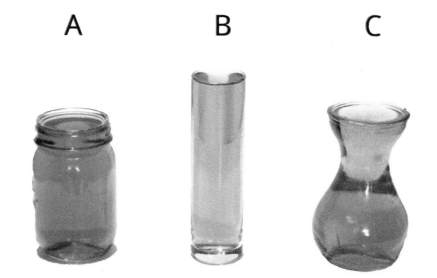

6.2: Rising Water Levels

1. Record data from your teacher's demonstration in the table. (You may not need all the rows.)

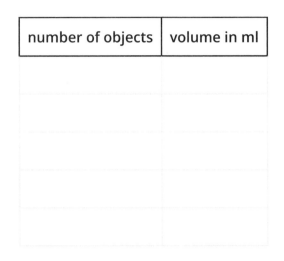

number of objects	volume in ml

2. What is the volume, V, in the cylinder after you add x objects? Explain your reasoning.

3. If you wanted to make the water reach the highest mark on the cylinder, how many objects would you need?

4. Plot and label points that show your measurements from the experiment.

5. The points should fall on a line. Use a ruler to graph this line.

6. Compute the slope of the line. What does the slope mean in this situation?

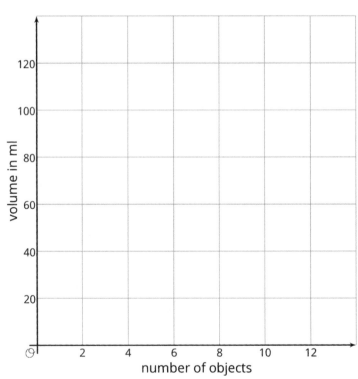

7. What is the vertical intercept? What does vertical intercept mean in this situation?

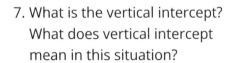

Are you ready for more?

A situation is represented by the equation $y = 5 + \frac{1}{2}x$.

   1. Invent a story for this situation.

   2. Graph the equation.

   3. What do the $\frac{1}{2}$ and the 5 represent in your situation?

   4. Where do you see the $\frac{1}{2}$ and 5 on the graph?

6.3: Calculate the Slope

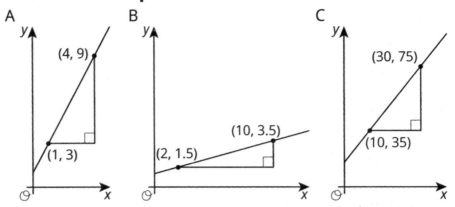

1. For each graph, record:

vertical change	horizontal change	slope

2. Describe a procedure for finding the slope between any two points on a line.

3. Write an expression for the slope of the line in the graph using the letters u, v, s, and t.

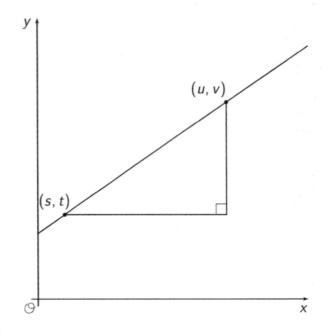

iM KH

Lesson 6 Summary

Let's say we have a glass cylinder filled with 50 ml of water and a bunch of marbles that are 3 ml in volume. If we drop marbles into the cylinder one at a time, we can watch the height of the water increase by the same amount, 3 ml, for each one added. This constant rate of change means there is a linear relationship between the number of marbles and the height of the water. Add one marble, the water height goes up 3 ml. Add 2 marbles, the water height goes up 6 ml. Add x marbles, the water height goes up $3x$ ml.

Reasoning this way, we can calculate that the height, y, of the water for x marbles is $y = 3x + 50$. Any linear relationships can be expressed in the form $y = mx + b$ using just the rate of change, m, and the initial amount, b. The 3 represents the rate of change, or slope of the graph, and the 50 represents the initial amount, or vertical intercept of the graph. We'll learn about some more ways to think about this equation in future lessons.

Now what if we didn't have a description to use to figure out the slope and the vertical intercept? That's okay so long as we can find some points on the line! For the line graphed here, two of the points on the line are $(3, 3)$ and $(9, 5)$ and we can use these points to draw in a slope triangle as shown:

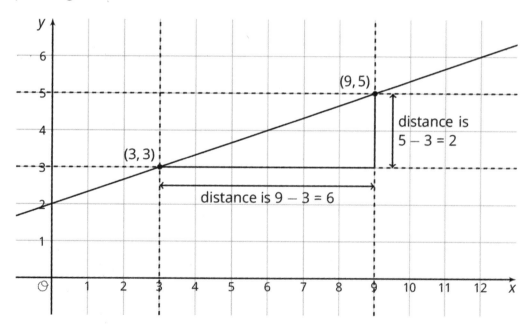

The slope of this line is the quotient of the length of the vertical side of the slope triangle and the length of the horizontal side of the slope triangle. So the slope, m, is $\frac{\text{vertical change}}{\text{horizontal change}} = \frac{2}{6} = \frac{1}{3}$. We can also see from the graph that the vertical intercept, b, is 2.

Putting these together, we can say that the equation for this line is $y = \frac{1}{3}x + 2$.

Lesson 6 Practice Problems

1. Create a graph that shows three linear relationships with different y-intercepts using the following slopes, and write an equation for each line.

   Slopes:

   - $\dfrac{1}{5}$

   - $\dfrac{3}{5}$

   - $\dfrac{6}{5}$

   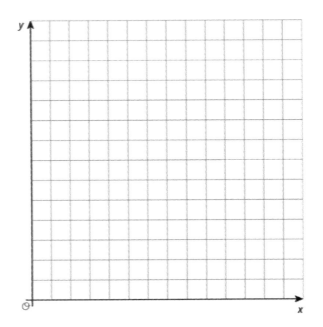

2. The graph shows the height in inches, h, of a bamboo plant t months after it has been planted.

   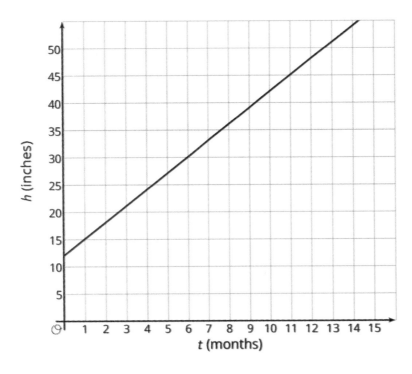

   a. Write an equation that describes the relationship between h and t.

   b. After how many months will the bamboo plant be 66 inches tall? Explain or show your reasoning.

iM KH

3. Here are recipes for two different banana cakes. Information for the first recipe is shown in the table.

sugar (cups)	flour (cups)
$\frac{1}{2}$	$\frac{3}{4}$
$2\frac{1}{2}$	$3\frac{3}{4}$
3	$4\frac{1}{2}$

The relationship between cups of flour y and cups of sugar x in the second recipe is $y = \frac{7}{4}x$

a. If you used 4 cups of sugar, how much flour does each recipe need?

b. What is the constant of proportionality for each situation and what does it mean?

(From Unit 5, Lesson 3.)

4. Show that the two figures are similar by identifying a sequence of translations, rotations, reflections, and dilations that takes the larger figure to the smaller one.

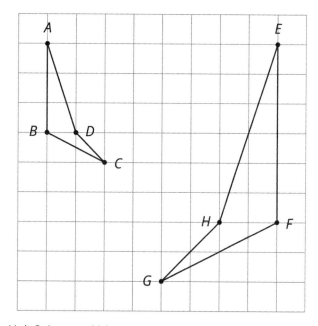

(From Unit 2, Lesson 11.)

Lesson 7: Translating to $y = mx + b$

Let's see what happens to the equations of translated lines.

7.1: Lines that Are Translations

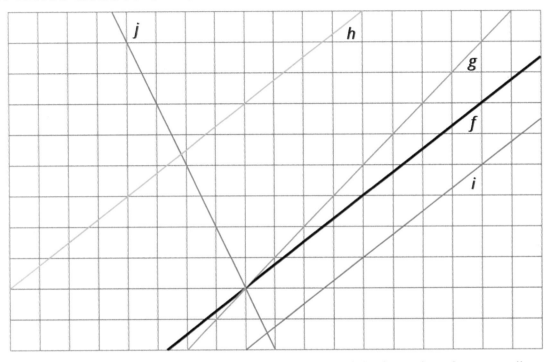

The diagram shows several lines. You can only see part of the lines, but they actually continue forever in both directions.

1. Which lines are images of line f under a translation?

2. For each line that is a translation of f, draw an arrow on the grid that shows the vertical translation distance.

iM KH

7.2: Increased Savings

1. Diego earns $10 per hour babysitting. Assume that he has no money saved before he starts babysitting and plans to save all of his earnings. Graph how much money, y, he has after x hours of babysitting.

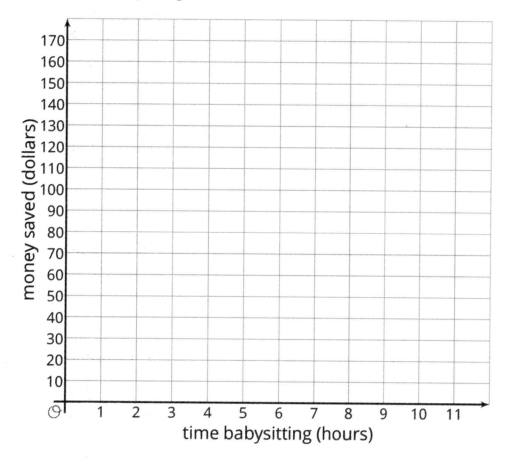

2. Now imagine that Diego started with $30 saved before he starts babysitting. On the same set of axes, graph how much money, y, he would have after x hours of babysitting.

3. Compare the second line with the first line. How much *more* money does Diego have after 1 hour of babysitting? 2 hours? 5 hours? x hours?

4. Write an equation for each line.

7.3: Translating a Line

This graph shows two lines.

Line a goes through the origin $(0, 0)$.

Line h is the image of line a under a translation.

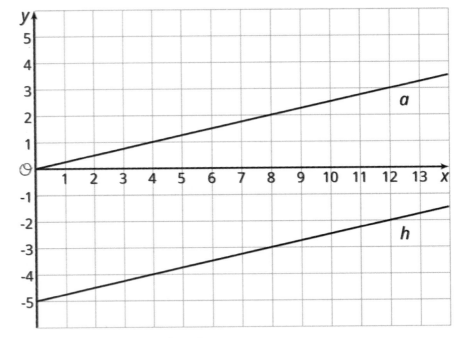

1. Select all of the equations whose graph is line h.

     a. $y = \frac{1}{4}x - 5$

     b. $y = \frac{1}{4}x + 5$

     c. $\frac{1}{4}x - 5 = y$

     d. $y = \text{-}5 + \frac{1}{4}x$

     e. $\text{-}5 + \frac{1}{4}x = y$

     f. $y = 5 - \frac{1}{4}x$

2. Your teacher will give you 12 cards. There are 4 pairs of lines, A–D, showing the graph, a, of a proportional relationship and the image, h, of a under a translation. Match each line h with an equation and either a table or description. For the line with no matching equation, write one on the blank card.

Are you ready for more?

A student says that the graph of the equation $y = 3(x + 8)$ is the same as the graph of $y = 3x$, only translated upwards by 8 units. Do you agree? Why or why not?

iM KH

Lesson 7 Summary

During an early winter storm, the snow fell at a rate of $\frac{1}{2}$ inch per hour. We can see the rate of change, $\frac{1}{2}$, in both the equation that represents this storm, $y = \frac{1}{2}x$, and in the slope of the line representing this storm.

In addition to being a linear relationship between the time since the beginning of the storm and the depth of the snow, we can also call this as a proportional relationship since the depth of snow was 0 at the beginning of the storm.

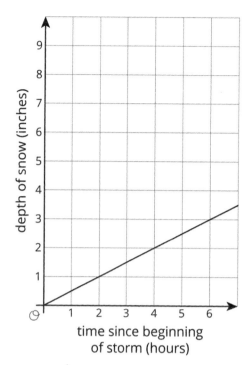

During a mid-winter storm, the snow again fell at a rate of $\frac{1}{2}$ inch per hour, but this time there was already 5 inches of snow on the ground.

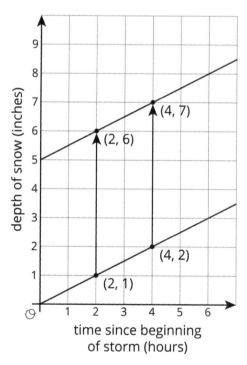

We can graph this storm on the same axes as the first storm by taking all the points on the graph of the first storm and translating them up 5 inches.

Two hours after each storm begins, 1 inch of new snow has fallen. For the first storm, this means there is now 1 inch of snow on the ground. For the second storm, this means there are now 6 inches of snow on the ground.

Unlike the first storm, the second is not a proportional relationship since the line representing the second storm has a vertical intercept of 5. The equation representing the storm, $y = \frac{1}{2}x + 5$, is of the form $y = mx + b$, where m is the rate of change, also the slope of the graph, and b is the initial amount, also the vertical intercept of the graph.

Lesson 7 Practice Problems

1. Select **all** the equations that have graphs with the same y-intercept.

   A. $y = 3x - 8$

   B. $y = 3x - 9$

   C. $y = 3x + 8$

   D. $y = 5x - 8$

   E. $y = 2x - 8$

   F. $y = \frac{1}{3}x - 8$

2. Create a graph showing the equations $y = \frac{1}{4}x$ and $y = \frac{1}{4}x - 5$. Explain how the graphs are the same and how they are different.

iM KH

3. A cable company charges $70 per month for cable service to existing customers.

    a. Find a linear equation representing the relationship between x, the number of months of service, and y, the total amount paid in dollars by an existing customer.

    b. For new customers, there is an additional one-time $100 service fee. Repeat the previous problem for new customers.

    c. When the two equations are graphed in the coordinate plane, how are they related to each other geometrically?

4. A mountain road is 5 miles long and gains elevation at a constant rate. After 2 miles, the elevation is 5500 feet above sea level. After 4 miles, the elevation is 6200 feet above sea level.

    a. Find the elevation of the road at the point where the road begins.

    b. Describe where you would see the point in part (a) on a graph where y represents the elevation in feet and x represents the distance along the road in miles.

(From Unit 5, Lesson 5.)

5. Match each graph to a situation.

A
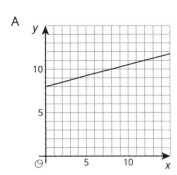

B
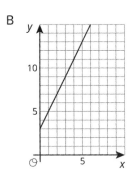

C
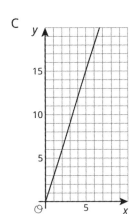

D
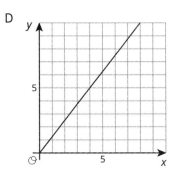

A. Graph A

B. Graph B

C. Graph C

D. Graph D

1. The graph represents the perimeter, y, in units, for an equilateral triangle with side length of x units. The slope of the line is 3.

2. The amount of money, y, in a cash box after x tickets are purchased for carnival games. The slope of the line is $\frac{1}{4}$.

3. The number of chapters read, y, after x days. The slope of the line is $\frac{5}{4}$.

4. The graph shows the cost in dollars, y, of a muffin delivery and the number of muffins, x, ordered. The slope of the line is 2.

(From Unit 5, Lesson 5.)

iM KH

Lesson 8: Slopes Don't Have to be Positive

Let's find out what a negative slope means.

8.1: Which One Doesn't Belong: Odd Line Out

Which line doesn't belong?

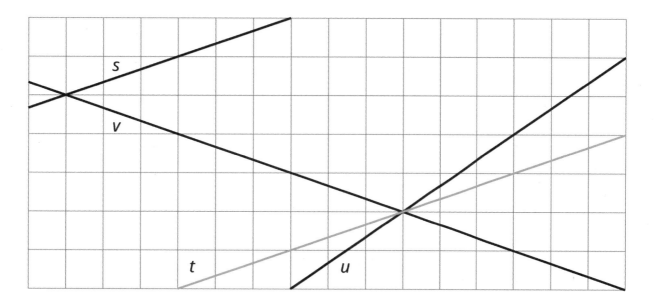

8.2: Stand Clear of the Closing Doors, Please

Noah put $40 on his fare card. Every time he rides public transportation, $2.50 is subtracted from the amount available on his card.

1. How much money, in dollars, is available on his card after he takes

    a. 0 rides?

    b. 1 ride?

    c. 2 rides?

    d. x rides?

2. Graph the relationship between amount of money on the card and number of rides.

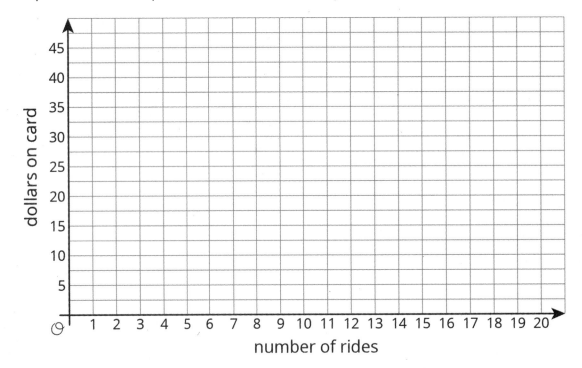

3. How many rides can Noah take before the card runs out of money? Where do you see this number of rides on your graph?

8.3: Travel Habits in July

Here is a graph that shows the amount on Han's fare card for every day of last July.

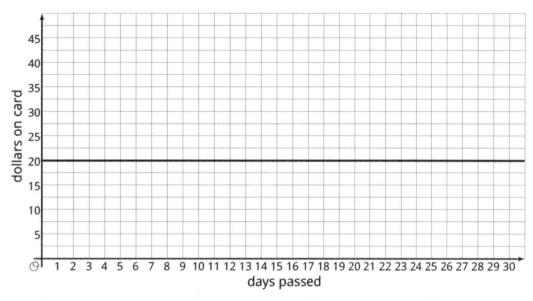

1. Describe what happened with the amount on Han's fare card in July.

2. Plot and label 3 different points on the line.

3. Write an equation that represents the amount on the card in July, y, after x days.

4. What value makes sense for the slope of the line that represents the amounts on Han's fare card in July?

Are you ready for more?

Let's say you have taken out a loan and are paying it back. Which of the following graphs have positive slope and which have negative slope?

1. Amount paid on the vertical axis and time since payments started on the horizontal axis.

2. Amount owed on the vertical axis and time remaining until the loan is paid off on the horizontal axis.

3. Amount paid on the vertical axis and time remaining until the loan is paid off on the horizontal axis.

8.4: Payback Plan

Elena borrowed some money from her brother. She pays him back by giving him the same amount every week. The graph shows how much she owes after each week.

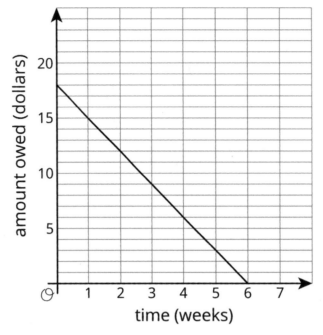

Answer and explain your reasoning for each question.

1. What is the slope of the line?

2. Explain how you know whether the slope is positive or negative.

3. What does the slope represent in this situation?

4. How much did Elena borrow?

5. How much time will it take for Elena to pay back all the money she borrowed?

iM KH

Lesson 8 Summary

At the end of winter in Maine, the snow on the ground was 30 inches deep. Then there was a particularly warm day and the snow melted at the rate of 1 inch per hour. The graph shows the relationship between the time since the snow started to melt and the depth of the snow.

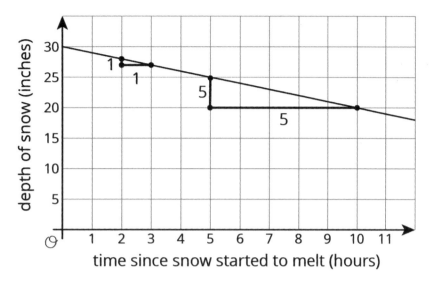

The slope of the graph is -1 since the rate of change is -1 inch per hour. That is, the depth goes *down* 1 inch per hour. The vertical intercept is 30 since the snow was 30 inches deep when the warmth started to melt the snow. The two slope triangles show how the rate of change is constant. It just also happens to be negative in this case since after each hour that passes, there is 1 inch *less* snow.

Graphs with negative slope often describe situations where some quantity is decreasing over time, like the depth of snow on warm days or the amount of money on a fare card being used to take rides on buses.

Slopes can be positive, negative, or even zero! A slope of 0 means there is no change in the *y*-value even though the *x*-value may be changing. For example, Elena won a contest where the prize was a special pass that gives her free bus rides for a year. Her fare card had $5 on it when she won the prize. Here is a graph of the amount of money on her fare card after winning the prize:

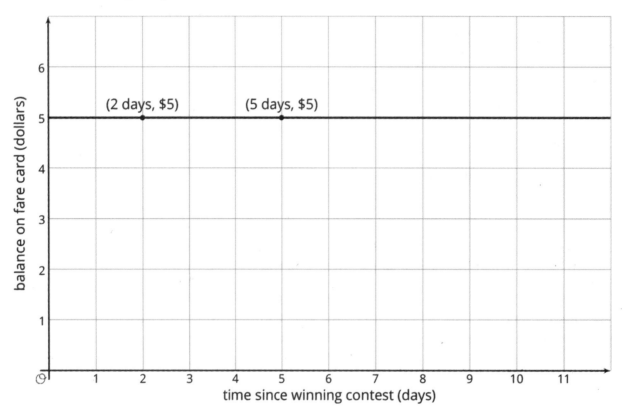

The vertical intercept is 5, since the graph starts when she has $5 on her fare card. The slope of the graph is 0 since she doesn't use her fare card for the next year, meaning the amount on her fare card doesn't change for a year. In fact, all graphs of linear relationships with slopes equal to 0 are horizontal—a rate of change of 0 means that, from one point to the next, the *y*-values remain the same.

iM KH

Lesson 8 Practice Problems

1. Suppose that during its flight, the elevation e (in feet) of a certain airplane and its time t, in minutes since takeoff, are related by a linear equation. Consider the graph of this equation, with time represented on the horizontal axis and elevation on the vertical axis. For each situation, decide if the slope is positive, zero, or negative.

   a. The plane is cruising at an altitude of 37,000 feet above sea level.

   b. The plane is descending at rate of 1000 feet per minute.

   c. The plane is ascending at a rate of 2000 feet per minute.

2. A group of hikers park their car at a trail head and walk into the forest to a campsite. The next morning, they head out on a hike from their campsite walking at a steady rate. The graph shows their distance in miles, d, from the car after h hours of hiking.

   a. How far is the campsite from their car? Explain how you know.

   b. Write an equation that describes the relationship between d and h.

   c. After how many hours of hiking will they be 16 miles from their car? Explain or show your reasoning.

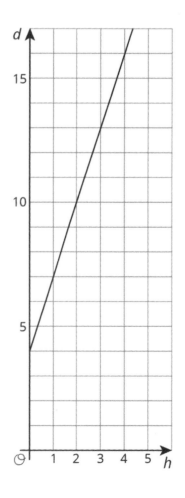

(From Unit 5, Lesson 6.)

3. Elena's aunt pays her $1 for each call she makes to let people know about her aunt's new business.

The table shows how much money Diego receives for washing windows for his neighbors.

number of windows	number of dollars
27	30
45	50
81	90

Select **all** the statements about the situation that are true.

   A. Elena makes more money for making 10 calls than Diego makes for washing 10 windows.

   B. Diego makes more money for washing each window than Elena makes for making each call.

   C. Elena makes the same amount of money for 20 calls as Diego makes for 18 windows.

   D. Diego needs to wash 35 windows to make as much money as Elena makes for 40 calls.

   E. The equation $y = \frac{9}{10}x$, where y is number of dollars and x is number of windows, represents Diego's situation.

   F. The equation $y = x$, where y is the number of dollars and x is the number of calls, represents Elena's situation.

(From Unit 5, Lesson 3.)

4. Each square on a grid represents 1 unit on each side. Match the graphs with the slopes of the lines.

A
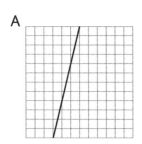

B
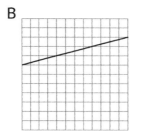

C
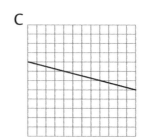

   ○ $-\frac{1}{4}$

   ○ $\frac{1}{4}$

   ○ 4

iM KH

5. Priya and Tyler are discussing the figures shown below. Priya thinks that B, C, and D are scaled copies of A. Tyler says B and D are scaled copies of A. Do you agree with Priya, or do you agree with Tyler? Explain your reasoning.

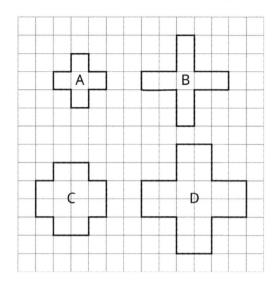

(From Unit 2, Lesson 1.)

6. Solve each equation, and check your solution.

$\frac{1}{9}(2m - 16) = \frac{1}{3}(2m + 4)$ $-4(r + 2) = 4(2 - 2r)$ $12(5 + 2y) = 4y - (6 - 9y)$

(From Unit 4, Lesson 13.)

Lesson 9: Slopes and Equations for All Kinds of Lines

Let's figure out the slope and equations for all kinds of lines.

9.1: Which One Doesn't Belong: Pairs of Lines

Which one doesn't belong?

A

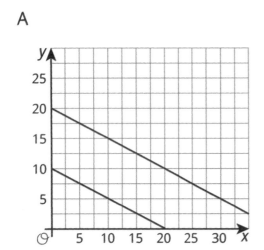

B

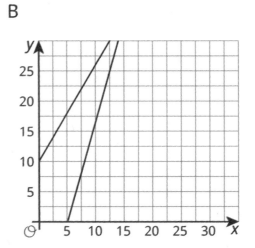

C

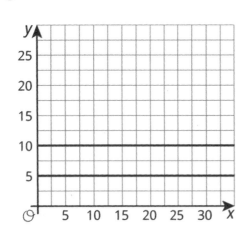

D

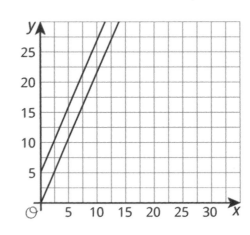

iM KH

9.2: Toward a More General Slope Formula

1. Plot the points $(1, 11)$ and $(8, 2)$, and use a ruler to draw the line that passes through them.

2. Without calculating, do you expect the slope of the line through $(1, 11)$ and $(8, 2)$ to be positive or negative? How can you tell?

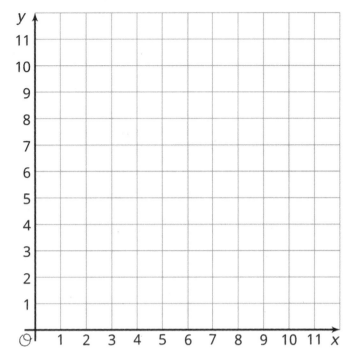

3. Calculate the slope of this line.

Are you ready for more?

Find the value of k so that the line passing through each pair of points has the given slope.

1. $(k, 2)$ and $(11, 14)$, slope = 2

2. $(1, k)$ and $(4, 1)$, slope = -2

3. $(3, 5)$ and $(k, 9)$, slope = $\frac{1}{2}$

4. $(-1, 4)$ and $(-3, k)$, slope = $\frac{-1}{2}$

5. $(\frac{-15}{2}, \frac{3}{16})$ and $(\frac{-13}{22}, k)$, slope = 0

9.3: Making Designs

Your teacher will give you either a design or a blank graph. Do not show your card to your partner.

If your teacher gives you the design:

1. Look at the design silently and think about how you could communicate what your partner should draw. Think about ways that you can describe what a line looks like, such as its slope or points that it goes through.

2. Describe each line, one at a time, and give your partner time to draw them.

3. Once your partner thinks they have drawn all the lines you described, only then should you show them the design.

If your teacher gives you the blank graph:

1. Listen carefully as your partner describes each line, and draw each line based on their description.

2. You are not allowed to ask for more information about a line than what your partner tells you.

3. Do not show your drawing to your partner until you have finished drawing all the lines they describe.

When finished, place the drawing next to the card with the design so that you and your partner can both see them. How is the drawing the same as the design? How is it different? Discuss any miscommunication that might have caused the drawing to look different from the design.

Pause here so your teacher can review your work. When your teacher gives you a new set of cards, switch roles for the second problem.

9.4: All the Same

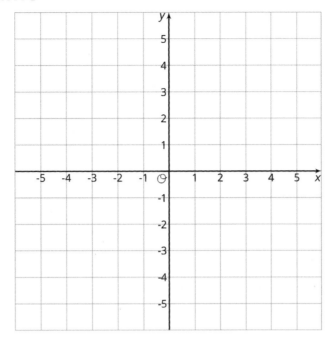

1. Plot at least 10 points whose y-coordinate is -4. What do you notice about them?

2. Which equation makes the most sense to represent all of the points with y-coordinate -4? Explain how you know.

   $x = -4$ $y = -4x$ $y = -4$ $x + y = -4$

3. Plot at least 10 points whose x-coordinate is 3. What do you notice about them?

4. Which equation makes the most sense to represent all of the points with x-coordinate 3? Explain how you know.

   $x = 3$ $y = 3x$ $y = 3$ $x + y = 3$

5. Graph the equation $x = -2$.

6. Graph the equation $y = 5$.

Are you ready for more?

1. Draw the rectangle with vertices $(2, 1)$, $(5, 1)$, $(5, 3)$, $(2, 3)$.

2. For each of the four sides of the rectangle, write an equation for a line containing the side.

3. A rectangle has sides on the graphs of $x = -1$, $x = 3$, $y = -1$, $y = 1$. Find the coordinates of each vertex.

Lesson 9 Summary

We learned earlier that one way to find the slope of a line is by drawing a slope triangle. For example, using the slope triangle shown here, the slope of the line is $-\frac{2}{4}$, or $-\frac{1}{2}$ (we know the slope is negative because the line is decreasing from left to right).

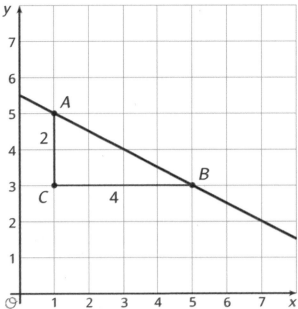

But slope triangles are only one way to calculate the slope of a line. Let's compute the slope of this line a different way using just the points $A = (1, 5)$ and $B = (5, 3)$. Since we know the slope is the vertical change divided by the horizontal change, we can calculate the change in the y-values and then the change in the x-values. Between points A and B, the y-value change is $3 - 5 = $ -2 and the x-value change is $5 - 1 = 4$. This means the slope is $-\frac{2}{4}$, or $-\frac{1}{2}$, which is the same as what we found using the slope triangle.

Notice that in each of the calculations, We subtracted the value from point A from the value from point B. If we had done it the other way around, then the y-value change would have been $5 - 3 = 2$ and the x-value change would have been $1 - 5 = $ -4, which still gives us a slope of $-\frac{1}{2}$. But what if we were to mix up the orders? If that had happened, we would think the slope of the line is *positive* $\frac{1}{2}$ since we would either have calculated $\frac{-2}{-4}$ or $\frac{2}{4}$. Since we already have a graph of the line and can see it has a negative slope, this is clearly incorrect. It we don't have a graph to check our calculation, we could think about how the point on the left, $(1, 5)$, is higher than the point on the right, $(5, 3)$, meaning the slope of the line must be negative.

Horizontal lines in the coordinate plane represent situations where the y value doesn't change at all while the x value changes, meaning they have a slope of 0. For example, the horizontal line that goes through the point $(0, 13)$ can be described in words as "for all points on the line, the y value is always 13." An equation that says the same thing is $y = 13$.

Vertical lines represent situations where the x value doesn't change at all while the y value changes. The equation $x = -4$ describes a vertical line through the point $(-4, 0)$.

Lesson 9 Practice Problems

1. For each graph, calculate the slope of the line.

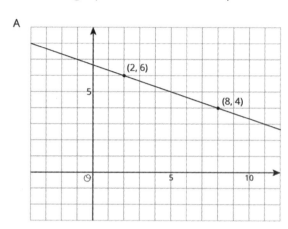

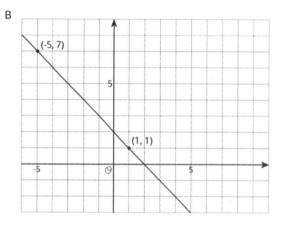

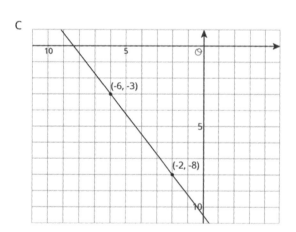

2. Match each pair of points to the slope of the line that joins them.

A. $(9, 10)$ and $(7, 2)$ 1. 4

B. $(-8, -11)$ and $(-1, -5)$ 2. -3

C. $(5, -6)$ and $(2, 3)$ 3. $-\frac{5}{2}$

D. $(6, 3)$ and $(5, -1)$ 4. $\frac{6}{7}$

E. $(4, 7)$ and $(6, 2)$

3. Draw a line with the given slope through the given point. What other point lies on that line?

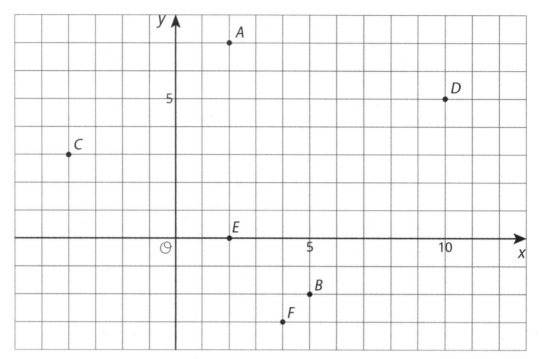

a. Point A, slope = -3

b. Point A, slope = $\frac{-1}{4}$

c. Point C, slope = $\frac{-1}{2}$

d. Point E, slope = $\frac{-2}{3}$

4. Suppose you wanted to graph the equation $y = -4x - 1$.

    a. Describe the steps you would take to draw the graph.

    b. How would you check that the graph you drew is correct?

iM KH

5. Write an equation for each line.

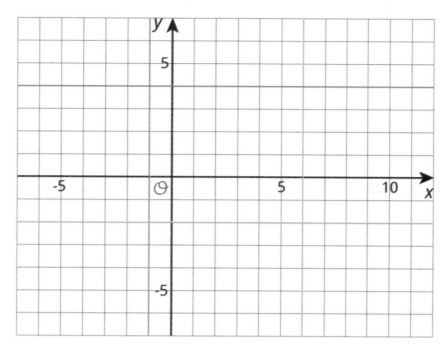

6. A publisher wants to figure out how thick their new book will be. The book has a front cover and a back cover, each of which have a thickness of $\frac{1}{4}$ of an inch. They have a choice of which type of paper to print the book on.

   a. Bond paper has a thickness of $\frac{1}{4}$ inch per one hundred pages. Write an equation for the width of the book, y, if it has x hundred pages, printed on bond paper.

   b. Ledger paper has a thickness of $\frac{2}{5}$ inch per one hundred pages. Write an equation for the width of the book, y, if it has x hundred pages, printed on ledger paper.

   c. If they instead chose front and back covers of thickness $\frac{1}{3}$ of an inch, how would this change the equations in the previous two parts?

   (From Unit 5, Lesson 6.)

Lesson 10: Solutions to Linear Equations

Let's think about what it means to be a solution to a linear equation with two variables in it.

10.1: Same Perimeter

There are many possible rectangles whose perimeter is 50 units. Complete the first 3 entries of the table with lengths, ℓ, and widths, w.

ℓ						
w						

10.2: Apples and Oranges

At the corner produce market, apples cost $1 each and oranges cost $2 each.

1. Find the cost of:

   a. 6 apples and 3 oranges

   b. 4 apples and 4 oranges

   c. 5 apples and 4 oranges

   d. 8 apples and 2 oranges

2. Noah has $10 to spend at the produce market. Can he buy 7 apples and 2 oranges? Explain or show your reasoning.

3. What combinations of apples and oranges can Noah buy if he spends all of his $10?

4. Use two variables to write an equation that represents $10-combinations of apples and oranges. Be sure to say what each variable means.

5. What are 3 combinations of apples and oranges that make your equation true? What are three combinations of apples and oranges that make it false?

Are you ready for more?

1. Graph the equation you wrote relating the number of apples and the number of oranges.

2. What is the slope of the graph? What is the meaning of the slope in terms of the context?

3. Suppose Noah has $20 to spend. Graph the equation describing this situation. What do you notice about the relationship between this graph and the earlier one?

10.3: Solutions and Everything Else

You have two numbers. If you double the first number and add it to the second number, the sum is 10.

1. Let x represent the first number and let y represent the second number. Write an equation showing the relationship between x, y, and 10.

2. Draw and label a set of x- and y-axes. Plot at least five points on this coordinate plane that make the statement and your equation true. What do you notice about the points you have plotted?

3. List ten points that do *not* make the statement true. Using a different color, plot each point in the same coordinate plane. What do you notice about these points compared to your first set of points?

Lesson 10 Summary

Think of all the rectangles whose perimeters are 8 units. If x represents the width and y represents the length, then

$$2x + 2y = 8$$

expresses the relationship between the width and length for all such rectangles.

For example, the width and length could be 1 and 3, since $2 \cdot 1 + 2 \cdot 3 = 8$ or the width and length could be 2.75 and 1.25, since $2 \cdot (2.75) + 2 \cdot (1.25) = 8$.

We could find many other possible pairs of width and length, (x, y), that make the equation true—that is, pairs (x, y) that when substituted into the equation make the left side and the right side equal.

A **solution to an equation with two variables** is any pair of values (x, y) that make the equation true.

We can think of the pairs of numbers that are solutions of an equation as points on the coordinate plane. Here is a line created by all the points (x, y) that are solutions to $2x + 2y = 8$. Every point on the line represents a rectangle whose perimeter is 8 units. All points not on the line are not solutions to $2x + 2y = 8$.

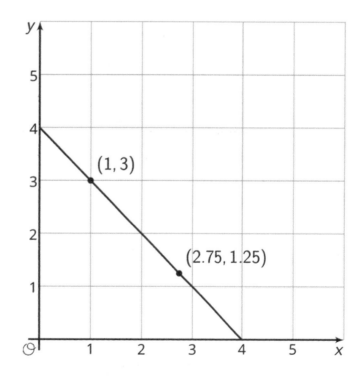

Glossary

- solution to an equation with two variables

Lesson 10 Practice Problems

1. Select **all** of the ordered pairs (x, y) that are solutions to the linear equation $2x + 3y = 6$.

   A. $(0, 2)$

   B. $(0, 6)$

   C. $(2, 3)$

   D. $(3, \text{-}2)$

   E. $(3, 0)$

   F. $(6, \text{-}2)$

2. The graph shows a linear relationship between x and y.

   x represents the number of comic books Priya buys at the store, all at the same price, and y represents the amount of money (in dollars) Priya has after buying the comic books.

   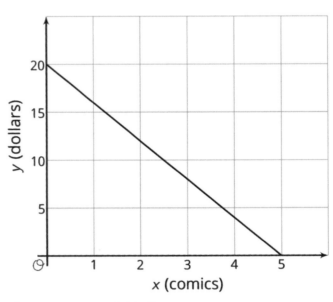

   a. Find and interpret the x- and y-intercepts of this line.

   b. Find and interpret the slope of this line.

   c. Find an equation for this line.

   d. If Priya buys 3 comics, how much money will she have remaining?

iM KH

3. Match each equation with its three solutions.

A. $y = 1.5x$

B. $2x + 3y = 7$

C. $x - y = 4$

D. $3x = \frac{y}{2}$

E. $y = -x + 1$

1. $(14, 21), (2, 3), (8, 12)$

2. $(-3, -7), (0, -4), (-1, -5)$

3. $\left(\frac{1}{8}, \frac{7}{8}\right), \left(\frac{1}{2}, \frac{1}{2}\right), \left(\frac{1}{4}, \frac{3}{4}\right)$

4. $\left(1, 1\frac{2}{3}\right), (-1, 3), \left(0, 2\frac{1}{3}\right)$

5. $(0.5, 3), (1, 6), (1.2, 7.2)$

4. A container of fuel dispenses fuel at the rate of 5 gallons per second. If y represents the amount of fuel remaining in the container, and x represents the number of seconds that have passed since the fuel started dispensing, then x and y satisfy a linear relationship.

In the coordinate plane, will the slope of the line representing that relationship have a positive, negative, or zero slope? Explain how you know.

(From Unit 5, Lesson 9.)

5. A sandwich store charges a delivery fee to bring lunch to an office building. One office pays $33 for 4 turkey sandwiches. Another office pays $61 for 8 turkey sandwiches. How much does each turkey sandwich add to the cost of the delivery? Explain how you know.

(From Unit 5, Lesson 4.)

Lesson 11: More Solutions to Linear Equations

Let's find solutions to more linear equations.

11.1: Coordinate Pairs

For each equation choose a value for x and then solve to find the corresponding y value that makes that equation true.

1. $6x = 7y$

2. $5x + 3y = 9$

3. $y + 5 - \frac{1}{3}x = 7$

11.2: True or False: Solutions in the Coordinate Plane

Here are graphs representing three linear relationships. These relationships could also be represented with equations.

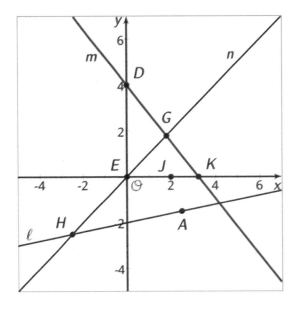

iM KH

For each statement below, decide if it is true or false. Explain your reasoning.

1. $(4, 0)$ is a solution of the equation for line m.

2. The coordinates of the point G make both the equation for line m and the equation for line n true.

3. $x = 0$ is a solution of the equation for line n.

4. $(2, 0)$ makes both the equation for line m and the equation for line n true.

5. There is no solution for the equation for line ℓ that has $y = 0$.

6. The coordinates of point H are solutions to the equation for line ℓ.

7. There are exactly two solutions of the equation for line ℓ.

8. There is a point whose coordinates make the equations of all three lines true.

After you finish discussing the eight statements, find another group and check your answers against theirs. Discuss any disagreements.

11.3: I'll Take an X, Please

One partner has 6 cards labeled A through F and one partner has 6 cards labeled a through f. In each pair of cards (for example, Cards A and a), there is an equation on one card and a coordinate pair, (x, y), that makes the equation true on the other card.

1. The partner with the equation asks the partner with a solution for either the x-value or the y-value and explains why they chose the one they did.

2. The partner with the equation uses this value to find the other value, explaining each step as they go.

3. The partner with the coordinate pair then tells the partner with the equation if they are right or wrong. If they are wrong, both partners should look through the steps to find and correct any errors. If they are right, both partners move onto the next set of cards.

4. Keep playing until you have finished Cards A through F.

Are you ready for more?

Consider the equation $ax + by = c$, where a, b, and c are positive numbers.

1. Find the coordinates of the x- and y-intercepts of the graph of the equation.

2. Find the slope of the graph.

iM KH

11.4: Making Signs

Clare and Andre are making signs for all the lockers as part of the decorations for the upcoming spirit week. Yesterday, Andre made 15 signs and Clare made 5 signs. Today, they need to make more signs. Each person's progress today is shown in the coordinate plane.

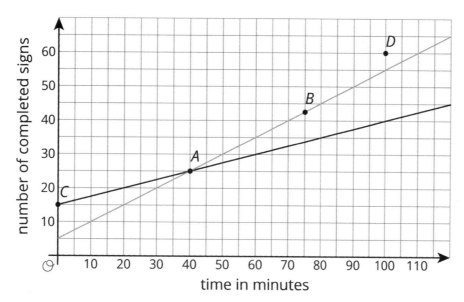

Based on the lines, mark the statements as true or false for each person.

point	what it says	Clare	Andre
A	At 40 minutes, I have 25 signs completed.		
B	At 75 minutes, I have 42 and a half signs completed.		
C	At 0 minutes, I have 15 signs completed.		
D	At 100 minutes, I have 60 signs completed.		

Are you ready for more?

- 4 toothpicks make 1 square

- 7 toothpicks make 2 squares

- 10 toothpicks make 3 squares

Do you see a pattern? If so, how many toothpicks would you need to make 10 squares according to your pattern? Can you represent your pattern with an expression?

Lesson 11 Summary

Let's think about the linear equation $2x - 4y = 12$. If we know $(0, \text{-}3)$ is a solution to the equation, then we also know $(0, \text{-}3)$ is a point on the graph of the equation. Since this point is on the y-axis, we also know that it is the vertical intercept of the graph. But what about the coordinate of the horizontal intercept, when $y = 0$? Well, we can use the equation to figure it out.

$$2x - 4y = 12$$
$$2x - 4(0) = 12$$
$$2x = 12$$
$$x = 6$$

Since $x = 6$ when $y = 0$, we know the point $(6, 0)$ is on the graph of the line. No matter the form a linear equation comes in, we can always find solutions to the equation by starting with one value and then solving for the other value.

Lesson 11 Practice Problems

1. For each equation, find y when $x = -3$. Then find x when $y = 2$

   a. $y = 6x + 8$

   b. $y = \frac{2}{3}x$

   c. $y = -x + 5$

   d. $y = \frac{3}{4}x - 2\frac{1}{2}$

   e. $y = 1.5x + 11$

2. True or false: The points $(6, 13)$, $(21, 33)$, and $(99, 137)$ all lie on the same line. The equation of the line is $y = \frac{4}{3}x + 5$. Explain or show your reasoning.

3. Here is a linear equation: $y = \frac{1}{4}x + \frac{5}{4}$

    a. Are $(1, 1.5)$ and $(12, 4)$ solutions to the equation? Explain or show your reasoning.

    b. Find the x-intercept of the graph of the equation. Explain or show your reasoning.

4. Find the coordinates of B, C, and D given that $AB = 5$ and $BC = 10$.

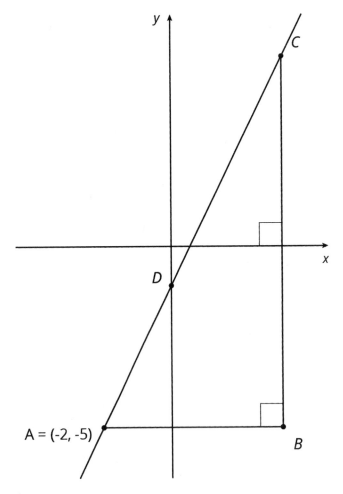

(From Unit 2, Lesson 16.)

iM KH

5. Match each graph of a linear relationship to a situation that most reasonably reflects its context.

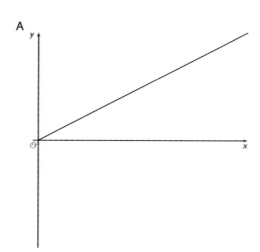

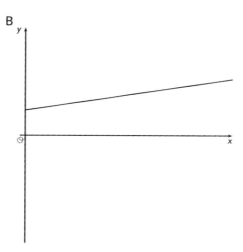

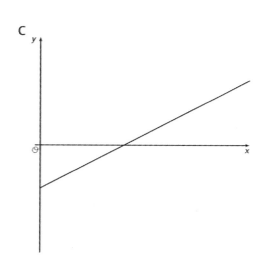

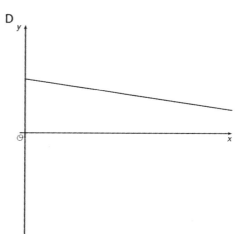

A. Graph A

B. Graph B

C. Graph C

D. Graph D

1. y is the weight of a kitten x days after birth.

2. y is the distance left to go in a car ride after x hours of driving at a constant rate toward its destination.

3. y is the temperature, in degrees C, of a gas being warmed in a laboratory experiment.

4. y is the amount of calories consumed eating x crackers.

(From Unit 5, Lesson 8.)

Lesson 12: On Both of the Lines

Let's use lines to think about situations.

12.1: Notice and Wonder: Bugs Passing in the Night

What do you notice? What do you wonder?

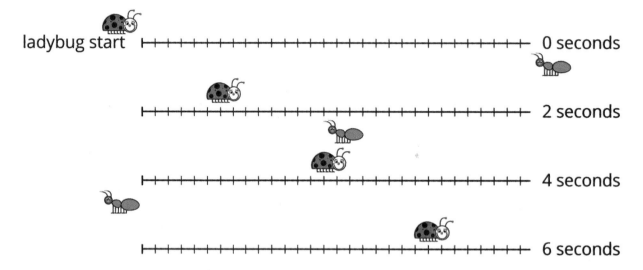

12.2: Bugs Passing in the Night, Continued

A different ant and ladybug are a certain distance apart, and they start walking toward each other. The graph shows the ladybug's distance from its starting point over time and the labeled point (2.5, 10) indicates when the ant and the ladybug pass each other.

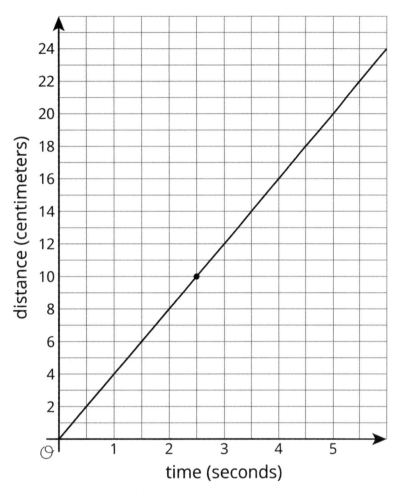

The ant is walking 2 centimeters per second.

1. Write an equation representing the relationship between the ant's distance from the ladybug's starting point and the amount of time that has passed.

2. If you haven't already, draw the graph of your equation on the same coordinate plane.

12.3: A Close Race

Elena and Jada were racing 100 meters on their bikes. Both racers started at the same time and rode at constant speed. Here is a table that gives information about Jada's bike race:

time from start (seconds)	distance from start (meters)
6	36
9	54

1. Graph the relationship between distance and time for Jada's bike race. Make sure to label and scale the axes appropriately.

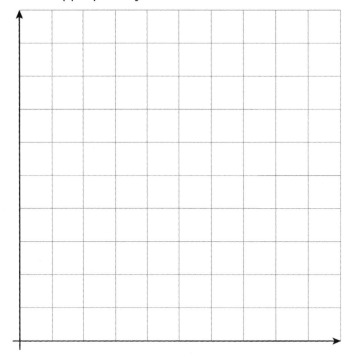

2. Elena traveled the entire race at a steady 6 meters per second. On the same set of axes, graph the relationship between distance and time for Elena's bike race.

3. Who won the race?

iV KH

Lesson 12 Summary

The solutions to an equation correspond to points on its graph. For example, if Car A is traveling 75 miles per hour and passes a rest area when $t = 0$, then the distance in miles it has traveled from the rest area after t hours is

$$d = 75t$$

The point $(2, 150)$ is on the graph of this equation because $150 = 75 \cdot 2$: two hours after passing the rest area, the car has traveled 150 miles.

If you have *two* equations, you can ask whether there is an ordered pair that is a solution to *both* equations simultaneously. For example, if Car B is traveling towards the rest area and its distance from the rest area is

$$d = 14 - 65t$$

We can ask if there is ever a time when the distance of Car A from the rest area is the same as the distance of Car B from the rest area. If the answer is "yes", then the solution will correspond to a point that is on both lines.

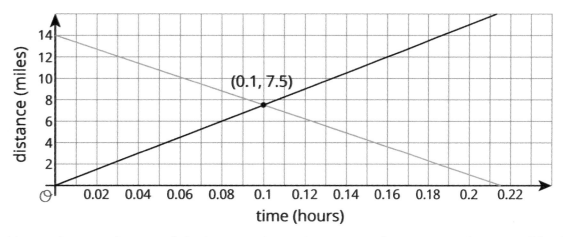

Looking at the coordinates of the intersection point, we see that Car A and Car B will both be 7.5 miles from the rest area after 0.1 hours (which is 6 minutes).

Now suppose another car, Car C, had also passed the rest stop at time $t = 0$ and traveled in the same direction as Car A, also going 75 miles per hour. It's equation would also be $d = 75t$. Any solution to the equation for Car A would also be a solution for Car C, and any solution to the equation for Car C would also be a solution for Car A. The line for Car C would land right on top of the line for Car A. In this case, every point on the graphed line is a solution to both equations, so that there are infinitely many solutions to the question "when are Car A and Car C the same distance from the rest stop?" This would mean that Car A and Car C were side by side for their whole journey.

When we have two linear equations that are equivalent to each other, like $y = 3x + 2$ and $2y = 6x + 4$, we will get two lines that are "right on top" of each other. Any solution to one equation is also solution to the other, so these two lines intersect at infinitely many points.

iM KH

Lesson 12 Practice Problems

1. Diego has $11 and begins saving $5 each week toward buying a new phone. At the same time that Diego begins saving, Lin has $60 and begins spending $2 per week on supplies for her art class. Is there a week when they have the same amount of money? How much do they have at that time?

2. Use a graph to find x and y values that make both $y = \frac{-2}{3}x + 3$ and $y = 2x - 5$ true.

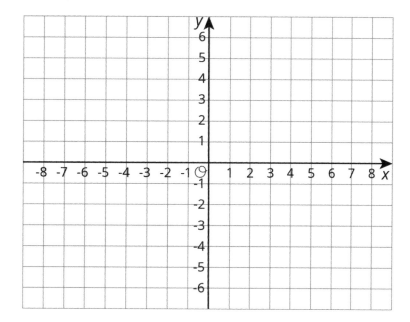

3. The point where the graphs of two equations intersect has y-coordinate 2. One equation is $y = -3x + 5$. Find the other equation if its graph has a slope of 1.

4. A farm has chickens and cows. All the cows have 4 legs and all the chickens have 2 legs. All together, there are 82 cow and chicken legs on the farm. Complete the table to show some possible combinations of chickens and cows to get 82 total legs.

number of chickens (x)	number of cows (y)
35	
7	
	10
19	
	5

Here is a graph that shows possible combinations of chickens and cows that add up to 30 animals:

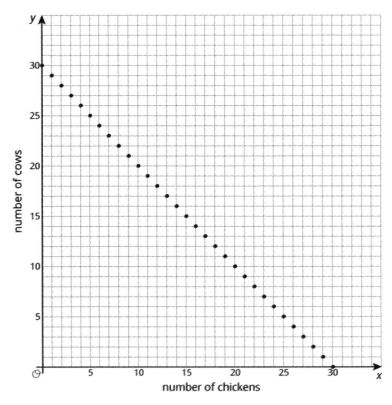

If the farm has 30 chickens and cows, and there are 82 chicken and cow legs all together, then how many chickens and how many cows could the farm have?

iM KH

5. a. Match the lines m and n to the statements they represent:

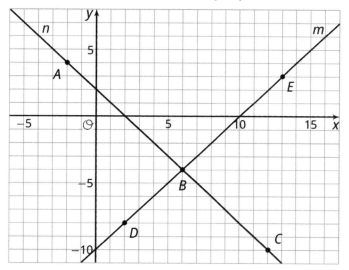

i. A set of points where the coordinates of each point have a sum of 2

ii. A set of points where the y-coordinate of each point is 10 less than its x-coordinate

b. Match the labeled points on the graph to statements about their coordinates:

i. Two numbers with a sum of 2

ii. Two numbers where the y-coordinate is 10 less than the x-coordinate

iii. Two numbers with a sum of 2 and where the y-coordinate is 10 less than the x-coordinate

6. Here is an equation: $4x - 4 = 4x +$ __. What could you write in the blank so the equation would be true for:

a. No values of x

b. All values of x

c. One value of x

(From Unit 4, Lesson 15.)

Lesson 13: Systems of Equations

Let's learn what a system of equations is.

13.1: Milkshakes

Diego and Lin are drinking milkshakes. Lin starts with 12 ounces and drinks $\frac{1}{4}$ ounce per second. Diego starts with 20 ounces and drinks $\frac{2}{3}$ ounce per second.

1. How long will it take Lin and Diego to finish their milkshakes?

2. Without graphing, explain what the graphs in this situation would look like. Think about slope, intercepts, axis labels, units, and intersection points to guide your thinking.

3. Discuss your description with your partner. If you disagree, work to reach an agreement.

13.2: Passing on the Trail

There is a hiking trail near the town where Han and Jada live that starts at a parking lot and ends at a lake. Han and Jada both decide to hike from the parking lot to the lake and back, but they start their hikes at different times.

At the time that Han reaches the lake and starts to turn back, Jada is 0.6 miles away from the parking lot and hiking at a constant speed of 3.2 miles per hour towards the lake. Han's distance, d, from the parking lot can be expressed as $d = -2.4t + 4.8$, where t represents the time in hours since he left the lake.

1. What is an equation for Jada's distance from the parking lot as she heads toward the lake?

2. Draw both graphs: one representing Han's equation and one representing Jada's equation. It is important to be very precise! Be careful, work in pencil, and use a ruler.

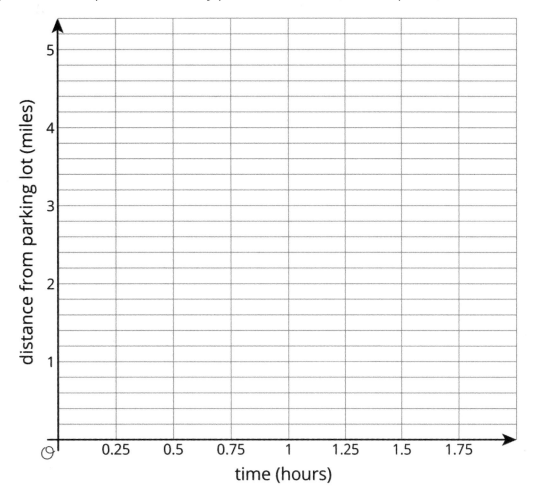

3. Find the point where the two graphs intersect each other. What are the coordinates of this point?

4. What do the coordinates mean in this situation?

5. What has to be true about the relationship between these coordinates and Jada's equation?

6. What has to be true about the relationship between these coordinates and Han's equation?

13.3: Stacks of Cups

A stack of n small cups has a height, h, in centimeters of $h = 1.5n + 6$. A stack of n large cups has a height, h, in centimeters of $h = 1.5n + 9$.

1. Graph the equations for each cup on the same set of axes. Make sure to label the axes and decide on an appropriate scale.

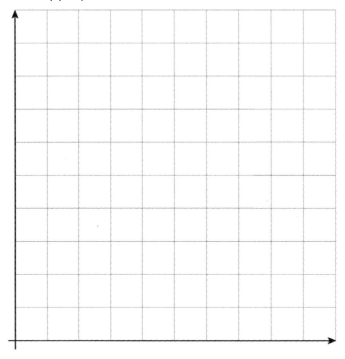

2. For what number of cups will the two stacks have the same height?

Lesson 13 Summary

A **system of equations** is a set of 2 (or more) equations where the variables represent the same unknown values. For example, suppose that two different kinds of bamboo are planted at the same time. Plant A starts at 6 ft tall and grows at a constant rate of $\frac{1}{4}$ foot each day. Plant B starts at 3 ft tall and grows at a constant rate of $\frac{1}{2}$ foot each day. We can write equations $y = \frac{1}{4}x + 6$ for Plant A and $y = \frac{1}{2}x + 3$ for Plant B, where x represents the number of days after being planted, and y represents height. We can write this system of equations.

$$\begin{cases} y = \frac{1}{4}x + 6 \\ y = \frac{1}{2}x + 3 \end{cases}$$

Solving a system of equations means to find the values of x and y that make both equations true at the same time. One way we have seen to find the solution to a system of equations is to graph both lines and find the intersection point. The intersection point represents the pair of x and y values that make both equations true. Here is a graph for the bamboo example:

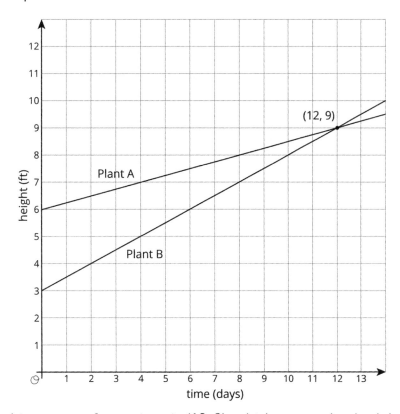

The solution to this system of equations is $(12, 9)$, which means that both bamboo plants will be 9 feet tall after 12 days.

We have seen systems of equations that have no solutions, one solution, and infinitely many solutions.

- When the lines do not intersect, there is no solution. (Lines that do not intersect are *parallel*.)

- When the lines intersect once, there is one solution.

- When the lines are right on top of each other, there are infinitely many solutions.

In future lessons, we will see that some systems cannot be easily solved by graphing, but can be easily solved using algebra.

Glossary

- system of equations

Lesson 13 Practice Problems

1. Here is the graph for one equation in a system of equations:

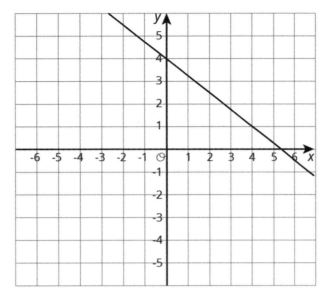

a. Write a second equation for the system so it has infinitely many solutions.

b. Write a second equation whose graph goes through $(0, 1)$ so the system has no solutions.

c. Write a second equation whose graph goes through $(0, 2)$ so the system has one solution at $(4, 1)$.

2. Create a second equation so the system has no solutions.

$$\begin{cases} y = \frac{3}{4}x - 4 \\ \end{cases}$$

3. Andre is in charge of cooking broccoli and zucchini for a large group. He has to spend all $17 he has and can carry 10 pounds of veggies. Zucchini costs $1.50 per pound and broccoli costs $2 per pound. One graph shows combinations of zucchini and broccoli that weigh 10 pounds and the other shows combinations of zucchini and broccoli that cost $17.

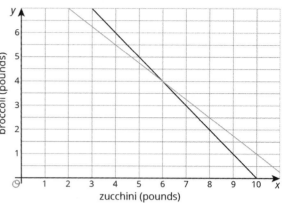

a. Name one combination of veggies that weighs 10 pounds but does not cost $17.

b. Name one combination of veggies that costs $17 but does not weigh 10 pounds.

c. How many pounds each of zucchini and broccoli can Andre get so that he spends all $17 and gets 10 pounds of veggies?

(From Unit 5, Lesson 12.)

4. The temperature in degrees Fahrenheit, F, is related to the temperature in degrees Celsius, C, by the equation

$$F = \frac{9}{5}C + 32$$

a. In the Sahara desert, temperatures often reach 50 degrees Celsius. How many degrees Fahrenheit is this?

b. In parts of Alaska, the temperatures can reach -60 degrees Fahrenheit. How many degrees Celsius is this?

c. There is one temperature where the degrees Fahrenheit and degrees Celsius are the same, so that $C = F$. Use the expression from the equation, where F is expressed in terms of C, to solve for this temperature.

(From Unit 4, Lesson 17.)

iM KH

Lesson 14: Solving Systems of Equations

Let's solve systems of equations.

14.1: True or False: Two Lines

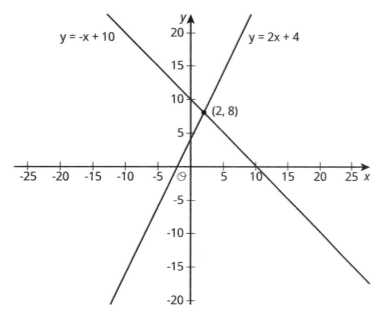

Use the lines to decide whether each statement is true or false. Be prepared to explain your reasoning using the lines.

1. A solution to $8 = -x + 10$ is 2.

2. A solution to $2 = 2x + 4$ is 8.

3. A solution to $-x + 10 = 2x + 4$ is 8.

4. A solution to $-x + 10 = 2x + 4$ is 2.

5. There are no values of x and y that make $y = -x + 10$ and $y = 2x + 4$ true at the same time.

14.2: Matching Graphs to Systems

Here are three **systems of equations** graphed on a coordinate plane:

A

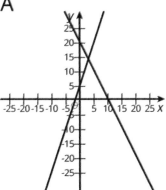

B

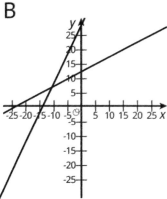

C

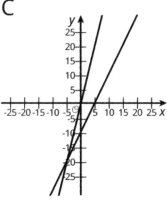

1. Match each figure to one of the systems of equations shown here.

   a. $\begin{cases} y = 3x + 5 \\ y = \text{-}2x + 20 \end{cases}$

   b. $\begin{cases} y = 2x - 10 \\ y = 4x - 1 \end{cases}$

   c. $\begin{cases} y = 0.5x + 12 \\ y = 2x + 27 \end{cases}$

2. Find the solution to each system and check that your solution is reasonable based on the graph.

14.3: Different Types of Systems

Your teacher will give you a page with some systems of equations.

1. Graph each system of equations carefully on the provided coordinate plane.

2. Describe what the graph of a system of equations looks like when it has . . .
   a. 1 solution

   b. 0 solutions

   c. infinitely many solutions

Are you ready for more?

The graphs of the equations $Ax + By = 15$ and $Ax - By = 9$ intersect at $(2, 1)$. Find A and B. Show or explain your reasoning.

Lesson 14 Summary

Sometimes it is easier to solve a system of equations without having to graph the equations and look for an intersection point. In general, whenever we are solving a system of equations written as

$$\begin{cases} y = [\text{some stuff}] \\ y = [\text{some other stuff}] \end{cases}$$

we know that we are looking for a pair of values (x, y) that makes both equations true. In particular, we know that the value for y will be the same in both equations. That means that

$$[\text{some stuff}] = [\text{some other stuff}]$$

For example, look at this system of equations:

$$\begin{cases} y = 2x + 6 \\ y = \text{-}3x - 4 \end{cases}$$

Since the y value of the solution is the same in both equations, then we know

$$2x + 6 = \text{-}3x - 4$$

We can solve this equation for x:

$$2x + 6 = \text{-}3x - 4$$
$$5x + 6 = \text{-}4 \qquad \text{add } 3x \text{ to each side}$$
$$5x = \text{-}10 \qquad \text{subtract 6 from each side}$$
$$x = \text{-}2 \qquad \text{divide each side by 5}$$

But this is only half of what we are looking for: we know the value for x, but we need the corresponding value for y. Since both equations have the same y value, we can use either equation to find the y-value:

$$y = 2(\text{-}2) + 6$$

Or

$$y = \text{-}3(\text{-}2) - 4$$

In both cases, we find that $y = 2$. So the solution to the system is (-2, 2). We can verify this by graphing both equations in the coordinate plane.

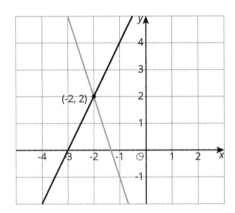

In general, a system of linear equations can have:

- No solutions. In this case, the lines that correspond to each equation never intersect.

- Exactly one solution. The lines that correspond to each equation intersect in exactly one point.

- An infinite number of solutions. The graphs of the two equations are the same line!

iM KH

Lesson 14 Practice Problems

1.   a. Write equations for the lines shown.

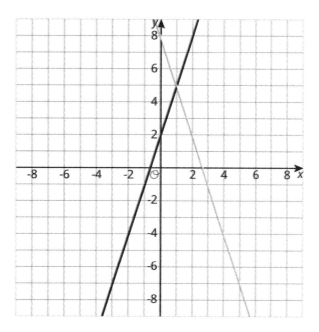

   b. Describe how to find the solution to the corresponding system by looking at the graph.

   c. Describe how to find the solution to the corresponding system by using the equations.

2. The solution to a system of equations is $(5, -19)$. Choose two equations that might make up the system.

   A. $y = -3x - 6$

   B. $y = 2x - 23$

   C. $y = -7x + 16$

   D. $y = x - 17$

   E. $y = -2x - 9$

3. Solve the system of equations: $\begin{cases} y = 4x - 3 \\ y = \text{-}2x + 9 \end{cases}$

4. Solve the system of equations: $\begin{cases} y = \frac{5}{4}x - 2 \\ y = \frac{\text{-}1}{4}x + 19 \end{cases}$

5. Here is an equation: $\frac{15(x-3)}{5} = 3(2x - 3)$

    a. Solve the equation by using the distributive property first.

    b. Solve the equation without using the distributive property.

    c. Check your solution.

    (From Unit 4, Lesson 14.)

iM KH

Lesson 15: Solving More Systems

Let's solve systems of equations.

15.1: Algebra Talk: Solving Systems Mentally

Solve these without writing anything down:

$$\begin{cases} x = 5 \\ y = x - 7 \end{cases}$$

$$\begin{cases} y = 4 \\ y = x + 3 \end{cases}$$

$$\begin{cases} x = 8 \\ y = \text{-}11 \end{cases}$$

15.2: Challenge Yourself

Here are a lot of systems of equations:

A $\begin{cases} y = 4 \\ x = \text{-}5y + 6 \end{cases}$

E $\begin{cases} y = \text{-}3x - 5 \\ y = 4x + 30 \end{cases}$

I $\begin{cases} 3x + 4y = 10 \\ x = 2y \end{cases}$

B $\begin{cases} y = 7 \\ x = 3y - 4 \end{cases}$

F $\begin{cases} y = 3x - 2 \\ y = \text{-}2x + 8 \end{cases}$

J $\begin{cases} y = 3x + 2 \\ 2x + y = 47 \end{cases}$

C $\begin{cases} y = \frac{3}{2}x + 7 \\ x = \text{-}4 \end{cases}$

G $\begin{cases} y = 3x \\ x = \text{-}2y + 56 \end{cases}$

K $\begin{cases} y = \text{-}2x + 5 \\ 2x + 3y = 31 \end{cases}$

D $\begin{cases} y = \text{-}3x + 10 \\ y = \text{-}2x + 6 \end{cases}$

H $\begin{cases} x = 2y - 15 \\ y = \text{-}2x \end{cases}$

L $\begin{cases} x + y = 10 \\ x = 2y + 1 \end{cases}$

1. Without solving, identify 3 systems that you think would be the least difficult to solve and 3 systems that you think would be the most difficult to solve. Be prepared to explain your reasoning.

2. Choose 4 systems to solve. At least one should be from your "least difficult" list and one should be from your "most difficult" list.

15.3: Five Does Not Equal Seven

Tyler was looking at this system of equations:

$$\begin{cases} x + y = 5 \\ x + y = 7 \end{cases}$$

He said, "Just looking at the system, I can see it has no solution. If you add two numbers, that sum can't be equal to two different numbers."

Do you agree with Tyler?

Are you ready for more?

In rectangle $ABCD$, side AB is 8 centimeters and side BC is 6 centimeters. F is a point on BC and E is a point on AB. The area of triangle DFC is 20 square centimeters, and the area of triangle DEF is 16 square centimeters. What is the area of triangle AED?

Lesson 15 Summary

When we have a system of linear equations where one of the equations is of the form $y = $ [stuff] or $x = $ [stuff], we can solve it algebraically by using a technique called *substitution*. The basic idea is to replace a variable with an expression it is equal to (so the expression is like a substitute for the variable). For example, let's start with the system:

$$\begin{cases} y = 5x \\ 2x - y = 9 \end{cases}$$

Since we know that $y = 5x$, we can substitute $5x$ for y in the equation $2x - y = 9$,

$$2x - (5x) = 9,$$

and then solve the equation for x,

$$x = \text{-}3.$$

We can find y using either equation. Using the first one: $y = 5 \cdot \text{-}3$. So

$$(\text{-}3, \text{-}15)$$

is the solution to this system. We can verify this by looking at the graphs of the equations in the system:

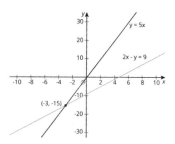

Sure enough! They intersect at (-3, -15).

We didn't know it at the time, but we were actually using substitution in the last lesson as well. In that lesson, we looked at the system

$$\begin{cases} y = 2x + 6 \\ y = \text{-}3x - 4 \end{cases}$$

and we substituted $2x + 6$ for y into the second equation to get $2x + 6 = \text{-}3x - 4$. Go back and check for yourself!

Lesson 15 Practice Problems

1. Solve: $\begin{cases} y = 6x \\ 4x + y = 7 \end{cases}$

2. Solve: $\begin{cases} y = 3x \\ x = -2y + 70 \end{cases}$

3. Which equation, together with $y = -1.5x + 3$, makes a system with one solution?

   A. $y = -1.5x + 6$

   B. $y = -1.5x$

   C. $2y = -3x + 6$

   D. $2y + 3x = 6$

   E. $y = -2x + 3$

4. The system $x - 6y = 4$, $3x - 18y = 4$ has no solution.

   a. Change one constant or coefficient to make a new system with one solution.

   b. Change one constant or coefficient to make a new system with an infinite number of solutions.

5. Match each graph to its equation.

A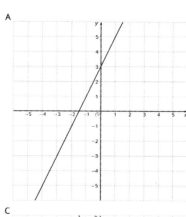

B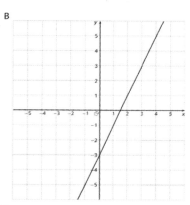

C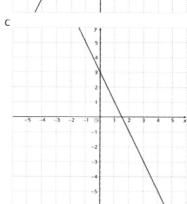

D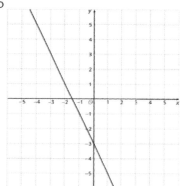

a. $y = 2x + 3$

b. $y = -2x + 3$

c. $y = 2x - 3$

d. $y = -2x - 3$

(From Unit 5, Lesson 9.)

6. Here are two points: $(-3, 4)$, $(1, 7)$. What is the slope of the line between them?

A. $\frac{4}{3}$

B. $\frac{3}{4}$

C. $\frac{1}{6}$

D. $\frac{2}{3}$

(From Unit 5, Lesson 9.)

Lesson 16: Writing Systems of Equations

Let's write systems of equations from real-world situations.

16.1: How Many Solutions? Matching

Match each system of equations with the number of solutions the system has.

1. $\begin{cases} y = -\frac{4}{3}x + 4 \\ y = -\frac{4}{3}x - 1 \end{cases}$

2. $\begin{cases} y = 4x - 5 \\ y = -2x + 7 \end{cases}$

3. $\begin{cases} 2x + 3y = 8 \\ 4x + 6y = 17 \end{cases}$

4. $\begin{cases} y = 5x - 15 \\ y = 5(x - 3) \end{cases}$

1. No solutions

2. One solution

3. Infinitely many solutions

16.2: Situations and Systems

For each situation:

- Create a system of equations.

- Then, without solving, interpret what the solution to the system would tell you about the situation.

1. Lin's family is out for a bike ride when her dad stops to take a picture of the scenery. He tells the rest of the family to keep going and that he'll catch up. Lin's dad spends 5 minutes taking the photo and then rides at 0.24 miles per minute until he meets up with the rest of the family further along the bike path. Lin and the rest were riding at 0.18 miles per minute.

2. Noah is planning a kayaking trip. Kayak Rental A charges a base fee of $15 plus $4.50 per hour. Kayak Rental B charges a base fee of $12.50 plus $5 per hour.

iM KH

3. Diego is making a large batch of pastries. The recipe calls for 3 strawberries for every apple. Diego used 52 fruits all together.

4. Flour costs $0.80 per pound and sugar costs $0.50 per pound. An order of flour and sugar weighs 15 pounds and costs $9.00.

16.3: Info Gap: Racing and Play Tickets

Your teacher will give you either a *problem card* or a *data card*. Do not show or read your card to your partner.

If your teacher gives you the *problem card*:

1. Silently read your card and think about what information you need to be able to answer the question.

2. Ask your partner for the specific information that you need.

3. Explain how you are using the information to solve the problem.

   Continue to ask questions until you have enough information to solve the problem.

4. Share the *problem card* and solve the problem independently.

5. Read the *data card* and discuss your reasoning.

If your teacher gives you the *data card*:

1. Silently read your card.

2. Ask your partner *"What specific information do you need?"* and wait for them to *ask* for information.

   If your partner asks for information that is not on the card, do not do the calculations for them. Tell them you don't have that information.

3. Before sharing the information, ask *"Why do you need that information?"* Listen to your partner's reasoning and ask clarifying questions.

4. Read the *problem card* and solve the problem independently.

5. Share the *data card* and discuss your reasoning.

16.4: Solving Systems Practice

Here are a lot of systems of equations:

- $\begin{cases} y = -2x + 6 \\ y = x - 3 \end{cases}$

- $\begin{cases} y = x - 6 \\ x = 6 + y \end{cases}$

- $\begin{cases} y = 5x - 4 \\ y = 4x + 12 \end{cases}$

- $\begin{cases} y = 0.24x \\ y = 0.18x + 0.9 \end{cases}$

- $\begin{cases} y = \frac{2}{3}x - 4 \\ y = -\frac{4}{3}x + 9 \end{cases}$

- $\begin{cases} y = 4.5x + 15 \\ y = 5x + 12.5 \end{cases}$

- $\begin{cases} 4y + 7x = 6 \\ 4y + 7x = -5 \end{cases}$

- $\begin{cases} y = 3x \\ x + y = 52 \end{cases}$

1. Without solving, identify 3 systems that you think would be the least difficult for you to solve and 3 systems you think would be the most difficult. Be prepared to explain your reasoning.

2. Choose 4 systems to solve. At least one should be from your "least difficult" list and one should be from your "most difficult" list.

Lesson 16 Summary

We have learned how to solve many kinds of systems of equations using algebra that would be difficult to solve by graphing. For example, look at

$$\begin{cases} y = 2x - 3 \\ x + 2y = 7 \end{cases}$$

The first equation says that $y = 2x - 3$, so wherever we see y, we can substitute the expression $2x - 3$ instead. So the second equation becomes $x + 2(2x - 3) = 7$.

We can solve for x:

$$x + 4x - 6 = 7 \qquad \text{distributive property}$$
$$5x - 6 = 7 \qquad \text{combine like terms}$$
$$5x = 13 \qquad \text{add 6 to each side}$$
$$x = \frac{13}{5} \qquad \text{multiply each side by } \frac{1}{5}$$

We know that the y value for the solution is the same for either equation, so we can use either equation to solve for it. Using the first equation, we get:

$$y = 2(\frac{13}{5}) - 3 \qquad \text{substitute } x = \frac{13}{5} \text{ into the equation}$$
$$y = \frac{26}{5} - 3 \qquad \text{multiply } 2(\frac{13}{5}) \text{ to make } \frac{26}{5}$$
$$y = \frac{26}{5} - \frac{15}{5} \qquad \text{rewrite 3 as } \frac{15}{5}$$
$$y = \frac{11}{5}$$

If we substitute $x = \frac{13}{5}$ into the other equation, $x + 2y = 7$, we get the same y value. So the solution to the system is $\left(\frac{13}{5}, \frac{11}{5} \right)$.

There are many kinds of systems of equations that we will learn how to solve in future grades, like $\begin{cases} 2x + 3y = 6 \\ -x + 2y = 3 \end{cases}$.

Or even $\begin{cases} y = x^2 + 1 \\ y = 2x + 3 \end{cases}$.

Lesson 16 Practice Problems

1. Kiran and his cousin work during the summer for a landscaping company. Kiran's cousin has been working for the company longer, so his pay is 30% more than Kiran's. Last week his cousin worked 27 hours, and Kiran worked 23 hours. Together, they earned $493.85. What is Kiran's hourly pay? Explain or show your reasoning.

2. Decide which story can be represented by the system of equations $y = x + 6$ and $x + y = 100$. Explain your reasoning.

   a. Diego's teacher writes a test worth 100 points. There are 6 more multiple choice questions than short answer questions.

   b. Lin and her younger cousin measure their heights. They notice that Lin is 6 inches taller, and their heights add up to exactly 100 inches.

3. Clare and Noah play a game in which they earn the same number of points for each goal and lose the same number of points for each penalty. Clare makes 6 goals and 3 penalties, ending the game with 6 points. Noah earns 8 goals and 9 penalties and ends the game with -22 points.

   a. Write a system of equations that describes Clare and Noah's outcomes. Use x to represent the number of points for a goal and y to represent the number of points for a penalty.

   b. Solve the system. What does your solution mean?

4. Solve: $\begin{cases} y = 6x - 8 \\ y = \text{-}3x + 10 \end{cases}$

(From Unit 5, Lesson 15.)

5. a. Estimate the coordinates of the point where the two lines meet.

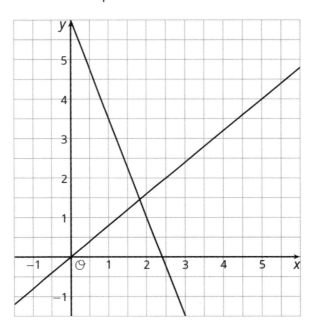

b. Choose two equations that make up the system represented by the graph.

   i. $y = \frac{5}{4}x$

   ii. $y = 6 - 2.5x$

   iii. $y = 2.5x + 6$

   iv. $y = 6 - 3x$

   v. $y = 0.8x$

c. Solve the system of equations and confirm the accuracy of your estimate.

(From Unit 5, Lesson 14.)

iM KH

Lesson 17: Organizing Data

Let's find ways to show patterns in data

17.1: Notice and Wonder: Messy Data

Here is a table of data. Each row shows two measurements of a triangle.

length of short side (cm)	length of perimeter (cm)
0.25	1
2	7.5
6.5	22
3	9.5
0.5	2
1.25	3.5
3.5	12.5
1.5	5
4	14
1	2.5

What do you notice? What do you wonder?

17.2: Seeing the Data

Here is the table of isosceles right triangle measurements from the warm-up and an empty table.

length of short sides (cm)	length of perimeter (cm)	length of short sides (cm)	length of perimeter (cm)
0.25	1		
2	7.5		
6.5	22		
3	9.5		
0.5	2		
1.25	3.5		
3.5	12.5		
1.5	5		
4	14		
1	2.5		

1. How can you organize the measurements from the first table so that any patterns are easier to see? Write the organized measurements in the empty table.

2. For each of the following lengths, estimate the perimeter of an isosceles right triangle whose short sides have that length. Explain your reasoning for each triangle.
   a. length of short sides is 0.75 cm

iM KH

b. length of short sides is 5 cm

c. length of short sides is 10 cm

Are you ready for more?

In addition to the graphic representations of data you have learned, there are others that make sense in other situations. Examine the maps showing the results of the elections for United States president for 2012 and 2016. In red are the states where a majority of electorate votes were cast for the Republican nominee. In blue are the states where a majority of the electorate votes were cast for the Democrat nominee.

1. What information can you see in these maps that would be more difficult to see in a bar graph showing the number of electorate votes for the 2 main candidates?

2. Why are these representations appropriate for the data that is shown?

17.3: Tables and Their Scatter Plots

Here are four **scatter plots**. Your teacher will give you four tables of data.

- Match each table with one of the scatter plots.

- Use information from the tables to label the axes for each scatter plot.

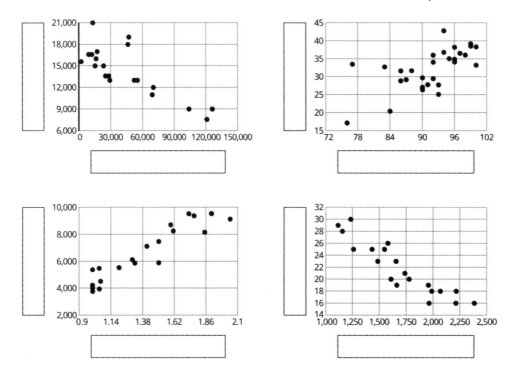

Lesson 17 Summary

Consider the data collected from pulling back a toy car and then letting it go forward. In the first table, the data may not seem to have an obvious pattern. The second table has the same data and shows that both values are increasing together.

<table>
<tr><td colspan="2" align="center">Unorganized table</td><td colspan="2" align="center">Organized table</td></tr>
<tr><td>distance pulled back (in)</td><td>distance traveled (in)</td><td>distance pulled back (in)</td><td>distance traveled (in)</td></tr>
<tr><td>6</td><td>23.57</td><td>1</td><td>8.95</td></tr>
<tr><td>4</td><td>18.48</td><td>2</td><td>13.86</td></tr>
<tr><td>10</td><td>38.66</td><td>4</td><td>18.48</td></tr>
<tr><td>8</td><td>31.12</td><td>6</td><td>23.57</td></tr>
<tr><td>2</td><td>13.86</td><td>8</td><td>31.12</td></tr>
<tr><td>1</td><td>8.95</td><td>10</td><td>38.66</td></tr>
</table>

A scatter plot of the data makes the pattern clear enough that we can estimate how far the car will travel when it is pulled back 5 inches.

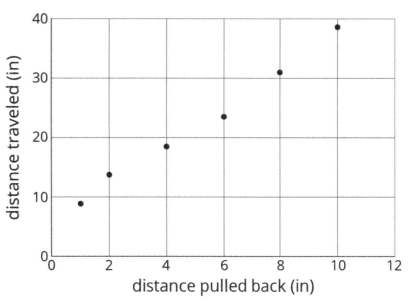

Patterns in data can sometimes become more obvious when reorganized in a table or when represented in **scatter plots** or other diagrams. If a pattern is observed, it can sometimes be used to make predictions.

Glossary

- scatter plot

Lesson 17 Practice Problems

1. Here is data on the number of cases of whooping cough from 1939 to 1955.

year	number of cases
1941	222,202
1950	120,718
1945	133,792
1942	191,383
1953	37,129
1939	103,188
1951	68,687
1948	74,715
1955	62,786
1952	45,030
1940	183,866
1954	60,866
1944	109,873
1946	109,860
1943	191,890
1949	69,479
1947	156,517

a. Make a new table that orders the data by year.

b. Circle the years in your table that had fewer than 100,000 cases of whooping cough.

c. Based on this data, would you expect 1956 to have closer to 50,000 cases or closer to 100,000 cases?

2. In volleyball statistics, a block is recorded when a player deflects the ball hit from the opposing team. Additionally, scorekeepers often keep track of the average number of blocks a player records in a game. Here is part of a table that records the number of blocks and blocks per game for each player in a women's volleyball tournament. A scatter plot that goes with the table follows.

blocks	blocks per game
13	1.18
1	0.17
5	0.42
0	0
0	0
7	0.64

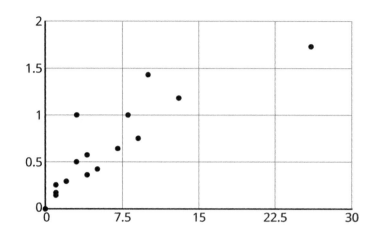

Label the axes of the scatter plot with the necessary information.

3. In hockey, a player gets credited with a "point" in their statistics when they get an assist or goal. The table shows the number of assists and number of points for 15 hockey players after a season.

assists	points
22	28
16	18
46	72
19	29
13	26
9	13
16	22
8	18
12	13
12	17
37	50
7	12
17	34
27	58
18	34

Make a scatter plot of this data. Make sure to scale and label the axes.

Lesson 18: What a Point in a Scatter Plot Means

Let's investigate points in scatter plots.

18.1: The Giant Panda

A giant panda lives in a zoo. What does the point on the graph tell you about the panda?

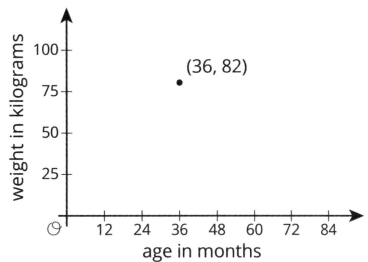

18.2: Weight and Fuel Efficiency

The table and scatter plot show weights and fuel efficiencies of 18 cars.

car	weight (kg)	fuel efficiency
A	1,549	25
B	1,610	20
C	1,737	21
D	1,777	20
E	1,486	23
F	1,962	16
G	2,384	16
H	1,957	19
I	2,212	16
J	1,115	29
K	2,068	18
L	1,663	19
M	2,216	18
N	1,432	25
O	1,987	18
P	1,580	26
Q	1,234	30
R	1,656	23

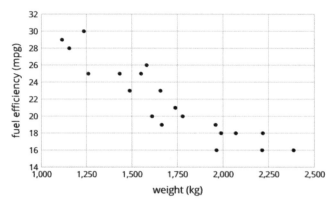

1. Which point in the scatter plot represents Car L's measurements?

2. What is the fuel efficiency of the car with the greatest weight?

3. What is the weight of the car with the greatest fuel efficiency?

4. Car S weighs 1,912 kilograms and gets 16 miles per gallon. On the scatter plot, plot a point that represents Car S's measurements.

5. Cars N and O, shown in the scatter plot, are made by the same company. Compare their weights and fuel efficiencies. Does anything surprise you about these cars?

6. A different company makes Cars F and G. Compare their weights and fuel efficiencies. Does anything surprise you about these cars?

Are you ready for more?

After a board game competition, the tournament director collects 50 dice from the games played and rolls each one until he gets bored and tries a different one. The scatter plot shows the number of times he rolled each die and the number of 6s that resulted during those rolls.

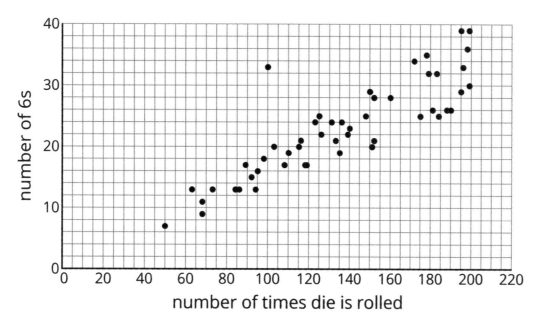

Select a point in the scatter plot and give its approximate coordinates, then tell the story of that point in the context of the problem.

18.3: Coat Sales

A clothing store keeps track of the average monthly temperature in degrees Celsius and coat sales in dollars.

temperature (degrees Celsius)	coat sales (dollars)
-5	1,550
-3	1,340
3	1,060
8	1,070
15	680
21	490
23	410
21	510
17	600
11	740
6	940
-2	1,390

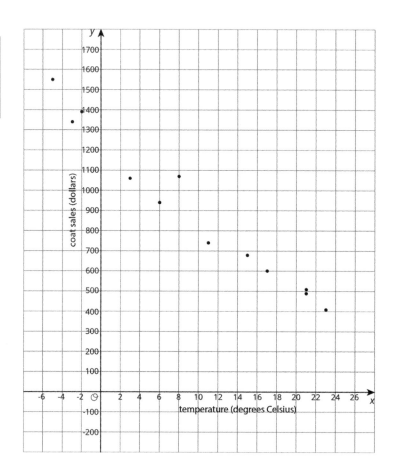

1. What does the point $(15, 680)$ represent?

2. For the month with the lowest average temperature, estimate the total amount made from coat sales. Explain how you used the table to find this information.

3. For the month with the smallest coat sales, estimate the average monthly temperature. Explain how you used the scatter plot to find this information.

4. If there were a point at $(0, A)$ what would it represent? Use the scatter plot to estimate a value for A.

5. What would a point at $(B, 0)$ represent? Use the scatter plot to estimate a value for B.

6. Would it make sense to use this trend to estimate the value of sales when the average monthly temperature is 60 degrees Celsius? Explain your reasoning.

Lesson 18 Summary

Scatter plots show two measurements for each individual from a group. For example, this scatter plot shows the weight and height for each dog from a group of 25 dogs.

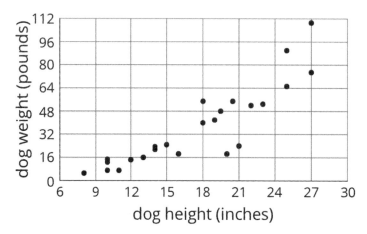

We can see that the tallest dogs are 27 inches, and that one of those tallest dogs weighs about 75 pounds while the other weighs about 110 pounds. This shows us that dog weight is not a function of dog height because there would be two different outputs for the same input. But we can see a general trend: Taller dogs tend to weigh more than shorter dogs. There are exceptions. For example, there is a dog that is 18 inches tall and weighs over 50 pounds, and there is another dog that is 21 inches tall but weighs less than 30 pounds.

When we collect data by measuring attributes like height, weight, area, or volume, we call the data *numerical data* (or measurement data), and we say that height, weight, area, or volume is a *numerical variable*. Upcoming lessons will discuss how to identify and describe trends in data that has been collected.

Lesson 18 Practice Problems

1. Here is a table and a scatter plot that compares points per game to free throw attempts for a basketball team during a tournament.

player	free throw attempts	points
player A	5.5	28.3
player B	2.1	18.6
player C	4.1	13.7
player D	1.6	10.6
player E	3.1	10.4
player F	1	5
player G	1.2	5
player H	0.7	4.7
player I	1.5	3.7
player J	1.5	3.5
player K	1.2	3.1
player L	0	1
player M	0	0.8
player N	0	0.6

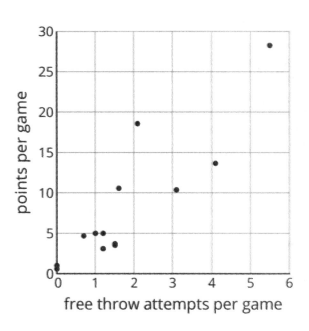

a. Circle the point that represents the data for Player E.

b. What does the point $(2.1, 18.6)$ represent?

c. In that same tournament, Player O on another team scored 14.3 points per game with 4.8 free throw attempts per game. Plot a point on the graph that shows this information.

2. Andre said, "I found two figures that are congruent, so they can't be similar."

   Diego said, "No, they are similar! The scale factor is 1."

   Do you agree with either of them? Use the definition of similarity to explain your answer.

(From Unit 2, Lesson 11.)

3. For each equation, explain what you could do first to each side of the equation so that there would be no fractions. You do not have to solve the equations (unless you want more practice).

   a. $\dfrac{3x - 4}{8} = \dfrac{x + 2}{3}$

   a. $\dfrac{4p + 3}{8} = \dfrac{p + 2}{4}$

   b. $\dfrac{3(2 - r)}{4} = \dfrac{3 + r}{6}$

   b. $\dfrac{2(a - 7)}{15} = \dfrac{a + 4}{6}$

(From Unit 4, Lesson 14.)

4. The points $(-2, 0)$ and $(0, -6)$ are each on the graph of a linear equation. Is $(2, 6)$ also on the graph of this linear equation? Explain your reasoning.

(From Unit 5, Lesson 11.)

iM KH

Lesson 19: Fitting a Line to Data

Let's look at the scatter plots as a whole.

19.1: Predict This

Here is a scatter plot that shows weights and fuel efficiencies of 20 different types of cars.

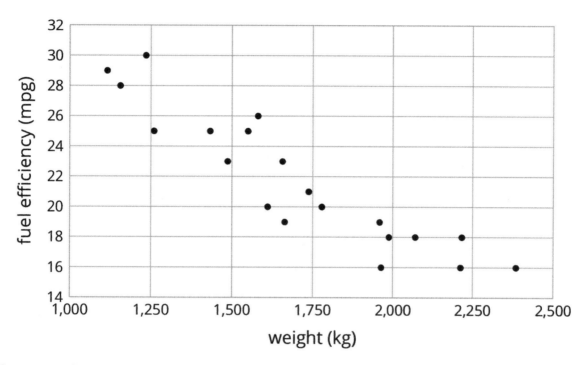

If a car weighs 1,750 kg, would you expect its fuel efficiency to be closer to 22 mpg or to 28 mpg? Explain your reasoning.

19.2: Shine Bright

Here is a table that shows weights and prices of 20 different diamonds.

weight (carats)	actual price (dollars)	predicted price (dollars)
1	3,772	4,429
1	4,221	4,429
1	4,032	4,429
1	5,385	4,429
1.05	3,942	4,705
1.05	4,480	4,705
1.06	4,511	4,760
1.2	5,544	5,533
1.3	6,131	6,085
1.32	5,872	6,195
1.41	7,122	6,692
1.5	7,474	7,189
1.5	5,904	7,189
1.59	8,706	7,686
1.61	8,252	7,796
1.73	9,530	8,459
1.77	9,374	8,679
1.85	8,169	9,121
1.9	9,541	9,397
2.04	9,125	10,170

The scatter plot shows the prices and weights of the 20 diamonds together with the graph of $y = 5{,}520x - 1{,}091$.

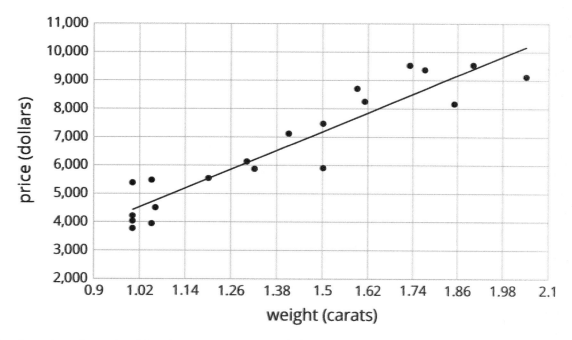

The function described by the equation $y = 5{,}520x - 1{,}091$ is a *model* of the relationship between a diamond's weight and its price.

This model *predicts* the price of a diamond from its weight. These predicted prices are shown in the third column of the table.

1. Two diamonds that both weigh 1.5 carats have different prices. What are their prices? How can you see this in the table? How can you see this in the graph?

2. The model predicts that when the weight is 1.5 carats, the price will be $7,189. How can you see this in the graph? How can you see this using the equation?

3. One of the diamonds weighs 1.9 carats. What does the model predict for its price? How does that compare to the actual price?

4. Find a diamond for which the model makes a very good prediction of the actual price. How can you see this in the table? In the graph?

5. Find a diamond for which the model's prediction is not very close to the actual price. How can you see this in the table? In the graph?

19.3: The Agony of the Feet

Here is a scatter plot that shows lengths and widths of 20 different left feet.

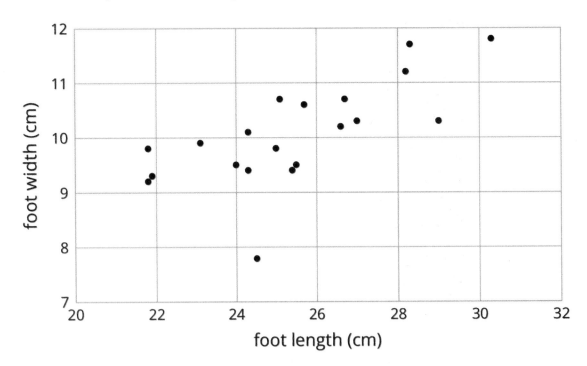

1. Estimate the widths of the longest foot and the shortest foot.

2. Estimate the lengths of the widest foot and the narrowest foot.

3. Here is the same scatter plot together with the graph of a model for the relationship between foot length and width.

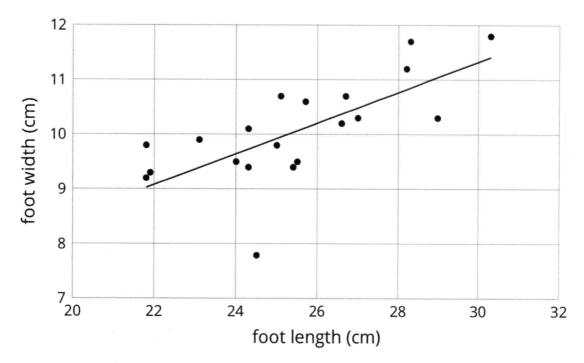

Circle the data point that seems weird when compared to the model. What length and width does that point represent?

Lesson 19 Summary

Sometimes, we can use a linear function as a model of the relationship between two variables. For example, here is a scatter plot that shows heights and weights of 25 dogs together with the graph of a linear function which is a model for the relationship between a dog's height and its weight.

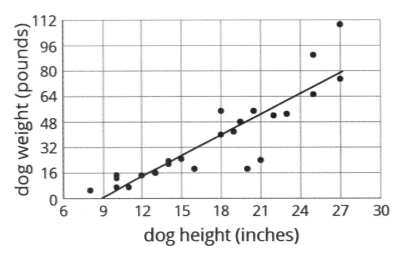

We can see that the model does a good job of predicting the weight given the height for some dogs. These correspond to points on or near the line. The model doesn't do a very good job of predicting the weight given the height for the dogs whose points are far from the line.

For example, there is a dog that is about 20 inches tall and weighs a little more than 16 pounds. The model predicts that the weight would be about 48 pounds. We say that the model *overpredicts* the weight of this dog. There is also a dog that is 27 inches tall and weighs about 110 pounds. The model predicts that its weight will be a little less than 80 pounds. We say the model *underpredicts* the weight of this dog.

Sometimes a data point is far away from the other points or doesn't fit a trend that all the other points fit. We call these **outliers**.

Glossary

- outlier

iM KH

Lesson 19 Practice Problems

1. The scatter plot shows the number of hits and home runs for 20 baseball players who had at least 10 hits last season. The table shows the values for 15 of those players.

The model, represented by $y = 0.15x - 1.5$, is graphed with a scatter plot.

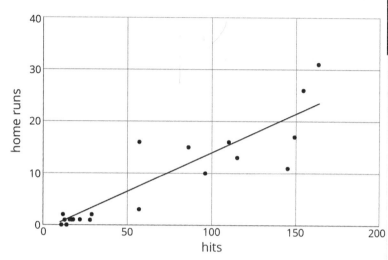

Use the graph and the table to answer the questions.

a. Player A had 154 hits in 2015. How many home runs did he have? How many was he predicted to have?

b. Player B was the player who most outperformed the prediction. How many hits did Player B have last season?

c. What would you expect to see in the graph for a player who hit many fewer home runs than the model predicted?

hits	home runs	predicted home runs
12	2	0.3
22	1	1.8
154	26	21.6
145	11	20.3
110	16	15
57	3	7.1
149	17	20.9
29	2	2.9
13	1	0.5
18	1	1.2
86	15	11.4
163	31	23
115	13	15.8
57	16	7.1
96	10	12.9

2. Here is a scatter plot that compares points per game to free throw attempts per game for basketball players in a tournament. The model, represented by $y = 4.413x + 0.377$, is graphed with the scatter plot. Here, x represents free throw attempts per game, and y represents points per game.

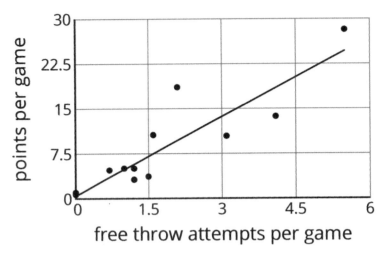

a. Circle any data points that appear to be outliers.

b. What does it mean for a point to be far above the line in this situation?

c. Based on the model, how many points per game would you expect a player who attempts 4.5 free throws per game to have? Round your answer to the nearest tenth of a point per game.

d. One of the players scored 13.7 points per game with 4.1 free throw attempts per game. How does this compare to what the model predicts for this player?

3. Choose the equation that has solutions $(5, 7)$ and $(8, 13)$.

    A. $3x - y = 8$

    B. $y = x + 2$

    C. $y - x = 5$

    D. $y = 2x - 3$

    (From Unit 5, Lesson 10.)

4. Solve each equation.

$$\frac{1}{7}\left(x + \frac{3}{4}\right) = \frac{1}{8} \qquad\qquad \frac{9}{2} = \frac{3}{4}\left(z + \frac{2}{3}\right)$$

$$1.5 = 0.6(w + 0.4) \qquad\qquad 0.08(7.97 + v) = 0.832$$

(From Unit 3, Lesson 8.)

Lesson 20: Describing Trends in Scatter Plots

Let's look for associations between variables.

20.1: Which One Doesn't Belong: Scatter Plots

Which one doesn't belong?

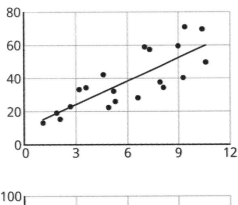
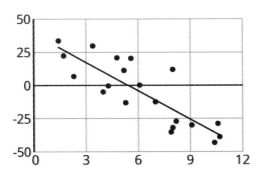
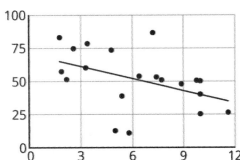
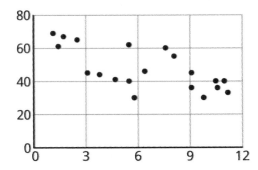

iM KH

20.2: Fitting Lines

Your teacher will give you a piece of pasta and a straightedge.

1. Here are two copies of the same scatter plot. Experiment with drawing lines to fit the data. Pick the line that you think best fits the data. Compare it with a partner's.

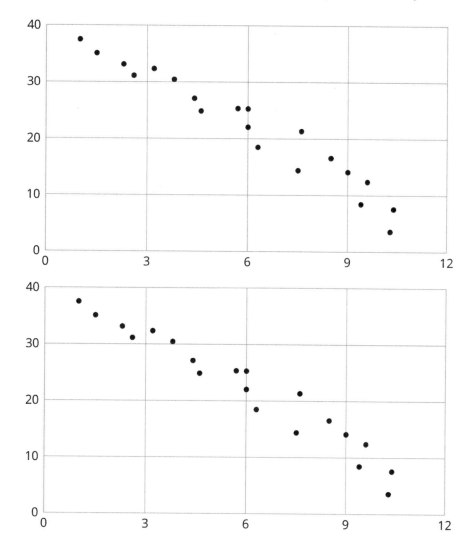

2. Here are two copies of another scatter plot. Experiment with drawing lines to fit the data. Pick the line that you think best fits the data. Compare it with a partner's.

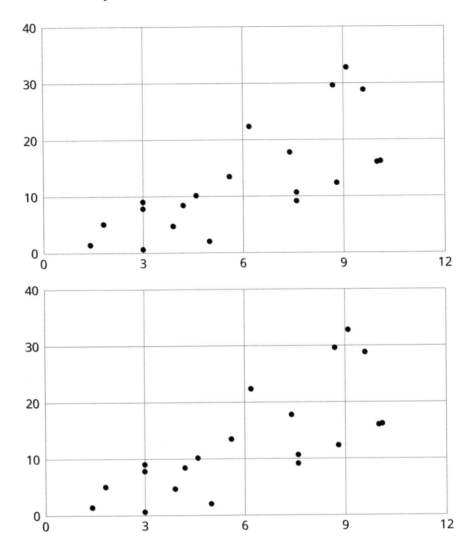

3. In your own words, describe what makes a line fit a data set well.

20.3: Good Fit Bad Fit

The scatter plots both show the year and price for the same 17 used cars. However, each scatter plot shows a different model for the relationship between year and price.

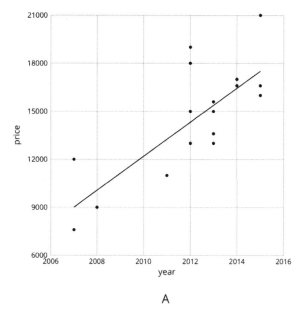

A

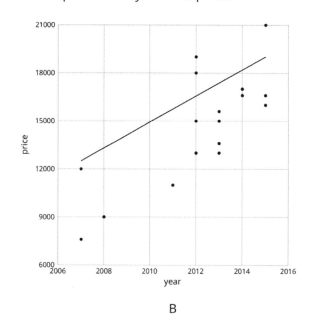

B

1. Look at Diagram A.

   a. For how many cars does the model in Diagram A make a good prediction of its price?

   b. For how many cars does the model underestimate the price?

   c. For how many cars does it overestimate the price?

2. Look at Diagram B.

   a. For how many cars does the model in Diagram B make a good prediction of its price?

   b. For how many cars does the model underestimate the price?

   c. For how many cars does it overestimate the price?

3. For how many cars does the prediction made by the model in Diagram A differ by more than $3,000? What about the model in Diagram B?

4. Which model does a better job of predicting the price of a used car from its year?

20.4: Practice Fitting Lines

1. Is this line a good fit for the data? Explain your reasoning.

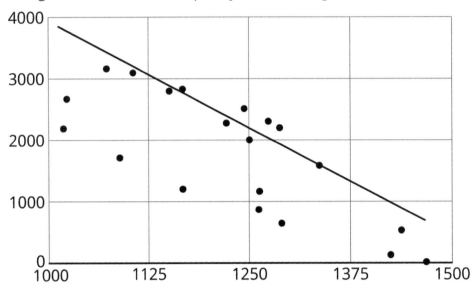

2. Draw a line that fits the data better.

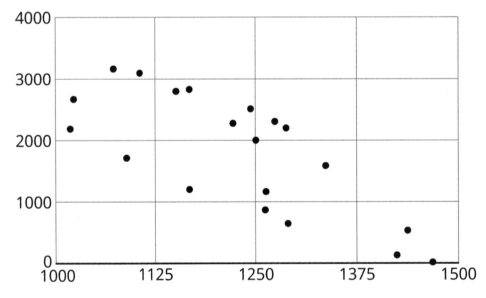

iM KH

3. Is this line a good fit for the data? Explain your reasoning.

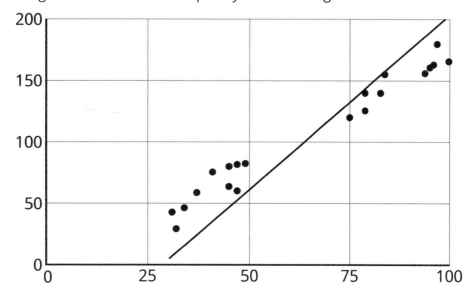

4. Draw a line that fits the data better.

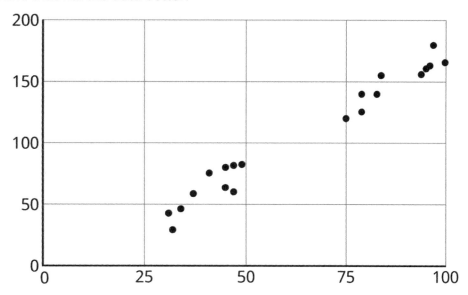

Are you ready for more?

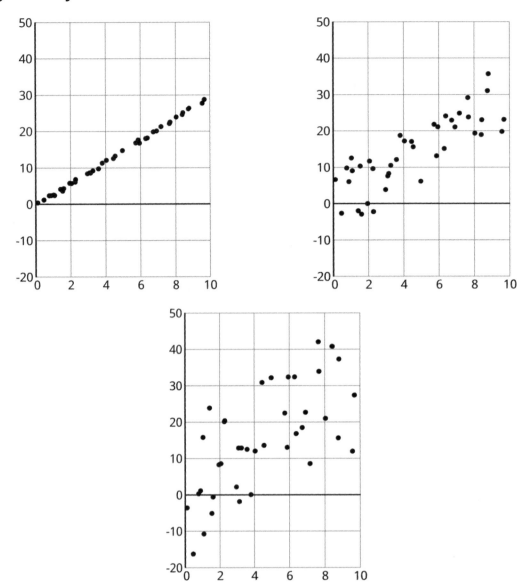

These scatter plots were created by multiplying the *x*-coordinate by 3 then adding a random number between two values to get the *y*-coordinate. The first scatter plot added a random number between -0.5 and 0.5 to the *y*-coordinate. The second scatter plot added a random number between -2 and 2 to the *y*-coordinate. The third scatter plot added a random number between -10 and 10 to the *y*-coordinate.

1. For each scatter plot, draw a line that fits the data.

2. Explain why some were easier to do than others.

iM KH

Lesson 20 Summary

When a linear function fits data well, we say there is a *linear association* between the variables. For example, the relationship between height and weight for 25 dogs with the linear function whose graph is shown in the scatter plot.

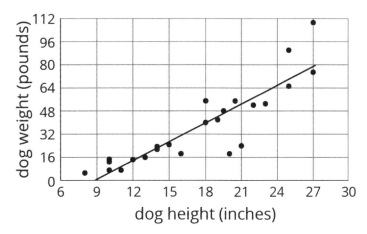

Because the model fits the data well and because the slope of the line is positive, we say that there is a **positive association** between dog height and dog weight.

What do you think the association between the weight of a car and its fuel efficiency is?

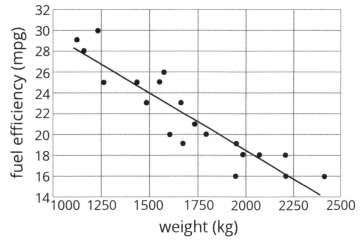

Because the slope of a line that fits the data well is negative, we say that there is a **negative association** between the fuel efficiency and weight of a car.

Glossary

- negative association
- positive association

Lesson 20 Practice Problems

1. a. Draw a line that you think is a good fit for this data. For this data, the inputs are the horizontal values, and the outputs are the vertical values.

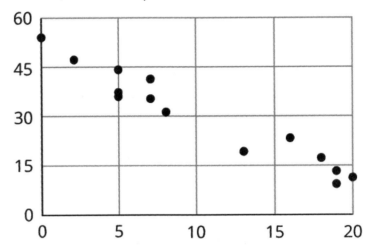

   b. Use your line of fit to estimate what you would expect the output value to be when the input is 10.

2. Here is a scatter plot that shows the most popular videos in a 10-year span.

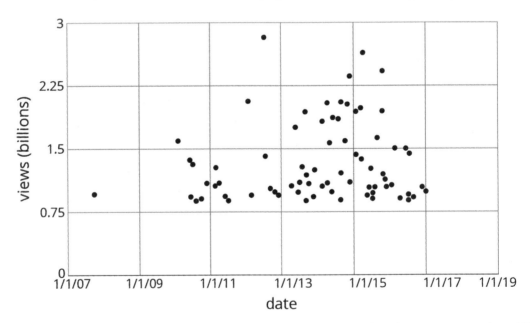

   a. Use the scatter plot to estimate the number of views for the most popular video in this 10-year span.

   b. Estimate when the 4th most popular video was released.

iM KH

(From Unit 5, Lesson 18.)

3. Here are Circles c and d. Point O is the center of dilation, and the dilation takes Circle c to Circle d.

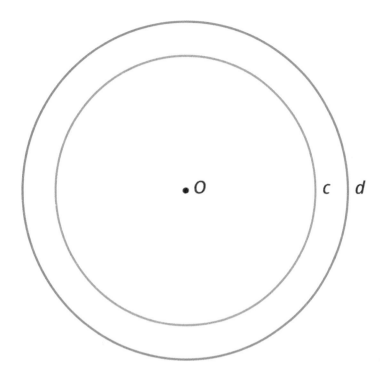

    a. Plot a point on Circle c. Label the point P. Plot where P goes when the dilation is applied.

    b. Plot a point on Circle d. Label the point Q. Plot a point that the dilation takes to Q.

(From Unit 2, Lesson 9.)

4. Triangle A is an isosceles triangle with two angles of measure x degrees and one angle of measure y degrees.

    a. Find three combinations of x and y that make this sentence true.

    b. Write an equation relating x and y.

    c. If you were to sketch the graph of this linear equation, what would its slope be? How can you interpret the slope in the context of the triangle?

(From Unit 5, Lesson 11.)

5. Mai earns $7 per hour mowing her neighbors' lawns. She also earned $14 for hauling away bags of recyclables for some neighbors.

Priya babysits her neighbor's children. The table shows the amount of money m she earns in h hours. Priya and Mai have agreed to go to the movies the weekend after they have earned the *same* amount of money for the *same* number of work hours.

h	m
1	$8.40
2	$16.80
4	$33.60

    a. How many hours do they each have to work before they go to the movies?

    b. How much will each of them have earned?

    c. Explain where the solution can be seen in tables of values, graphs, and equations that represent Priya's and Mai's hourly earnings.

(From Unit 5, Lesson 12.)

iM KH

Lesson 21: The Slope of a Fitted Line

Let's look at how changing one variable changes another.

21.1: Estimating Slope

Estimate the slope of the line.

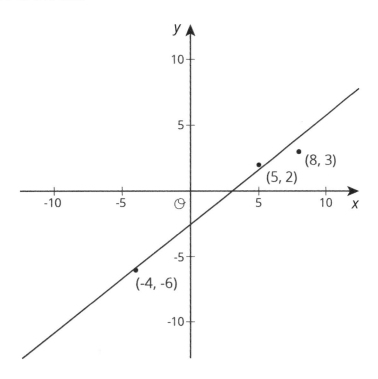

21.2: Describing Linear Associations

For each scatter plot, decide if there is an association between the two variables, and describe the situation using one of these sentences:

- For these data, as _____ increases, _____ tends to increase.

- For these data, as _____ increases, _____ tends to decrease.

- For these data, _____ and _____ do not appear to be related.

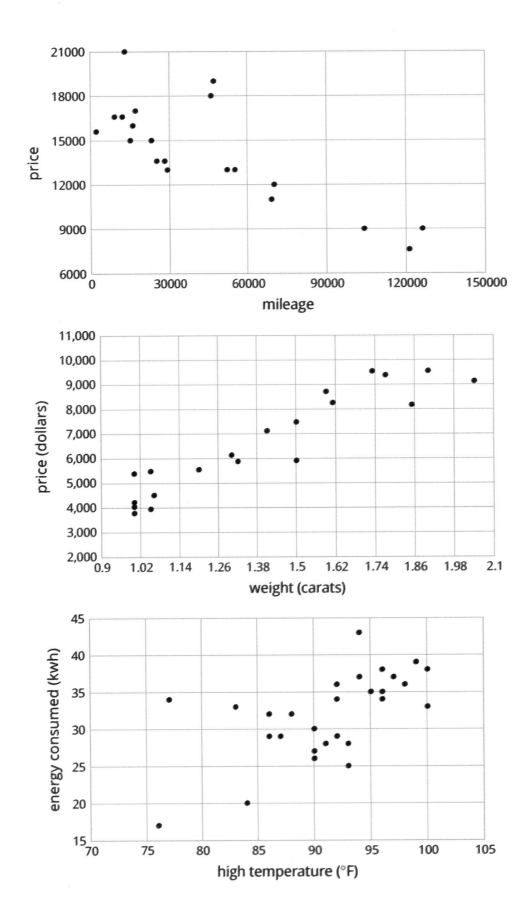

21.3: Interpreting Slopes

For each of the situations, a linear model for some data is shown.

1. What is the slope of the line in the scatter plot for each situation?

2. What is the meaning of the slope in that situation?

$$y = 5{,}520.619x - 1{,}091.393$$

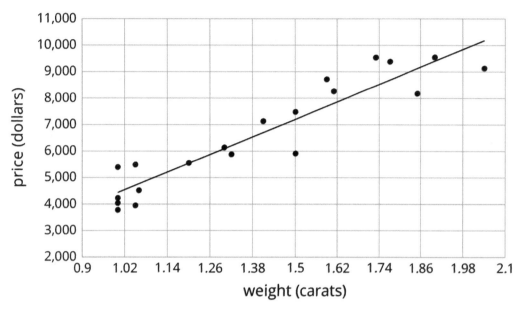

$$y = -0.011x + 40.604$$

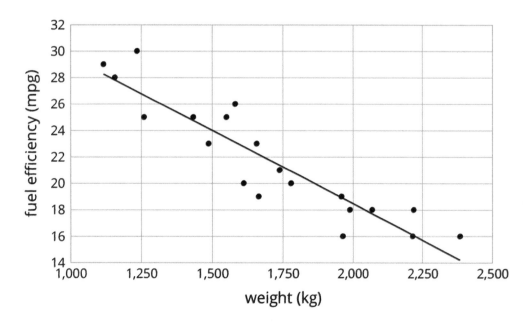

$y = 0.59x - 21.912$

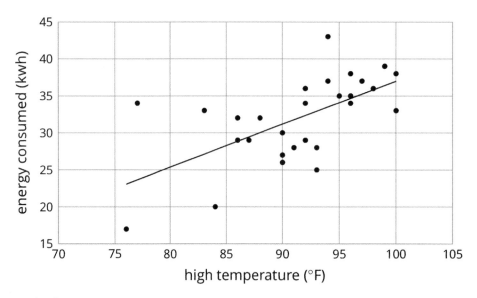

Are you ready for more?

The scatter plot shows the weight and fuel efficiency data used in an earlier lesson along with a linear model represented by the equation $y = -0.0114x + 41.3021$.

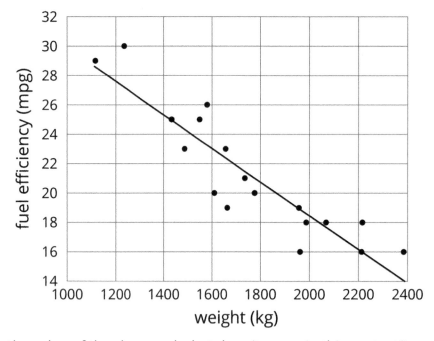

1. What is the value of the slope and what does it mean in this context?

2. What does the other number in the equation represent on the graph? What does it mean in context?

iM KH

3. Use the equation to predict the fuel efficiency of a car that weighs 100 kilograms.

4. Use the equation to predict the weight of a car that has a fuel efficiency of 22 mpg.

5. Which of these two predictions probably fits reality better? Explain.

21.4: Positive or Negative?

1. For each of the scatter plots, decide whether it makes sense to fit a linear model to the data. If it does, would the graph of the model have a positive slope, a negative slope, or a slope of zero?

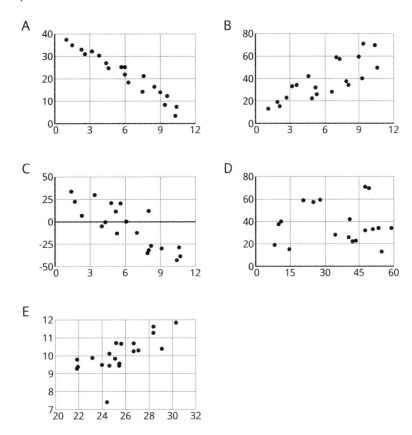

2. Which of these scatter plots show evidence of a positive association between the variables? Of a negative association? Which do not appear to show an association?

Lesson 21 Summary

Here is a scatter plot that we have seen before. As noted earlier, we can see from the scatter plot that taller dogs tend to weigh more than shorter dogs. Another way to say it is that weight tends to increase as height increases. When we have a positive association between two variables, an increase in one means there tends to be an increase in the other.

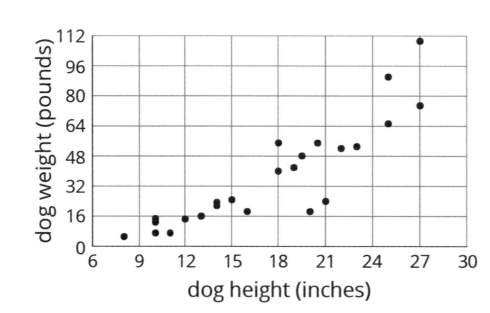

We can quantify this tendency by fitting a line to the data and finding its slope. For example, the equation of the fitted line is

$$w = 4.27h - 37$$

where h is the height of the dog and w is the predicted weight of the dog.

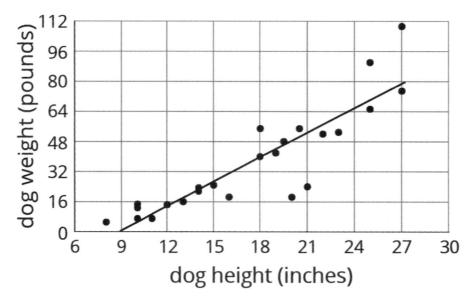

The slope is 4.27, which tells us that for every 1-inch increase in dog height, the weight is predicted to increase by 4.27 pounds.

iM KH

In our example of the fuel efficiency and weight of a car, the slope of the fitted line shown is -0.01.

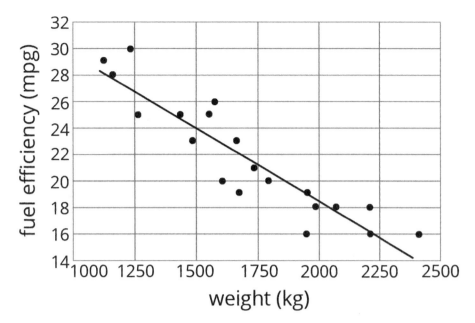

This tells us that for every 1-kilogram increase in the weight of the car, the fuel efficiency is predicted to decrease by 0.01 miles per gallon. When we have a negative association between two variables, an increase in one means there tends to be a decrease in the other.

Lesson 21 Practice Problems

1. Which of these statements is true about the data in the scatter plot?

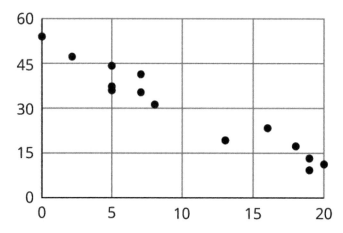

A. As x increases, y tends to increase.

B. As x increases, y tends to decrease.

C. As x increases, y tends to stay unchanged.

D. x and y are unrelated.

2. Here is a scatter plot that compares hits to at bats for players on a baseball team.

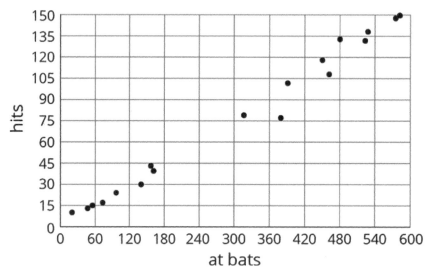

Describe the relationship between the number of at bats and the number of hits using the data in the scatter plot.

3. The linear model for some butterfly data is given by the equation
   $y = 0.238x + 4.642$. Which of the following best describes the slope of the model?

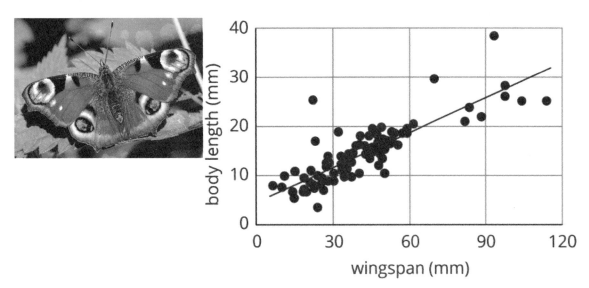

A. For every 1 mm the wingspan increases, the length of the butterfly increases 0.238 mm.

B. For every 1 mm the wingspan increases, the length of the butterfly increases 4.642 mm.

C. For every 1 mm the length of the butterfly increases, the wingspan increases 0.238 mm.

D. For every 1 mm the length of the butterfly increases, the wingspan increases 4.642 mm.

4. Solve: $\begin{cases} y = -3x + 13 \\ y = -2x + 1 \end{cases}$

(From Unit 5, Lesson 15.)

5. Nonstop, one-way flight times from O'Hare Airport in Chicago and prices of a one-way ticket are shown in the scatter plot.

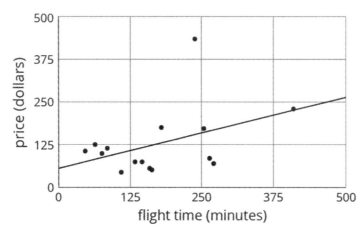

a. Circle any data that appear to be outliers.

b. Use the graph to estimate the difference between any outliers and their predicted values.

(From Unit 5, Lesson 19.)

6. Consider the following graphs of linear equations. Decide which line has a positive slope, and which has a negative slope. Then calculate each line's exact slope.

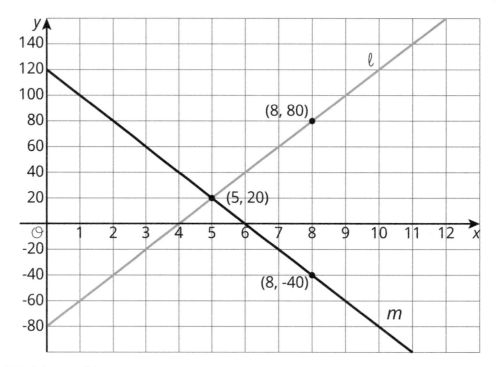

(From Unit 5, Lesson 9.)

iM KH

Lesson 22: Observing More Patterns in Scatter Plots

Let's look for other patterns in data.

22.1: Notice and Wonder: Clustering

What do you Notice? What do you Wonder?

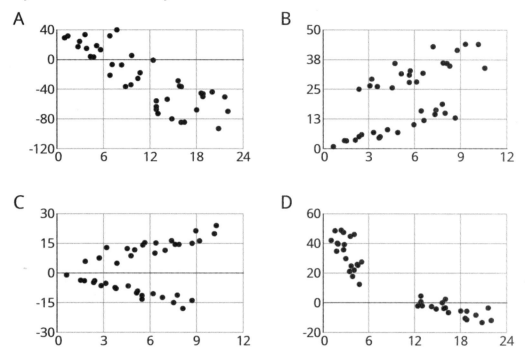

22.2: Scatter Plot City

Your teacher will give you a set of cards. Each card shows a scatter plot.

1. Sort the cards into categories and describe each category.

2. Explain the reasoning behind your categories to your partner. Listen to your partner's reasoning for their categories.

3. Sort the cards into two categories: positive associations and negative associations. Compare your sorting with your partner's and discuss any disagreements.

4. Sort the cards into two categories: linear associations and non-linear associations. Compare your sorting with your partner's and discuss any disagreements.

22.3: Animal Brains

Is there an association between the weight of an animal's body and the weight of the animal's brain?

Use the data in the table to make a scatter plot. Are there any outliers?

animal	body weight (kg)	brain weight (g)
cow	465	423
grey wolf	36	120
goat	28	115
donkey	187	419
horse	521	655
potar monkey	10	115
cat	3	26
giraffe	529	680
gorilla	207	406
human	62	1,320
rhesus monkey	7	179
kangaroo	35	56
sheep	56	175
jaguar	100	157
chimpanzee	52	440
pig	192	180

iM KH

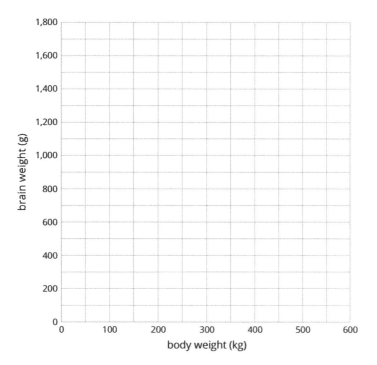

1. After removing the outliers, does there appear to be an association between body weight and brain weight? Describe the association in a sentence.

2. Using a piece of pasta and a straightedge, fit a line to your scatter plot, and estimate its slope. What does this slope mean in the context of brain and body weight?

3. Does the fitted line help you identify more outliers?

Are you ready for more?

Use one of the suggestions or find another set of data that interested you to look for associations between the variables.

- Number of wins vs number of points per game for your favorite sports team in different seasons

- Amount of money grossed vs critic rating for your favorite movies

- Price of a ticket vs stadium capacity for popular bands on tour

After you have collected the data,

1. Create a scatter plot for the data.

2. Are any of the points very far away from the rest of the data?

3. Would a linear model fit the data in your scatter plot? If so, draw it. If not, explain why a line would be a bad fit.

4. Is there an association between the two variables? Explain your reasoning.

Lesson 22 Summary

Sometimes a scatter plot shows an association that is *not* linear:

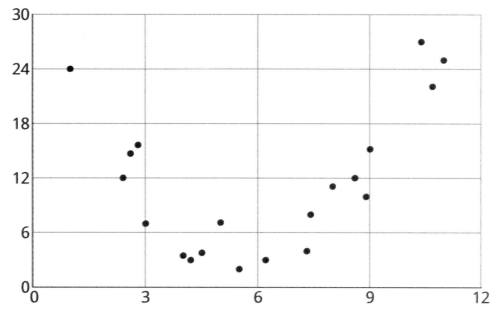

We call such an association a *non-linear association*. In later grades, you will study equations that can be models for non-linear associations.

Sometimes in a scatter plot we can see separate groups of points.

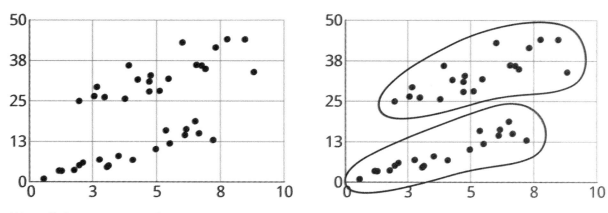

We call these groups *clusters*.

People often collect data in two variables to investigate possible associations between two numerical variables and use the connections that they find to predict more values of the variables. Data analysis usually follows these steps:

1. Collect data.

2. Organize and represent the data, and look for an association.

3. Identify any outliers and try to explain why these data points are exceptions to the trend that describes the association.

4. Find n equation that fits the data well.

Although computational systems can help with data analysis by graphing the data, finding an equation that might fit the data, and using that equation to make predictions, it is important to understand the process and think about what is happening. A computational system may find an equation that does not make sense or use a line when the situation suggests that a different model would be more appropriate.

Lesson 22 Practice Problems

1. Literacy rate and population for the 12 countries with more than 100 million people are shown in the scatter plot. Circle any clusters in the data.

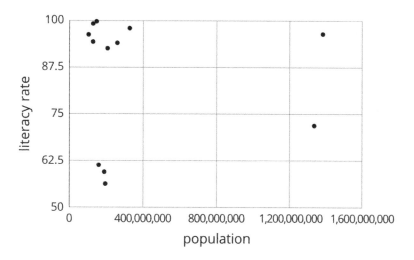

2. Here is a scatter plot:

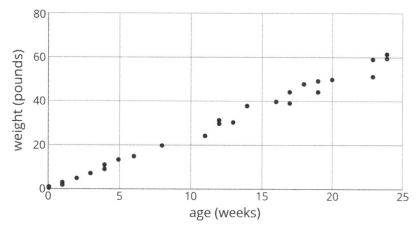

Select **all** the following that describe the association in the scatter plot:

    A. Linear association

    B. Non-linear association

    C. Positive association

    D. Negative association

    E. No association

3. For the same data, two different models are graphed. Which model more closely matches the data? Explain your reasoning.

A
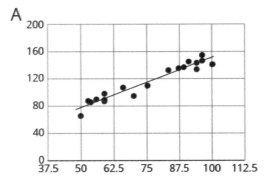

B
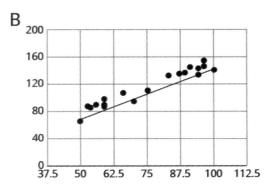

(From Unit 5, Lesson 20.)

4. Here is a scatter plot of data for some of the tallest mountains on Earth.

The heights in meters and year of first recorded ascent is shown. Mount Everest is the tallest mountain in this set of data.

  a. Estimate the height of Mount Everest.

  b. Estimate the year of the first recorded ascent of Mount Everest.

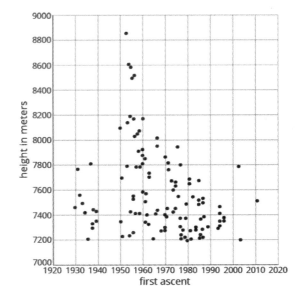

(From Unit 5, Lesson 18.)

iM KH

5. Different stores across the country sell a book for different prices. The table shows the price of the book in dollars and the number of books sold at that price.

price in dollars	number sold
11.25	53
10.50	60
12.10	30
8.45	81
9.25	70
9.75	80
7.25	120
12	37
9.99	130
7.99	100
8.75	90

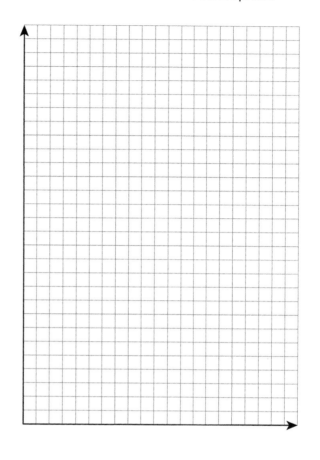

a. Draw a scatter plot of this data. Label the axes.

b. Are there any outliers? Explain your reasoning.

c. If there is a relationship between the variables, explain what it is.

d. Remove any outliers, and draw a line that you think is a good fit for the data.

Lesson 23: Looking for Associations

Let's look for associations in data.

23.1: Notice and Wonder: Bar Association

What do you notice? What do you wonder?

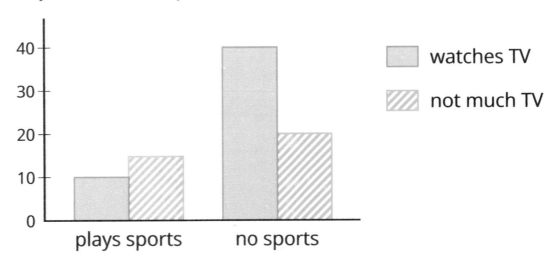

23.2: Card Sort: Matching Representations

Your teacher will hand out some cards.

Some cards show **two-way tables** like this:

	has cell phone	does not have cell phone	total
10 to 12 years old	25	35	60
13 to 15 years old	40	10	50
16 to 18 years old	50	10	60
total	115	55	170

Some cards show bar graphs like this:

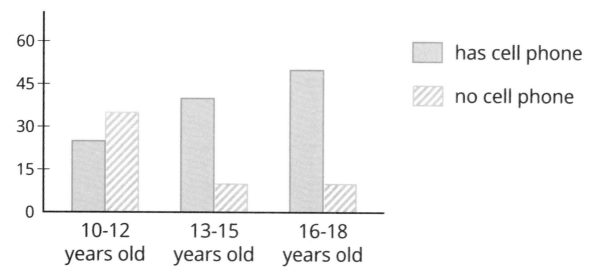

Some cards show **segmented bar graphs** like this:

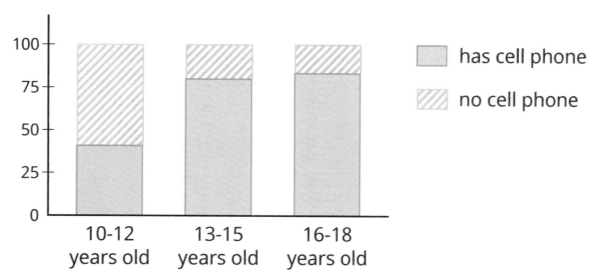

The bar graphs and segmented bar graphs have their labels removed.

1. Put all the cards that describe the same situation in the same group.

2. One of the groups does not have a two-way table. Make a two-way table for the situation described by the graphs in the group.

3. Label the bar graphs and segmented bar graphs so that the categories represented by each bar are indicated.

4. Describe in your own words the kind of information shown by a segmented bar graph.

One of the segmented bar graphs is missing. Construct a segmented bar graph that matches the other representations.

23.3: Building Another Type of Two-Way Table

Here is a two-way table that shows data about cell phone usage among children aged 10 to 18.

	has cell phone	does not have cell phone	total
10 to 12 years old	25	35	60
13 to 15 years old	40	10	50
16 to 18 years old	50	10	60
total	115	55	170

1. Complete the table. In each row, the entries for "has cell phone" and "does not have cell phone" should have the total 100%. Round entries to the nearest percentage point.

	has cell phone	does not have cell phone	total
10 to 12 years old	42%		
13 to 15 years old			100%
16 to 18 years old		17%	

This is still a two-way table. Instead of showing *frequency*, this table shows **relative frequency**.

2. Two-way tables that show relative frequencies often don't include a "total" row at the bottom. Why?

3. Is there an association between age and cell phone use? How does the two-way table of relative frequencies help to illustrate this?

Are you ready for more?

A pollster attends a rally and surveys many of the participants about whether they associate with political Party A or political Party B and whether they are for or against Proposition 3.14 going up for vote soon. The results are sorted into the table shown.

	for	against
party A	832	165
party B	80	160

- A news station reports these results by saying, "A poll shows that about the same number of people from both parties are voting against Proposition 3.14."

- A second news station shows this graphic.

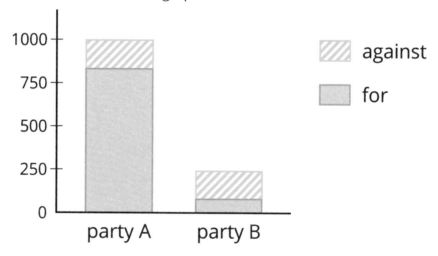

1. Are any of the news reports misleading? Explain your reasoning.

2. Create a headline, graphic, and short description that more accurately represents the data in the table.

Lesson 23 Summary

When we collect data by counting things in various categories, like red, blue, or yellow, we call the data *categorical data*, and we say that color is a *categorical variable*.

We can use **two-way tables** to investigate possible connections between two categorical variables. For example, this two-way table of frequencies shows the results of a study of meditation and state of mind of athletes before a track meet.

	meditated	did not meditate	total
calm	45	8	53
agitated	23	21	44
total	68	29	97

If we are interested in the question of whether there is an association between meditating and being calm, we might present the frequencies in a bar graph, grouping data about meditators and grouping data about non-meditators, so we can compare the numbers of calm and agitated athletes in each group.

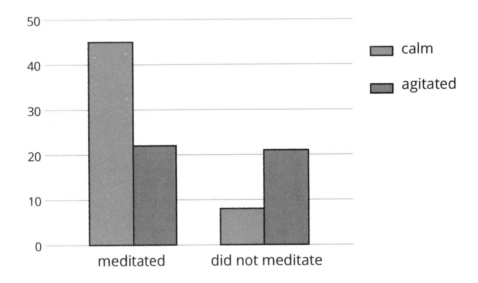

Notice that the number of athletes who did not meditate is small compared to the number who meditated (29 as compared to 68, as shown in the table).

If we want to know the proportions of calm meditators and calm non-meditators, we can make a two-way table of **relative frequencies** and present the relative frequencies in a **segmented bar graph**.

	meditated	did not meditate
calm	66%	28%
agitated	34%	72%
total	100%	100%

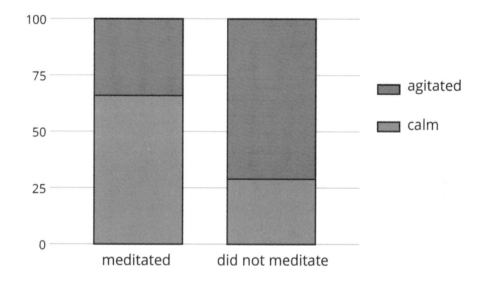

Glossary

- relative frequency
- segmented bar graph
- two-way table

Lesson 23 Practice Problems

1. A scientist wants to know if the color of the water affects how much animals drink. The average amount of water each animal drinks was recorded in milliliters for a week and then graphed. Is there evidence to suggest an association between water color and animal?

	cat intake (ml)	dog intake (ml)	total (ml)
blue water	210	1200	1410
green water	200	1100	1300
total	410	2300	2710

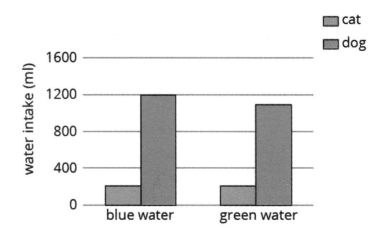

2. A farmer brings his produce to the farmer's market and records whether people buy lettuce, apples, both, or something else.

	bought apples	did not buy apples
bought lettuce	14	58
did not buy lettuce	8	29

Make a table that shows the relative frequencies for each row. Use this table to decide if there is an association between buying lettuce and buying apples.

3. Researchers at a media company want to study news-reading habits among different age groups. They tracked print and online subscription data and made a 2-way table.

	internet media	print media
18-25 year olds	151	28
26-45 year olds	132	72
46-65 year olds	48	165

    a. Create a segmented bar graph using one bar for each row of the table.

    b. Is there an association between age groups and the method they use to read articles? Explain your reasoning.

4. Using the data in the scatter plot, what is a reasonable slope of a model that fits this data?

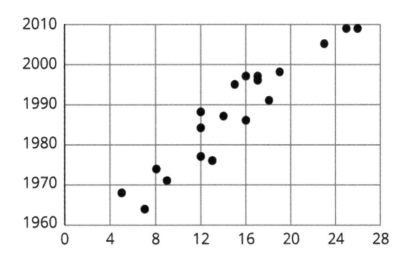

    A. -2.5

    B. -1

    C. 1

    D. 2.5

(From Unit 5, Lesson 21.)

Lesson 24: Using Data Displays to Find Associations

Let's use data displays to find associations.

24.1: Sports and Musical Instruments

For a survey, students in a class answered these questions:

- Do you play a sport?

- Do you play a musical instrument?

1. Here is a two-way table that gives some results from the survey. Complete the table, assuming that all students answered both questions.

	plays instrument	does not play instrument	total
plays sport	5		16
does not play sport			
total		15	25

2. To the nearest percentage point, what percentage of students who play a sport *don't* play a musical instrument?

3. To the nearest percentage point, what percentage of students who *don't* play a sport also *don't* play a musical instrument?

24.2: Sports and Music Association

Your teacher will give you a two-way table with information about the number of people in your class who play sports or musical instruments.

1. Complete this table to make a two-way table for the data from earlier. The table will show relative frequencies *by row*.

	plays instrument	does not play instrument	row total
plays sport			100%
does not play sport			100%

2. Make a segmented bar graph for the table. Use one bar of the graph for each row of the table.

3. Complete the table to make a two-way table for the data from earlier. The table will show relative frequencies *by column*.

	plays instrument	does not play instrument
plays sport		
does not play sport		
column total	100%	100%

4. Using the values in the table, make a segmented bar graph. Use one bar of the graph for each column of the table.

100 ─────────────────────────

75 ─────────────────────────

50 ─────────────────────────

25 ─────────────────────────

0 ─────────────────────────
　　plays instrument　　no instrument

5. Based on the two-way tables and segmented bar graphs, do you think there is an association between playing a sport and playing a musical instrument? Explain how you know.

iM KH

24.3: Colored Erasers

An eraser factory has five machines. One machine makes the eraser shapes. Then each shape goes through the red machine, blue machine, yellow machine, or green machine to have a side colored.

The manager notices that an uncolored side of some erasers is flawed at the end of the process and wants to know which machine needs to be fixed: the shape machine or some of the color machines. The manager collected data on the number of flawed and unflawed erasers of each color.

	unflawed	flawed	total
red	285	15	300
blue	223	17	240
yellow	120	80	200
green	195	65	260
total	823	177	1000

1. Work with a partner. Each of you should make one segmented bar graph for the data in the table. One segmented bar graph should have a bar for each *row* of the table. The other segmented bar graph should have one bar for each *column* of the table.

2. Are the flawed erasers associated with certain colors? If so, which colors? Explain your reasoning.

Are you ready for more?

Based on the federal budgets for 2009, the table shows where some of the federal money was expected to go. The values are in billions of U.S. Dollars.

	United States	Japan	United Kingdom
defense	718.4	42.8	49.2
education	44.9	47.5	113.9

1. Why would a segmented bar graph be more useful than the table of data to see any associations between the country and where the money is spent?

2. Create a segmented bar graph that represents the data from the table.

3. Is there an association between the country's budget and their spending in these areas? Explain your reasoning.

iV KH

Lesson 24 Summary

In an earlier lesson, we looked at data on meditation and state of mind in athletes.

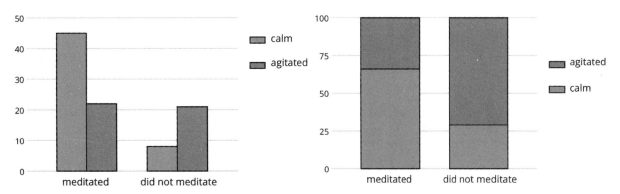

Is there an association between meditation and state of mind?

The bar graph shows that more athletes were calm than agitated among the group that meditated, and more athletes were agitated than calm among the group that did not. We can see the proportions of calm meditators and calm non-meditators from the segmented bar graph, which shows that about 66% of athletes who meditated were calm, whereas only about 27% of those who did not meditate were calm.

This does not necessarily mean that meditation causes calm; it could be the other way around, that calm athletes are more inclined to meditate. But it does suggest that there is an association between meditating and calmness.

Lesson 24 Practice Problems

1. An ecologist is studying a forest with a mixture of tree types. Since the average tree height in the area is 40 feet, he measures the height of the tree against that. He also records the type of tree. The results are shown in the table and segmented bar graph. Is there evidence of an association between tree height and tree type? Explain your reasoning.

	under 40 feet	40 feet or taller	total
deciduous	45	30	75
evergreen	14	10	24
total	59	40	99

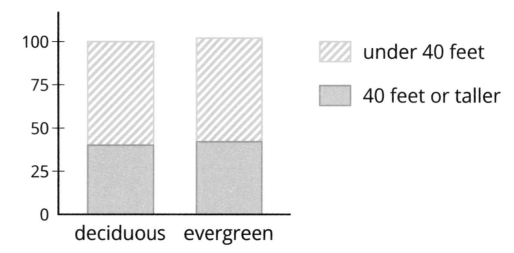

iM KH

2. Workers at an advertising agency are interested in people's TV viewing habits. They take a survey of people in two cities to try to find patterns in the types of shows they watch. The results are recorded in a table and shown in a segmented bar graph. Is there evidence of different viewing habits? If so, explain.

	reality	news	comedy	drama
Chicago	50	40	90	20
Topeka	45	70	40	45

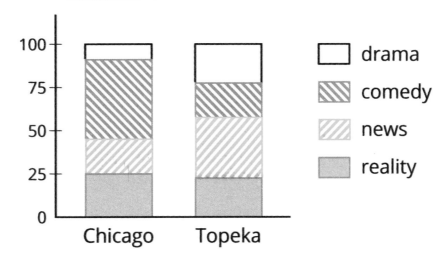

3. A scientist is interested in whether certain species of butterflies like certain types of local flowers. The scientist captures butterflies in two zones with different flower types and records the number caught. Do these data show an association between butterfly type and zone? Explain your reasoning.

	zone 1	zone 2
eastern tiger swallowtail	16	34
monarch	24	46

Lesson 25: Using Linear Relations to Solve Problems

Let's write equations for real-world situations and think about their solutions.

25.1: Buying Fruit

For each relationship described, write an equation to represent the relationship.

1. Grapes cost $2.39 per pound. Bananas cost $0.59 per pound. You have $15 to spend on g pounds of grapes and b pounds of bananas.

2. A savings account has $50 in it at the start of the year and $20 is deposited each week. After x weeks, there are y dollars in the account.

25.2: Five Savings Accounts

Each line represents one person's weekly savings account balance from the start of the year.

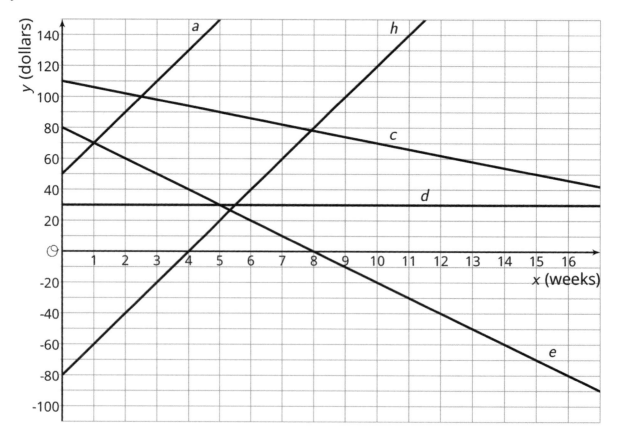

iM KH

1. Choose one line and write a description of what happens to that person's account over the first 17 weeks of the year. Do not tell your group which line you chose.

2. Share your story with your group and see if anyone can guess your line.

3. Write an equation for each line on the graph. What do the slope, m, and vertical intercept, b, in each equation mean in the situation?

4. For which equation is $(1, 70)$ a solution? Interpret this solution in terms of your story.

5. Predict the balance in each account after 20 weeks.

25.3: Fabulous Fish

The Fabulous Fish Market orders tilapia, which costs $3 per pound, and salmon, which costs $5 per pound. The market budgets $210 to spend on this order each day.

    1. What are five different combinations of salmon and tilapia that the market can order?

    2. Define variables and write an equation representing the relationship between the amount of each fish bought and how much the market spends.

    3. Sketch a graph of the relationship. Label your axes.

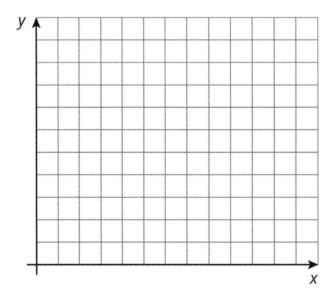

    4. On your graph, plot and label the combinations A—F.

	A	B	C	D	E	F
pounds of tilapia	5	19	27	25	65	55
pounds of salmon	36	30.6	25	27	6	4

5. Which of these combinations can the market order? Explain or show your reasoning.

6. List two ways you can tell if a pair of numbers is a solution to an equation.

Lesson 26: Solving Problems with Systems of Equations

Let's solve some gnarly problems.

26.1: Are We There Yet?

A car is driving towards home at 0.5 miles per minute. If the car is 4 miles from home at $t = 0$, which of the following can represent the distance that the car has left to drive?

- $0.5t$

- $4 + 0.5t$

- $4 - 0.5t$

- $4 \cdot (0.5t)$

26.2: Cycling, Fundraising, Working, and ___?

Solve each problem. Explain or show your reasoning.

1. Two friends live 7 miles apart. One Saturday, the two friends set out on their bikes at 8 am and started riding towards each other. One rides at 0.2 miles per minute, and the other rides at 0.15 miles per minute. At what time will the two friends meet?

2. Students are selling grapefruits and nuts for a fundraiser. The grapefruits cost $1 each and a bag of nuts cost $10 each. They sold 100 items and made $307. How many grapefruits did they sell?

3. Jada earns $7 per hour mowing her neighbors' lawns. Andre gets paid $5 per hour for the first hour of babysitting and $8 per hour for any additional hours he babysits. What is the number of hours they both can work so that they get paid the same amount?

4. Pause here so your teacher can review your work. Then, invent another problem that is like one of these, but with different numbers. Solve your problem.

5. Create a visual display that includes:
   - The new problem you wrote, without the solution.

   - Enough work space for someone to show a solution.

6. Trade your display with another group, and solve each other's new problem. Make sure that you explain your solution carefully. Be prepared to share this solution with the class.

7. When the group that got the problem you invented shares their solution, check that their answer is correct.

Are you ready for more?

On a different Saturday, two friends set out on bikes at 8:00 am and met up at 8:30 am. (The same two friends who live 7 miles apart.) If one was riding at 10 miles per hour, how fast was the other riding?

Lesson 27: Gone In 30 Seconds

Let's gather and analyze some timing data.

27.1: Measuring 30 Seconds

In this activity, you'll get two chances to guess at how long 30 seconds is, then look for an association between the two guesses of all students.

1. Work with a partner. Follow the instructions listed here to gather your data.
   - One of you will hold a stopwatch where the other person cannot see it.
   - The person holding the stopwatch says "go" and starts the timer.
   - The other person says "stop" when they think 30 seconds have passed.
   - The person holding the stopwatch will stop the timer, then report and record the time to the nearest second.
   - The person holding the stopwatch will give a second chance, repeating the experiment.
   - After *both* times are recorded, switch roles.

2. Record the group data in this table. When you finish, a group member should give the data to the teacher.

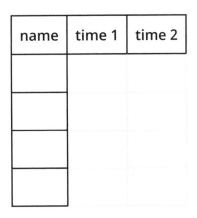

name	time 1	time 2

3. Look at your data. Comparing Time 1 to Time 2, do you think there is a positive association, a negative association, or no association? Discuss your thinking with your group.

4. What are some ways you could organize and represent the entire class's data?

5. Make a scatter plot of the entire class's data and look for patterns. Identify any outliers and the type of any association you observe.

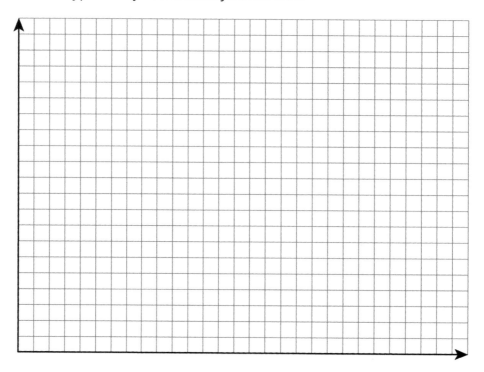

6. Draw two lines on your scatter plot: a vertical line and a horizontal line, each representing 30 seconds for one trial. Use the table for the class's data to complete this two-way table.

	time 2 < 30 sec	time 2 = 30 sec	time 2 > 30 sec	total
time 1 < 30 sec				
time 1 = 30 sec				
time 1 > 30 sec				
total				

7. Use the two-way table to decide whether there is an association between Time 1 and Time 2. Explain how you know.

iM KH

Learning Targets

Lesson 1: Understanding Proportional Relationships

- I can graph a proportional relationship from a story.

- I can use the constant of proportionality to compare the pace of different animals.

Lesson 2: Representing Proportional Relationships

- I can graph a proportional relationship from an equation.

- I can scale and label coordinate axes in order to graph a proportional relationship.

- I can tell when two graphs are of the same proportional relationship even if the scales are different.

Lesson 3: Comparing Proportional Relationships

- I can compare proportional relationships represented in different ways.

Lesson 4: Introduction to Linear Relationships

- I can find the rate of change of a linear relationship by figuring out the slope of the line representing the relationship.

Lesson 5: More Linear Relationships

- I can interpret the vertical intercept of a graph of a real-world situation.

- I can match graphs to the real-world situations they represent by identifying the slope and the vertical intercept.

Lesson 6: Representations of Linear Relationships

- I can use patterns to write a linear equation to represent a situation.

- I can write an equation for the relationship between the total volume in a graduated cylinder and the number of objects added to the graduated cylinder.

Lesson 7: Translating to $y = mx + b$

- I can explain where to find the slope and vertical intercept in both an equation and its graph.

- I can write equations of lines using y=mx+b.

Lesson 8: Slopes Don't Have to be Positive

- I can give an example of a situation that would have a negative slope when graphed.

- I can look at a graph and tell if the slope is positive or negative and explain how I know.

Lesson 9: Slopes and Equations for All Kinds of Lines

- I can calculate positive and negative slopes given two points on the line.

- I can write equations of vertical and horizontal lines.

Lesson 10: Solutions to Linear Equations

- I know that the graph of an equation is a visual representation of all the solutions to the equation.

- I understand what the solution to an equation in two variables is.

Lesson 11: More Solutions to Linear Equations

- I can find solutions (x, y) to linear equations given either the x- or the y-value to start from.

Lesson 12: On Both of the Lines

- I can use graphs to find an ordered pair that two real-world situations have in common.

Lesson 13: Systems of Equations

- I can explain the solution to a system of equations in a real-world context.

- I can explain what a system of equations is.

- I can make graphs to find an ordered pair that two real-world situations have in common.

Lesson 14: Solving Systems of Equations

- I can graph a system of equations.

- I can solve systems of equations using algebra.

Lesson 15: Solving More Systems

- I can use the structure of equations to help me figure out how many solutions a system of equations has.

Lesson 16: Writing Systems of Equations

- I can write a system of equations from a real-world situation.

Lesson 17: Organizing Data

- I can organize data to see patterns more clearly.

Lesson 18: What a Point in a Scatter Plot Means

- I can describe the meaning of a point in a scatter plot in context.

Lesson 19: Fitting a Line to Data

- I can pick out outliers on a scatter plot.

- I can use a model to predict values for data.

Lesson 20: Describing Trends in Scatter Plots

- I can draw a line to fit data in a scatter plot.

- I can say whether data in a scatter plot has a positive or negative association (or neither).

Lesson 21: The Slope of a Fitted Line

- I can use the slope of a line fit to data in a scatter plot to say how the variables are connected in real-world situations.

Lesson 22: Observing More Patterns in Scatter Plots

- I can analyze a set of data to determine associations between two variables.

- I can pick out clusters in data from a scatter plot.

- I can use a scatter plot to decide if two variables have a linear association.

Lesson 23: Looking for Associations

- I can identify the same data represented in a bar graph, a segmented bar graph, and a two-way table.

- I can use a two-way frequency table or relative frequency table to find associations among variables.

Lesson 24: Using Data Displays to Find Associations

- I can create relative frequency tables, bar graphs, and segmented bar graphs from frequency tables to find associations among variables.

Lesson 25: Using Linear Relations to Solve Problems

- I can write linear equations to reason about real-world situations.

Lesson 26: Solving Problems with Systems of Equations

- I can use a system of equations to represent a real-world situation and answer questions about the situation.

Lesson 27: Gone In 30 Seconds

- I can collect data and analyze it for associations using scatter plots, two-way tables, and segmented bar graphs.

ACCELERATED

7

Unit

6

STUDENT WORKBOOK

Book 2

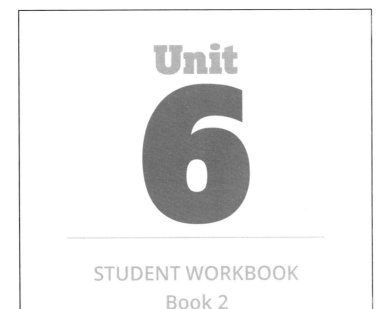

Kendall Hunt | iM CERTIFIED

Lesson 1: Inputs and Outputs

Let's make some rules.

1.1: Dividing by 0

Study the statements carefully.

- $12 \div 3 = 4$ because $12 = 4 \cdot 3$

- $6 \div 0 = x$ because $6 = x \cdot 0$

What value can be used in place of x to create true statements? Explain your reasoning.

1.2: Guess My Rule

Keep the rule cards face down. Decide who will go first.

1. Player 1 picks up a card and silently reads the rule without showing it to Player 2.

2. Player 2 chooses an integer and asks Player 1 for the result of applying the rule to that number.

3. Player 1 gives the result, without saying how they got it.

4. Keep going until Player 2 correctly guesses the rule.

After each round, the players switch roles.

Are you ready for more?

If you have a rule, you can apply it several times in a row and look for patterns. For example, if your rule was "add 1" and you started with the number 5, then by applying that rule over and over again you would get 6, then 7, then 8, etc., forming an obvious pattern.

Try this for the rules in this activity. That is, start with the number 5 and apply each of the rules a few times. Do you notice any patterns? What if you start with a different starting number?

1.3: Making Tables

For each input-output rule, fill in the table with the outputs that go with a given input. Add two more input-output pairs to the table.

1.

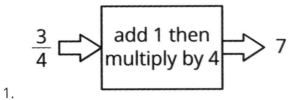

input	output
$\frac{3}{4}$	7
2.35	
42	

2.

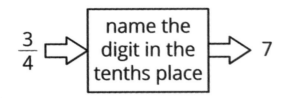

input	output
$\frac{3}{4}$	7
2.35	
42	

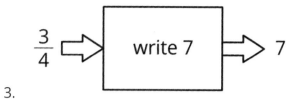

3.

input	output
$\frac{3}{4}$	7
2.35	
42	

Pause here until your teacher directs you to the last rule.

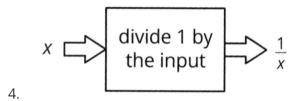

4.

input	output
$\frac{3}{7}$	$\frac{7}{3}$
1	
0	

iM KH

Lesson 1 Summary

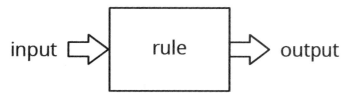

An *input-output rule* is a rule that takes an allowable input and uses it to determine an output. For example, the following diagram represents the rule that takes any number as an input, then adds 1, multiplies by 4, and gives the resulting number as an output.

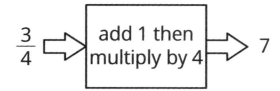

In some cases, not all inputs are allowable, and the rule must specify which inputs will work. For example, this rule is fine when the input is 2:

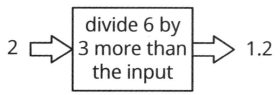

But if the input is -3, we would need to evaluate $6 \div 0$ to get the output.

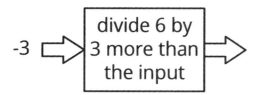

So, when we say that the rule is "divide 6 by 3 more than the input," we also have to say that -3 is not allowed as an input.

Lesson 1 Practice Problems

1. Given the rule:

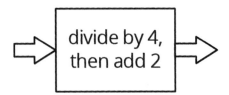

Complete the table for the function rule for the following input values:

input	0	2	4	6	8	10
output						

2. Here is an input-output rule:

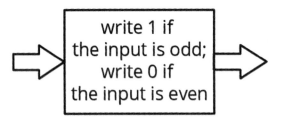

Complete the table for the input-output rule:

input	-3	-2	-1	0	1	2	3
output							

iM KH

3. Andre's school orders some new supplies for the chemistry lab. The online store shows a pack of 10 test tubes costs $4 less than a set of nested beakers. In order to fully equip the lab, the school orders 12 sets of beakers and 8 packs of test tubes.

a. Write an equation that shows the cost of a pack of test tubes, t, in terms of the cost of a set of beakers, b.

b. The school office receives a bill for the supplies in the amount of $348. Write an equation with t and b that describes this situation.

c. Since t is in terms of b from the first equation, this expression can be substituted into the second equation where t appears. Write an equation that shows this substitution.

d. Solve the equation for b.

e. How much did the school pay for a set of beakers? For a pack of test tubes?

(From Unit 5, Lesson 16.)

4. Solve: $\begin{cases} y = x - 4 \\ y = 6x - 10 \end{cases}$

(From Unit 5, Lesson 15.)

5. For what value of x do the expressions $2x + 3$ and $3x - 6$ have the same value?

(From Unit 4, Lesson 17.)

Lesson 2: Introduction to Functions

Let's learn what a function is.

2.1: Square Me

Here are some numbers in a list:

$$1, -3, -\frac{1}{2}, 3, 2, \frac{1}{4}, 0.5$$

1. How many different numbers are in the list?

2. Make a new list containing the squares of all these numbers.

3. How many different numbers are in the new list?

4. Explain why the two lists do not have the same number of different numbers.

2.2: You Know This, Do You Know That?

Say yes or no for each question. If yes, draw an input-output diagram. If no, give examples of two different outputs that are possible for the same input.

1. A person is 5.5 feet tall. Do you know their height in inches?

2. A number is 5. Do you know its square?

3. The square of a number is 16. Do you know the number?

4. A square has a perimeter of 12 cm. Do you know its area?

5. A rectangle has an area of 16 cm^2. Do you know its length?

6. You are given a number. Do you know the number that is $\frac{1}{5}$ as big?

7. You are given a number. Do you know its reciprocal?

2.3: Using Function Language

Here are the questions from the previous activity. For the ones you said yes to, write a statement like, "The height a rubber ball bounces to depends on the height it was dropped from" or "Bounce height is a **function** of drop height." For all of the ones you said no to, write a statement like, "The day of the week does not determine the temperature that day" or "The temperature that day is not a function of the day of the week."

1. A person is 5.5 feet tall. Do you know their height in inches?

2. A number is 5. Do you know its square?

3. The square of a number is 16. Do you know the number?

4. A square has a perimeter of 12 cm. Do you know its area?

5. A rectangle has an area of 16 cm^2. Do you know its length?

6. You are given a number. Do you know the number that is $\frac{1}{5}$ as big?

7. You are given a number. Do you know its reciprocal?

2.4: Same Function, Different Rule?

Which input-output rules could describe the same function (if any)? Be prepared to explain your reasoning.

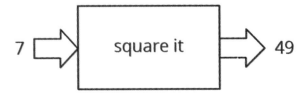

iM KH

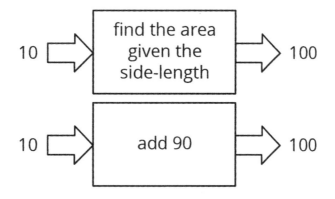

Are you ready for more?

The phrase "is a function of" gets used in non-mathematical speech as well as mathematical speech in sentences like, "The range of foods you like is a function of your upbringing." What is that sentence trying to convey? Is it the same use of the word "function" as the mathematical one?

Lesson 2 Summary

Let's say we have an input-output rule that for each allowable input gives exactly one output. Then we say the output *depends* on the input, or the output is a **function** of the input.

For example, the area of a square is a function of the side length, because you can find the area from the side length by squaring it. So when the input is 10 cm, the output is 100 cm^2.

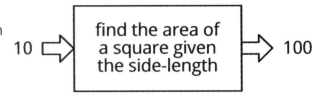

Sometimes we might have two different rules that describe the same function. As long as we always get the same, single output from the same input, the rules describe the same function.

Glossary

- function

iM KH

Lesson 2 Practice Problems

1. Here are several function rules. Calculate the output for each rule when you use -6 as the input.

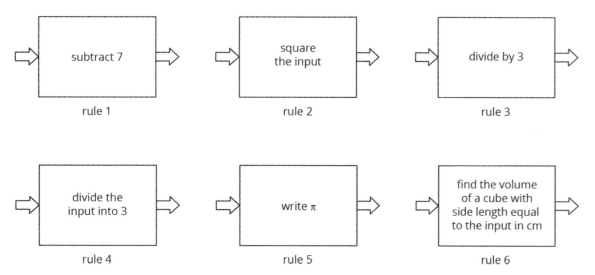

2. A group of students is timed while sprinting 100 meters. Each student's speed can be found by dividing 100 m by their time. Is each statement true or false? Explain your reasoning.

   a. Speed is a function of time.

   b. Time is a function of distance.

   c. Speed is a function of number of students racing.

   d. Time is a function of speed.

3. Diego's history teacher writes a test for the class with 26 questions. The test is worth 123 points and has two types of questions: multiple choice worth 3 points each, and essays worth 8 points each. How many essay questions are on the test? Explain or show your reasoning.

(From Unit 5, Lesson 16.)

4. These tables correspond to inputs and outputs. Which of these input and output tables could represent a function rule, and which ones could not? Explain or show your reasoning.

Table A:

input	output
-2	4
-1	1
0	0
1	1
2	4

Table B:

input	output
4	-2
1	-1
0	0
1	1
4	2

Table C:

input	output
1	0
2	0
3	0

Table D:

input	output
0	1
0	2
0	3

iM KH

Lesson 3: Equations for Functions

Let's find outputs from equations.

3.1: A Square's Area

Fill in the table of input-output pairs for the given rule. Write an algebraic expression for the rule in the box in the diagram.

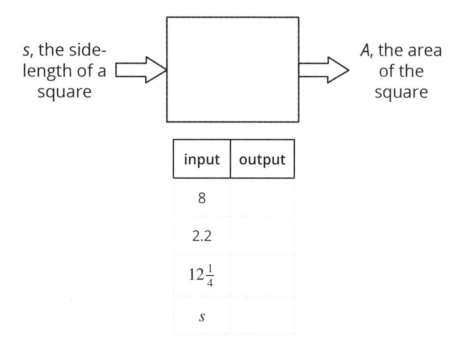

input	output
8	
2.2	
$12\frac{1}{4}$	
s	

3.2: Diagrams, Equations, and Descriptions

Record your answers to these questions in the table provided.

1. Match each of these descriptions with a diagram:
   a. the circumference, C, of a circle with **radius**, r

   b. the distance in miles, d, that you would travel in t hours if you drive at 60 miles per hour

   c. the output when you triple the input and subtract 4

   d. the volume of a cube, v given its edge length, s

2. Write an equation for each description that expresses the output as a function of the input.

3. Find the output when the input is 5 for each equation.

4. Name the **independent** and **dependent variables** of each equation.

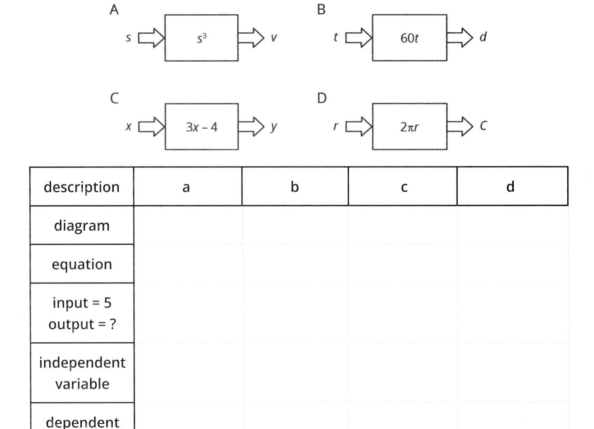

description	a	b	c	d
diagram				
equation				
input = 5 output = ?				
independent variable				
dependent variable				

iM KH

Are you ready for more?

Choose a 3-digit number as an input.

Apply the following rule to it, one step at a time:

- Multiply your number by 7.

- Add one to the result.

- Multiply the result by 11.

- Subtract 5 from the result.

- Multiply the result by 13

- Subtract 78 from the result to get the output.

Can you describe a simpler way to describe this rule? Why does this work?

3.3: Dimes and Quarters

Jada had some dimes and quarters that had a total value of $12.50. The relationship between the number of dimes, d, and the number of quarters, q, can be expressed by the equation $0.1d + 0.25q = 12.5$.

1. If Jada has 4 quarters, how many dimes does she have?

2. If Jada has 10 quarters, how many dimes does she have?

3. Is the number of dimes a function of the number of quarters? If yes, write a rule (that starts with $d =$...) that you can use to determine the output, d, from a given input, q. If no, explain why not.

4. If Jada has 25 dimes, how many quarters does she have?

5. If Jada has 30 dimes, how many quarters does she have?

6. Is the number of quarters a function of the number of dimes? If yes, write a rule (that starts with $q =$...) that you can use to determine the output, q, from a given input, d. If no, explain why not.

Lesson 3 Summary

We can sometimes represent functions with equations. For example, the area, A, of a circle is a function of the radius, r, and we can express this with an equation:

$$A = \pi r^2$$

We can also draw a diagram to represent this function:

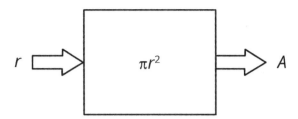

In this case, we think of the radius, r, as the input, and the area of the circle, A, as the output. For example, if the input is a radius of 10 cm, then the output is an area of 100π cm^2, or about 314 square cm. Because this is a function, we can find the area, A, for any given radius, r.

Since it is the input, we say that r is the **independent variable** and, as the output, A is the **dependent variable**.

Sometimes when we have an equation we get to choose which variable is the independent variable. For example, if we know that

$$10A - 4B = 120$$

then we can think of A as a function of B and write

$$A = 0.4B + 12$$

or we can think of B as a function of A and write

$$B = 2.5A - 30$$

Glossary

- dependent variable
- independent variable
- radius

Lesson 3 Practice Problems

1. Here is an equation that represents a function: $72x + 12y = 60$.

   Select **all** the different equations that describe the same function:

   A. $120y + 720x = 600$

   B. $y = 5 - 6x$

   C. $2y + 12x = 10$

   D. $y = 5 + 6x$

   E. $x = \frac{5}{6} - \frac{y}{6}$

   F. $7x + 2y = 6$

   G. $x = \frac{5}{6} + \frac{y}{6}$

2.   a. Graph a system of linear equations with no solutions.

      b. Write an equation for each line you graph.

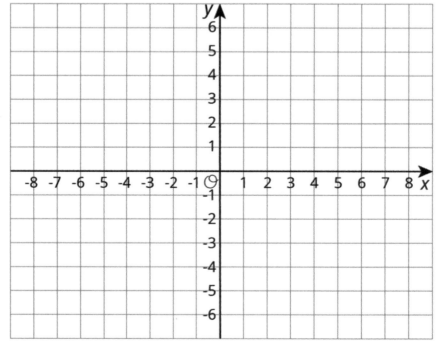

(From Unit 5, Lesson 14.)

3. Brown rice costs $2 per pound, and beans cost $1.60 per pound. Lin has $10 to spend on these items to make a large meal of beans and rice for a potluck dinner. Let b be the number of pounds of beans Lin buys and r be the number of pounds of rice she buys when she spends all her money on this meal.

    a. Write an equation relating the two variables.

    b. Rearrange the equation so b is the independent variable.

    c. Rearrange the equation so r is the independent variable.

4. Solve each equation and check your answer.

$$2x + 4(3 - 2x) = \frac{3(2x+2)}{6} + 4 \qquad\qquad 4z + 5 = \text{-}3z - 8$$

$$\frac{1}{2} - \frac{1}{8}q = \frac{q-1}{4}$$

(From Unit 4, Lesson 14.)

Lesson 4: Tables, Equations, and Graphs of Functions

Let's connect equations and graphs of functions.

4.1: Notice and Wonder: Doubling Back

What do you notice? What do you wonder?

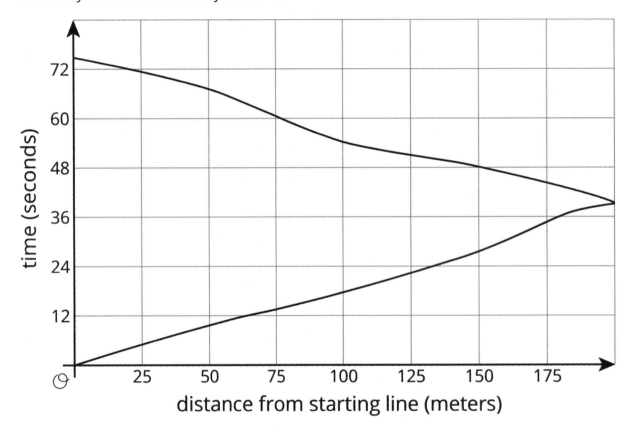

iM **KH**

4.2: Equations and Graphs of Functions

The graphs of three functions are shown.

A

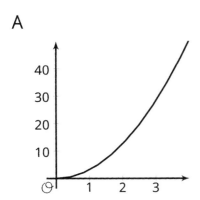

B

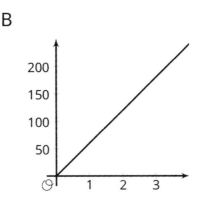

C

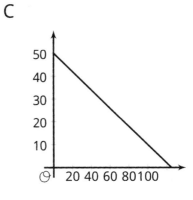

1. Match one of these equations to each of the graphs.
    a. $d = 60t$, where d is the distance in miles that you would travel in t hours if you drove at 60 miles per hour.

    b. $q = 50 - 0.4d$, where q is the number of quarters, and d is the number of dimes, in a pile of coins worth $12.50.

    c. $A = \pi r^2$, where A is the area in square centimeters of a circle with radius r centimeters.

2. Label each of the axes with the independent and dependent variables and the quantities they represent.

3. For each function: What is the output when the input is 1? What does this tell you about the situation? Label the corresponding point on the graph.

4. Find two more input-output pairs. What do they tell you about the situation? Label the corresponding points on the graph.

A function inputs fractions $\frac{a}{b}$ between 0 and 1 where a and b have no common factors, and outputs the fraction $\frac{1}{b}$. For example, given the input $\frac{3}{4}$ the function outputs $\frac{1}{4}$, and to the input $\frac{1}{2}$ the function outputs $\frac{1}{2}$. These two input-output pairs are shown on the graph.

Plot at least 10 more points on the graph of this function. Are most points on the graph above or below a height of 0.3? Of height 0.01?

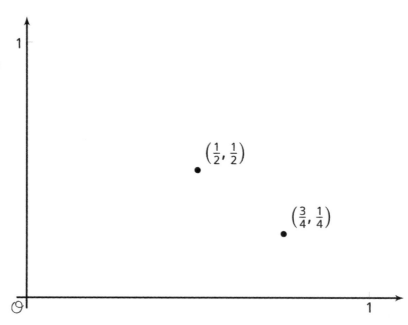

4.3: Running around a Track

1. Kiran was running around the track. The graph shows the time, t, he took to run various distances, d. The table shows his time in seconds after every three meters.

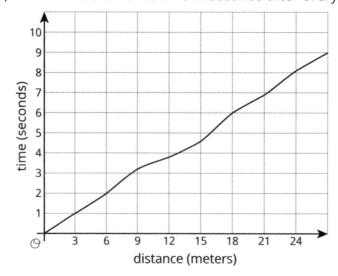

iM KH

d	0	3	6	9	12	15	18	21	24	27
t	0	1.0	2.0	3.2	3.8	4.6	6.0	6.9	8.09	9.0

a. How long did it take Kiran to run 6 meters?

b. How far had he gone after 6 seconds?

c. Estimate when he had run 19.5 meters.

d. Estimate how far he ran in 4 seconds.

e. Is Kiran's time a function of the distance he has run? Explain how you know.

2. Priya is running once around the track. The graph shows her time given how far she is from her starting point.

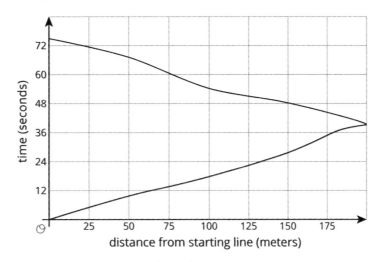

a. What was her farthest distance from her starting point?

b. Estimate how long it took her to run around the track.

c. Estimate when she was 100 meters from her starting point.

d. Estimate how far she was from the starting line after 60 seconds.

e. Is Priya's time a function of her distance from her starting point? Explain how you know.

Lesson 4 Summary

Here is the graph showing Noah's run.

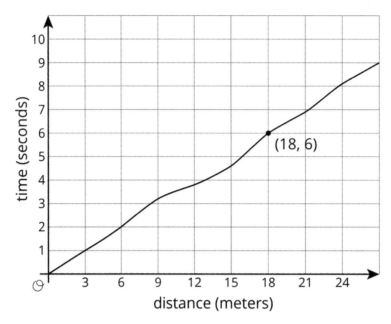

The time in seconds since he started running is a function of the distance he has run. The point (18,6) on the graph tells you that the time it takes him to run 18 meters is 6 seconds. The input is 18 and the output is 6.

The graph of a function is all the coordinate pairs, (input, output), plotted in the coordinate plane. By convention, we always put the input first, which means that the inputs are represented on the horizontal axis and the outputs, on the vertical axis.

Lesson 4 Practice Problems

1. The graph and the table show the high temperatures in a city over a 10-day period.

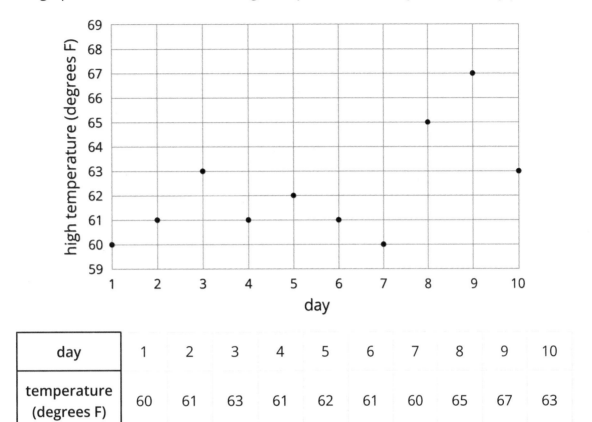

day	1	2	3	4	5	6	7	8	9	10
temperature (degrees F)	60	61	63	61	62	61	60	65	67	63

a. What was the high temperature on Day 7?

b. On which days was the high temperature 61 degrees?

c. Is the high temperature a function of the day? Explain how you know.

d. Is the day a function of the high temperature? Explain how you know.

2. The amount Lin's sister earns at her part-time job is proportional to the number of hours she works. She earns $9.60 per hour.

    a. Write an equation in the form $y = kx$ to describe this situation, where x represents the hours she works and y represents the dollars she earns.

    b. Is y a function of x? Explain how you know.

    c. Write an equation describing x as a function of y.

3. Use the equation $2m + 4s = 16$ to complete the table, then graph the line using s as the dependent variable.

m	0		-2	
s		3		0

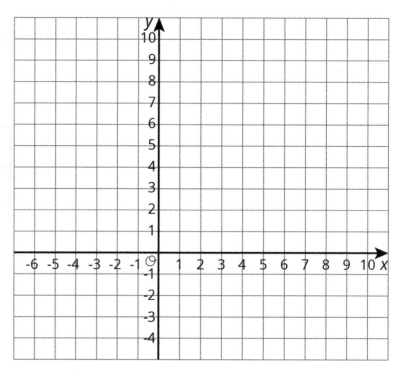

4. Solve the system of equations: $\begin{cases} y = 7x + 10 \\ y = \text{-}4x - 23 \end{cases}$

(From Unit 5, Lesson 14.)

iM KH

Lesson 5: More Graphs of Functions

Let's interpret graphs of functions.

5.1: Which One Doesn't Belong: Graphs

Which graph doesn't belong?

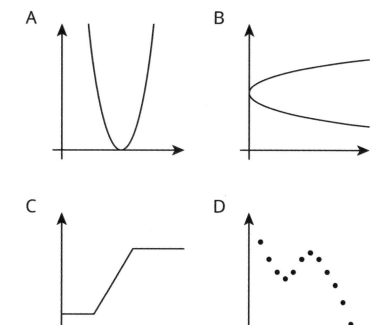

5.2: Time and Temperature

The graph shows the temperature between noon and midnight in one day in a certain city.

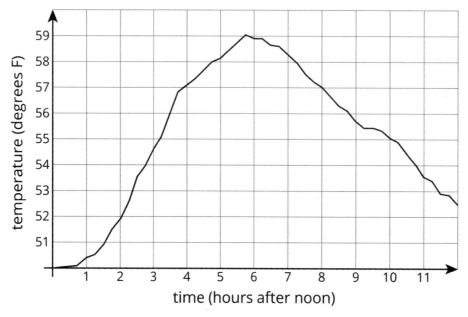

1. Was it warmer at 3:00 p.m. or 9:00 p.m.?

2. Approximately when was the temperature highest?

3. Find another time that the temperature was the same as it was at 4:00 p.m.

4. Did the temperature change more between 1:00 p.m. and 3:00 p.m. or between 3:00 p.m. and 5:00 p.m.?

5. Does this graph show that temperature is a function of time, or time is a function of temperature?

6. When the input for the function is 8, what is the output? What does that tell you about the time and temperature?

5.3: Garbage

1. The graph shows the amount of garbage produced in the US each year between 1991 and 2013.

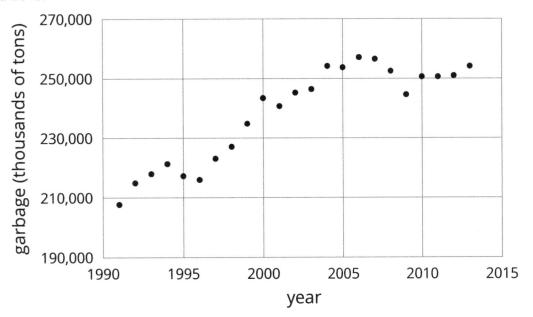

a. Did the amount of garbage increase or decrease between 1999 and 2000?

b. Did the amount of garbage increase or decrease between 2005 and 2009?

c. Between 1991 and 1995, the garbage increased for three years, and then it decreased in the fourth year. Describe how the amount of garbage changed in the years between 1995 and 2000.

2. The graph shows the percentage of garbage that was recycled between 1991 and 2013.

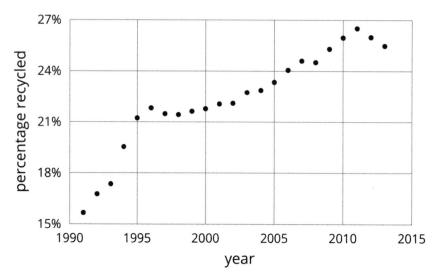

a. When was it increasing?

b. When was it decreasing?

c. Tell the story of the change in the percentage of garbage recycled in the US over this time period.

Are you ready for more?

Refer to the graph in the first part of the activity.

1. Find a year where the amount of garbage produced increased from the previous year, but not by as much it increased the following year.

2. Find a year where the amount of garbage produced increased from the previous year, and then increased by a smaller amount the following year.

3. Find a year where the amount of garbage produced decreased from the previous year, but not by as much it decreased the following year.

4. Find a year where the amount of garbage produced decreased from the previous year, and then decreased by a smaller amount the following year.

Lesson 5 Summary

Here is a graph showing the temperature in a town as a function of time after 8:00 p.m.

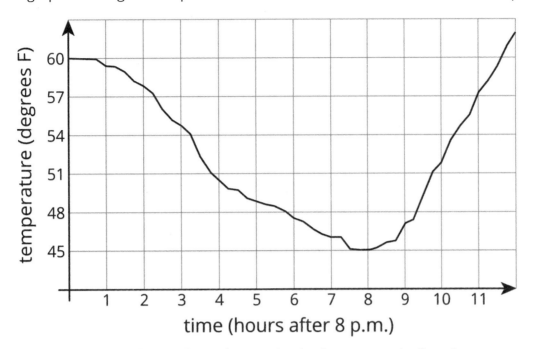

The graph of a function tells us what is happening in the context the function represents. In this example, the temperature starts out at $60°$ F at 8:00 p.m. It decreases during the night, reaching its lowest point at 8 hours after 8:00 p.m., or 4:00 a.m. Then it starts to increase again.

Lesson 5 Practice Problems

1. The solution to a system of equations is $(6, -3)$. Choose two equations that might make up the system.

    A. $y = -3x + 6$

    B. $y = 2x - 9$

    C. $y = -5x + 27$

    D. $y = 2x - 15$

    E. $y = -4x + 27$

    (From Unit 5, Lesson 14.)

2. A car is traveling on a small highway and is either going 55 miles per hour or 35 miles per hour, depending on the speed limits, until it reaches its destination 200 miles away. Letting x represent the amount of time in hours that the car is going 55 miles per hour, and y being the time in hours that the car is going 35 miles per hour, an equation describing the relationship is:
$$55x + 35y = 200$$

    a. If the car spends 2.5 hours going 35 miles per hour on the trip, how long does it spend going 55 miles per hour?

    b. If the car spends 3 hours going 55 miles per hour on the trip, how long does it spend going 35 miles per hour?

    c. If the car spends no time going 35 miles per hour, how long would the trip take? Explain your reasoning.

    (From Unit 6, Lesson 3.)

iM KH

3. The graph represents an object that is shot upwards from a tower and then falls to the ground. The independent variable is time in seconds and the dependent variable is the object's height above the ground in meters.

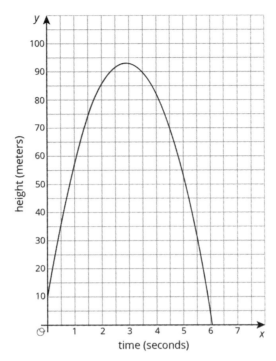

a. How tall is the tower from which the object was shot?

b. When did the object hit the ground?

c. Estimate the greatest height the object reached and the time it took to reach that height. Indicate this situation on the graph.

Lesson 6: Even More Graphs of Functions

Let's draw a graph from a story.

6.1: Dog Run

Here are five pictures of a dog taken at equal intervals of time.

Diego and Lin drew different graphs to represent this situation:

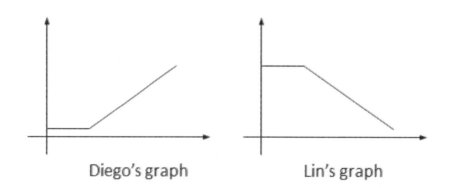

They both used time as the independent variable. What do you think each one used for the dependent variable? Explain your reasoning.

6.2: Which Graph is It?

For each situation,

- name the independent and dependent variables

- pick the graph that best fits the situation, or sketch the graph if one isn't provided

- label the axes

- answer the question: which quantity is a function of which? Be prepared to explain your reasoning.

1. Jada is training for a swimming race. The more she practices, the less time it takes for her to swim one lap.

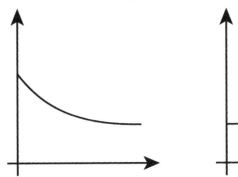 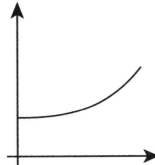 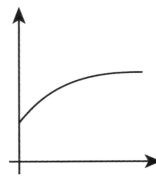

2. Andre adds some money to a jar in his room each week for 3 weeks and then takes some out in week 4.

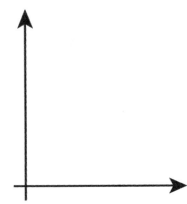

6.3: Sketching a Story about a Boy and a Bike

Your teacher will give you tools for creating a visual display. With your group, create a display that shows your response to each question.

Here is a story: "Noah was at home. He got on his bike and rode to his friend's house and stayed there for awhile. Then he rode home again. Then he rode to the park. Then he rode home again."

1. Create a set of axes and sketch a graph of this story.

2. What are the two quantities? Label the axes with their names and units of measure. (For example, if this were a story about pouring water into a pitcher, one of your labels might say "volume (liters).")

3. Which quantity is a function of which? Explain your reasoning.

4. Based on your graph, is his friend's house or the park closer to Noah's home? Explain how you know.

5. Read the story and all your responses again. Does everything make sense? If not, make changes to your work.

Are you ready for more?

It is the year 3000. Noah's descendants are still racing around the park, but thanks to incredible technological advances, now with much more powerful gadgets at their disposal. How might their newfound access to teleportation and time-travel devices alter the graph of stories of their daily adventures? Could they affect whether or not the distance from home is a function of the time elapsed?

Lesson 6 Summary

Here is a graph showing Andre's distance as a function of time.

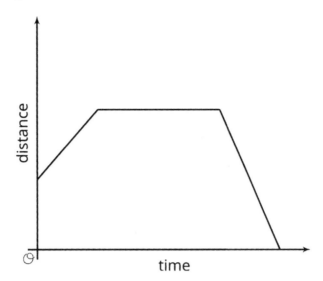

For a graph representing a context, it is important to specify the quantities represented on each axis. For example, if this is showing distance from home, then Andre starts at some distance from home (maybe at his friend's house), moves further away (maybe to a park), then returns home. If instead the graph is showing distance from school, the story may be Andre starts out at home, moves further away (maybe to a friend's house), then goes to school. What could the story be if the graph is showing distance from a park?

Lesson 6 Practice Problems

1. Match the graph to the following situations (you can use a graph multiple times). For each match, name possible independent and dependent variables and how you would label the axes.

A   B   C

   a. Tyler pours the same amount of milk from a bottle every morning.

   b. A plant grows the same amount every week.

   c. The day started very warm but then it got colder.

   d. A carnival has an entry fee of $5 and tickets for rides cost $1 each.

2. Jada fills her aquarium with water.

The graph shows the height of the water, in cm, in the aquarium as a function of time in minutes. Invent a story of how Jada fills the aquarium that fits the graph.

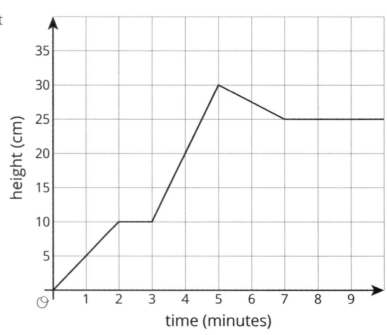

iM KH

3. Recall the formula for area of a circle.

   a. Write an equation relating a circle's radius, r, and area, A.

   b. Is area a function of the radius? Is radius a function of the area?

   c. Fill in the missing parts of the table.

r	3		$\frac{1}{2}$	
A		16π		100π

(From Unit 6, Lesson 4.)

4. The points with coordinates $(4, 8)$, $(2, 10)$, and $(5, 7)$ all lie on the line $2x + 2y = 24$.

   a. Create a graph, plot the points, and sketch the line.

   b. What is the slope of the line you graphed?

   c. What does this slope tell you about the relationship between lengths and widths of rectangles with perimeter 24?

(From Unit 5, Lesson 9.)

Lesson 7: Connecting Representations of Functions

Let's connect tables, equations, graphs, and stories of functions.

7.1: Which are the Same? Which are Different?

Here are three different ways of representing functions. How are they alike? How are they different?

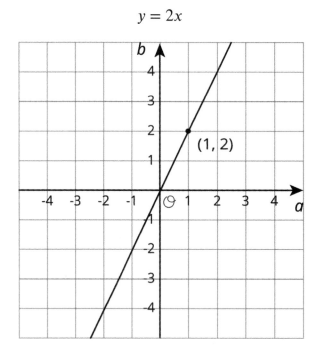

$$y = 2x$$

p	-2	-1	0	1	2	3
q	4	2	0	-2	-4	-6

7.2: Comparing Temperatures

The graph shows the temperature between noon and midnight in City A on a certain day.

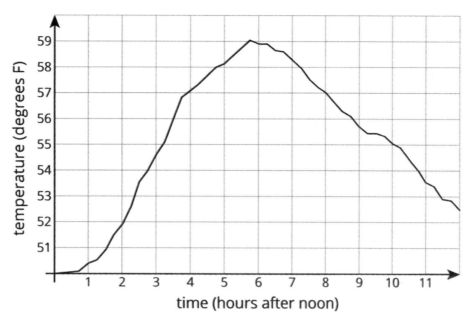

The table shows the temperature, T, in degrees Fahrenheit, for h hours after noon, in City B.

h	1	2	3	4	5	6
T	82	78	75	62	58	59

1. Which city was warmer at 4:00 p.m.?

2. Which city had a bigger change in temperature between 1:00 p.m. and 5:00 p.m.?

3. How much greater was the highest recorded temperature in City B than the highest recorded temperature in City A during this time?

4. Compare the outputs of the functions when the input is 3.

7.3: Comparing Volumes

The **volume**, V, of a cube with edge length s cm is given by the equation $V = s^3$.

The volume of a sphere is a function of its radius (in centimeters), and the graph of this relationship is shown here.

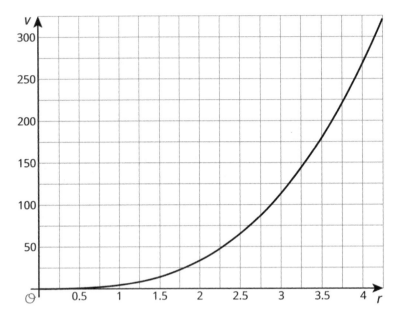

1. Is the volume of a cube with edge length $s = 3$ greater or less than the volume of a sphere with radius 3?

2. If a sphere has the same volume as a cube with edge length 5, estimate the radius of the sphere.

3. Compare the outputs of the two volume functions when the inputs are 2.

Are you ready for more?

Estimate the edge length of a cube that has the same volume as a sphere with radius 2.5.

7.4: It's Not a Race

Elena's family is driving on the freeway at 55 miles per hour.

Andre's family is driving on the same freeway, but not at a constant speed. The table shows how far Andre's family has traveled, d, in miles, every minute for 10 minutes.

t	1	2	3	4	5	6	7	8	9	10
d	0.9	1.9	3.0	4.1	5.1	6.2	6.8	7.4	8	9.1

1. How many miles per minute is 55 miles per hour?

2. Who had traveled farther after 5 minutes? After 10 minutes?

3. How long did it take Elena's family to travel as far as Andre's family had traveled after 8 minutes?

4. For both families, the distance in miles is a function of time in minutes. Compare the outputs of these functions when the input is 3.

Lesson 7 Summary

Functions are all about getting outputs from inputs. For each way of representing a function—equation, graph, table, or verbal description—we can determine the output for a given input.

Let's say we have a function represented by the equation $y = 3x + 2$ where y is the dependent variable and x is the independent variable. If we wanted to find the output that goes with 2, we can input 2 into the equation for x and finding the corresponding value of y. In this case, when x is 2, y is 8 since $3 \cdot 2 + 2 = 8$.

If we had a graph of this function instead, then the coordinates of points on the graph are the input-output pairs. So we would read the y-coordinate of the point on the graph that corresponds to a value of 2 for x. Looking at the graph of this function here, we can see the point $(2, 8)$ on it, so the output is 8 when the input is 2.

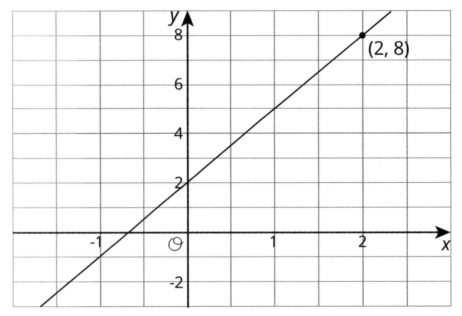

A table representing this function shows the input-output pairs directly (although only for select inputs).

x	-1	0	1	2	3
y	-1	2	5	8	11

Again, the table shows that if the input is 2, the output is 8.

Glossary

• volume

iM KH

Lesson 7 Practice Problems

1. The equation and the tables represent two different functions. Use the equation $b = 4a - 5$ and the table to answer the questions. This table represents c as a function of a.

a	-3	0	2	5	10	12
c	-20	7	3	21	19	45

a. When a is -3, is b or c greater?

b. When c is 21, what is the value of a? What is the value of b that goes with this value of a?

c. When a is 6, is b or c greater?

d. For what values of a do we know that c is greater than b?

2. Elena and Lin are training for a race. Elena runs her mile at a constant speed of 7.5 miles per hour.

Lin's total distances are recorded every minute:

time (minutes)	1	2	3	4	5	6	7	8	9
distance (miles)	0.11	0.21	0.32	0.41	0.53	0.62	0.73	0.85	1

a. Who finished their mile first?

b. This is a graph of Lin's progress. Draw a graph to represent Elena's mile on the same axes.

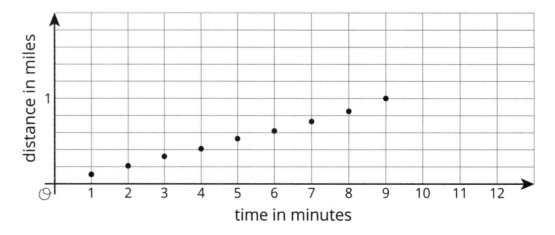

c. For these models, is distance a function of time? Is time a function of distance? Explain how you know.

iM KH

3. Match each function rule with the value that could not be a possible input for that function.

    A. 3 divided by the input   1. 3

    B. Add 4 to the input, then divide this   2. 4
       value into 3

                                       3. -4

    C. Subtract 3 from the input, then
       divide this value into 1   4. 0

                                       5. 1

(From Unit 6, Lesson 2.)

4. Find a value of x that makes the equation true. Explain your reasoning, and check that your answer is correct.

$$\text{-}(\text{-}2x + 1) = 9 - 14x$$

(From Unit 4, Lesson 13.)

Lesson 8: Linear Functions

Let's investigate linear functions.

8.1: Bigger and Smaller

Diego said that these graphs are ordered from smallest to largest. Mai said they are ordered from largest to smallest. But these are graphs, not numbers! What do you think Diego and Mai are thinking?

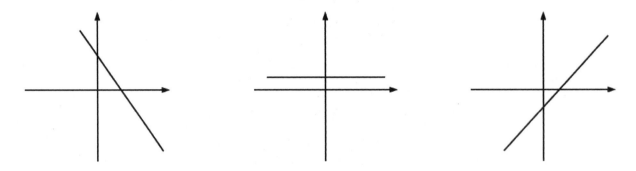

8.2: Proportional Relationships Define Linear Functions

1. Jada earns $7 per hour mowing her neighbors' lawns.

    a. Name the two quantities in this situation that are in a functional relationship. Which did you choose to be the independent variable? What is the variable that depends on it?

    b. Write an equation that represents the function.

    c. Here is a graph of the function. Label the axes. Label at least two points with input-output pairs.

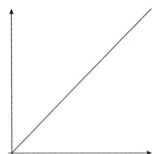

2. To convert feet to yards, you multiply the number of feet by $\frac{1}{3}$.

    a. Name the two quantities in this situation that are in a functional relationship. Which did you choose to be the independent variable? What is the variable that depends on it?

    b. Write an equation that represents the function.

    c. Draw the graph of the function. Label at least two points with input-output pairs.

8.3: Is it Filling Up or Draining Out?

There are four tanks of water.

- The amount of water in gallons, A, in Tank A is given by the function $A = 200 + 8t$, where t is in minutes.

- The amount of water in gallons, B, in Tank B starts at 400 gallons and is decreasing at 5 gallons per minute. These functions work when $t \geq 0$ and $t \leq 80$.

1. Which tank started out with more water?

2. Write an equation representing the relationship between B and t.

3. One tank is filling up. The other is draining out. Which is which? How can you tell?

4. The amount of water in gallons, C, in Tank C is given by the function $C = 800 - 7t$. Is it filling up or draining out? Can you tell just by looking at the equation?

5. The graph of the function for the amount of water in gallons, D, in Tank D at time t is shown. Is it filling up or draining out? How do you know?

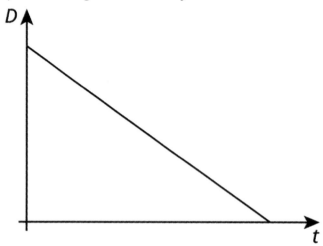

Are you ready for more?

- Pick a tank that was draining out. How long did it take for that tank to drain? What percent full was the tank when 30% of that time had elapsed? When 70% of the time had elapsed?

- What point in the plane is 30% of the way from $(0, 15)$ to $(5, 0)$? 70% of the way?

- What point in the plane is 30% of the way from $(3, 5)$ to $(8, 6)$? 70% of the way?

iM KH

8.4: Which is Growing Faster?

Noah is depositing money in his account every week to save money. The graph shows the amount he has saved as a function of time since he opened his account.

Elena opened an account the same day as Noah. The amount of money E in her account is given by the function $E = 8w + 60$, where w is the number of weeks since the account was opened.

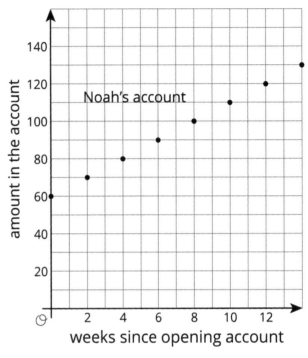

1. Who started out with more money in their account? Explain how you know.

2. Who is saving money at a faster rate? Explain how you know.

3. How much will Noah save over the course of a year if he does not make any withdrawals? How long will it take Elena to save that much?

Lesson 8 Summary

Suppose a car is traveling at 30 miles per hour. The relationship between the time in hours and the distance in miles is a proportional relationship. We can represent this relationship with an equation of the form $d = 30t$, where distance is a function of time (since each input of time has exactly one output of distance). Or we could write the equation $t = \frac{1}{30}d$ instead, where time is a function of distance (since each input of distance has exactly one output of time).

More generally, if we represent a linear function with an equation like $y = mx + b$, then b is the initial value (which is 0 for proportional relationships), and m is the rate of change of the function. If m is positive, the function is increasing. If m is negative, the function is decreasing. If we represent a linear function in a different way, say with a graph, we can use what we know about graphs of lines to find the m and b values and, if needed, write an equation.

iM KH

Lesson 8 Practice Problems

1. Two cars drive on the same highway in the same direction. The graphs show the distance, d, of each one as a function of time, t. Which car drives faster? Explain how you know.

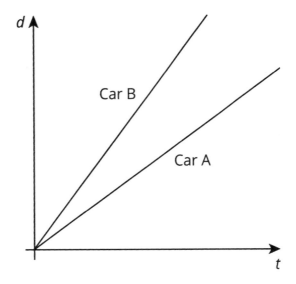

2. Two car services offer to pick you up and take you to your destination. Service A charges 40 cents to pick you up and 30 cents for each mile of your trip. Service B charges $1.10 to pick you up and charges c cents for each mile of your trip.

   a. Match the services to the Lines ℓ and m.

   b. For Service B, is the additional charge per mile greater or less than 30 cents per mile of the trip? Explain your reasoning.

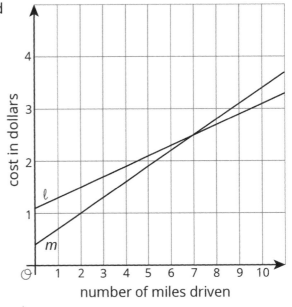

3. Kiran and Clare like to race each other home from school. They run at the same speed, but Kiran's house is slightly closer to school than Clare's house. On a graph, their distance from their homes in meters is a function of the time from when they begin the race in seconds.

    a. As you read the graphs left to right, would the lines go up or down?

    b. What is different about the lines representing Kiran's run and Clare's run?

    c. What is the same about the lines representing Kiran's run and Clare's run?

4. Write an equation for each line.

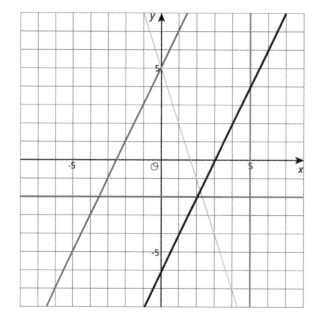

(From Unit 5, Lesson 9.)

iM KH

Lesson 9: Linear Models

Let's model situations with linear functions.

9.1: Candlelight

A candle is burning. It starts out 12 inches long. After 1 hour, it is 10 inches long. After 3 hours, it is 5.5 inches long.

1. When do you think the candle will burn out completely?

2. Is the height of the candle a function of time? If yes, is it a linear function? Explain your thinking.

9.2: Shadows

When the Sun was directly overhead, the stick had no shadow. After 20 minutes, the shadow was 10.5 cm long. After 60 minutes, it was 26 cm long.

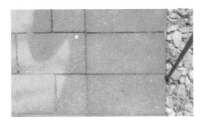 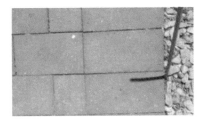 

1. Based on this information, estimate how long it will be after 95 minutes.

2. After 95 minutes, the shadow measured 38.5 cm. How does this compare to your estimate?

3. Is the length of the shadow a function of time? If so, is it linear? Explain your reasoning.

9.3: Recycling

In an earlier lesson, we saw this graph that shows the percentage of all garbage in the U.S. that was recycled between 1991 and 2013.

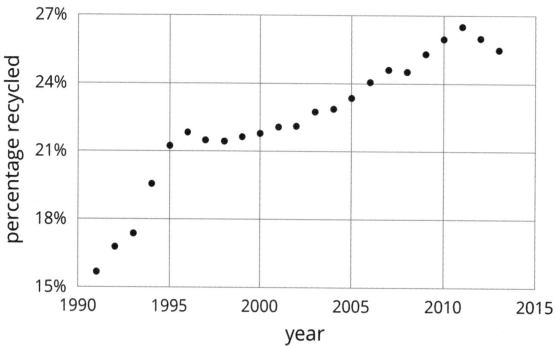

1. Sketch a linear function that models the change in the percentage of garbage that was recycled between 1991 and 1995. For which years is the model good at predicting the percentage of garbage that is produced? For which years is it not as good?

2. Pick another time period to model with a sketch of a linear function. For which years is the model good at making predictions? For which years is it not very good?

iM KH

Lesson 9 Summary

Water has different boiling points at different elevations. At 0 m above sea level, the boiling point is 100° C. At 2,500 m above sea level, the boiling point is 91.3° C. If we assume the boiling point of water is a linear function of elevation, we can use these two data points to calculate the slope of the line:

$$m = \frac{91.3 - 100}{2,500 - 0} = \frac{-8.7}{2,500}$$

This slope means that for each increase of 2,500 m, the boiling point of water decreases by 8.7° C. Next, we already know the y-intercept is 100° C from the first point, so a linear equation representing the data is

$$y = \frac{-8.7}{2,500}x + 100$$

This equation is an example of a mathematical *model*. A mathematical model is a mathematical object like an equation, a function, or a geometric figure that we use to represent a real-life situation. Sometimes a situation can be modeled by a linear function. We have to use judgment about whether this is a reasonable thing to do based on the information we are given. We must also be aware that the model may make imprecise predictions, or may only be appropriate for certain ranges of values.

Testing our model for the boiling point of water, it accurately predicts that at an elevation of 1,000 m above sea level (when $x = 1,000$), water will boil at 96.5° C since $y = \frac{-8.7}{2500} \cdot 1000 + 100 = 96.5$. For higher elevations, the model is not as accurate, but it is still close. At 5,000 m above sea level, it predicts 82.6° C, which is 0.6° C off the actual value of 83.2° C. At 9,000 m above sea level, it predicts 68.7° C, which is about 3° C less than the actual value of 71.5° C. The model continues to be less accurate at even higher elevations since the relationship between the boiling point of water and elevation isn't linear, but for the elevations in which most people live, it's pretty good.

Lesson 9 Practice Problems

1. On the first day after the new moon, 2% of the Moon's surface is illuminated. On the second day, 6% is illuminated.

   a. Based on this information, predict the day on which the Moon's surface is 50% illuminated and 100% illuminated.

   b. The Moon's surface is 100% illuminated on day 14. Does this agree with the prediction you made?

   c. Is the percentage illumination of the Moon's surface a linear function of the day?

iM KH

2. In science class, Jada uses a graduated cylinder with water in it to measure the volume of some marbles. After dropping in 4 marbles so they are all under water, the water in the cylinder is at a height of 10 milliliters. After dropping in 6 marbles so they are all under water, the water in the cylinder is at a height of 11 milliliters.

    a. What is the volume of 1 marble?

    b. How much water was in the cylinder before any marbles were dropped in?

    c. What should be the height of the water after 13 marbles are dropped in?

    d. Is the relationship between volume of water and number of marbles a linear relationship? If so, what does the slope of a line representing this relationship mean? If not, explain your reasoning.

3. Solve each of these equations. Explain or show your reasoning.

$$2(3x + 2) = 2x + 28 \qquad 5y + 13 = \text{-}43 - 3y \qquad 4(2a + 2) = 8(2 - 3a)$$

(From Unit 4, Lesson 13.)

4. For a certain city, the high temperatures (in degrees Celsius) are plotted against the number of days after the new year.

   Based on this information, is the high temperature in this city a linear function of the number of days after the new year?

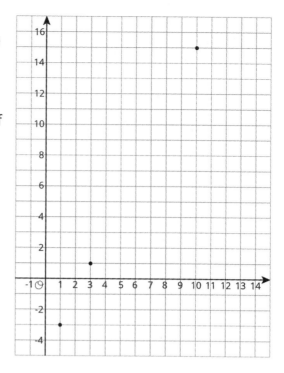

5. The school designed their vegetable garden to have a perimeter of 32 feet with the length measuring two feet more than twice the width.

   a. Using ℓ to represent the length of the garden and w to represent its width, write and solve a system of equations that describes this situation.

   b. What are the dimensions of the garden?

   (From Unit 5, Lesson 16.)

iM KH

Lesson 10: Piecewise Linear Functions

Let's explore functions built out of linear pieces.

10.1: Notice and Wonder: Lines on Dots

What do you notice? What do you wonder?

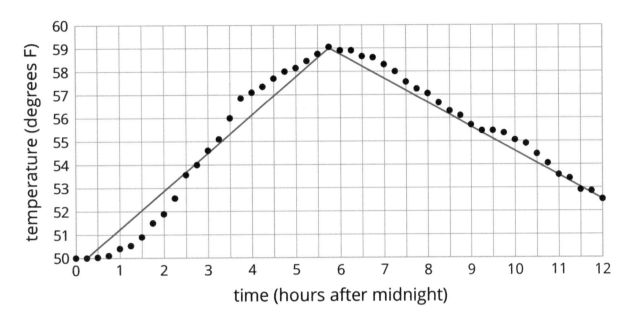

10.2: Modeling Recycling

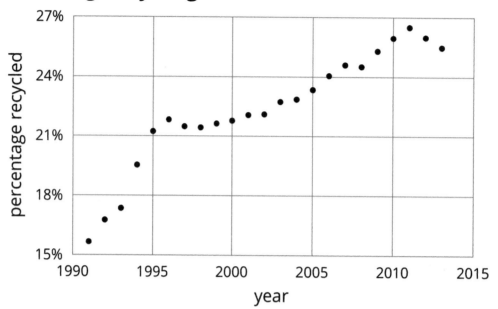

1. Approximate the percentage recycled each year with a piecewise linear function by drawing between three and five line segments to approximate the graph.

2. Find the slope for each piece. What do these slopes tell you?

10.3: Dog Bath

Elena filled up the tub and gave her dog a bath. Then she let the water out of the tub.

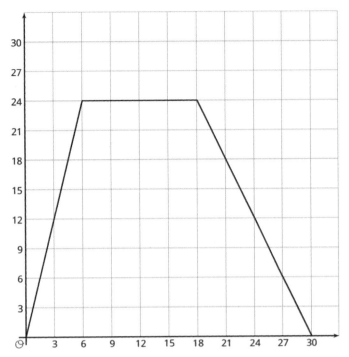

1. The graph shows the amount of water in the tub, in gallons, as a function of time, in minutes. Add labels to the graph to show this.

2. When did she turn off the water faucet?

3. How much water was in the tub when she bathed her dog?

4. How long did it take for the tub to drain completely?

5. At what rate did the faucet fill the tub?

6. At what rate did the water drain from the tub?

10.4: Distance and Speed

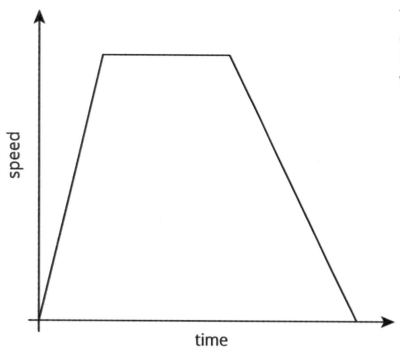

The graph shows the speed of a car as a function of time. Describe what a person watching the car would see.

Are you ready for more?

The graph models the speed of a car over a function of time during a 3-hour trip. How far did the car go over the course of the trip?

There is a nice way to visualize this quantity in terms of the graph. Can you find it?

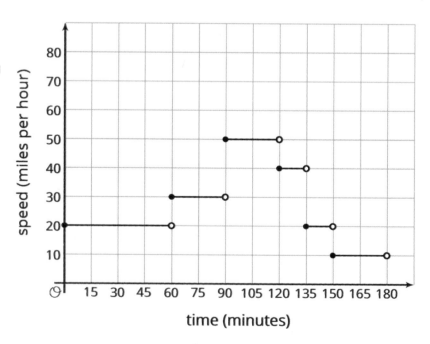

iM KH

Lesson 10 Summary

This graph shows Andre biking to his friend's house where he hangs out for a while. Then they bike together to the store to buy some groceries before racing back to Andre's house for a movie night. Each line segment in the graph represents a different part of Andre's travels.

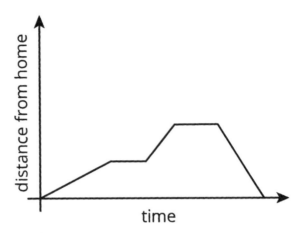

This is an example of a piecewise linear function, which is a function whose graph is pieced together out of line segments. It can be used to model situations in which a quantity changes at a constant rate for a while, then switches to a different constant rate.

We can use piecewise functions to represent stories, or we can use them to model actual data. In the second example, temperature recordings at several times throughout a day are modeled with a piecewise function made up of two line segments. Which line segment do you think does the best job of modeling the data?

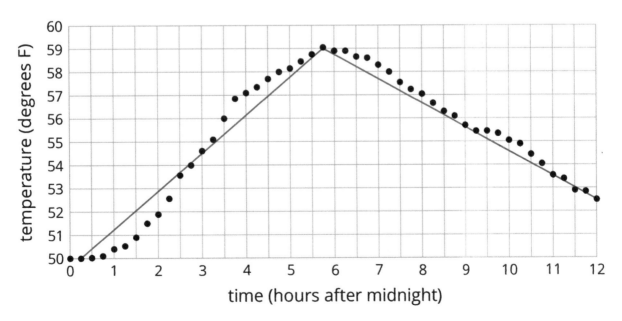

Lesson 10 Practice Problems

1. The graph shows the distance of a car from home as a function of time.

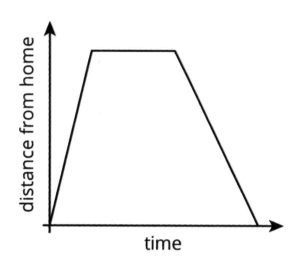

Describe what a person watching the car may be seeing.

2. The equation and the graph represent two functions. Use the equation $y = 4$ and the graph to answer the questions.

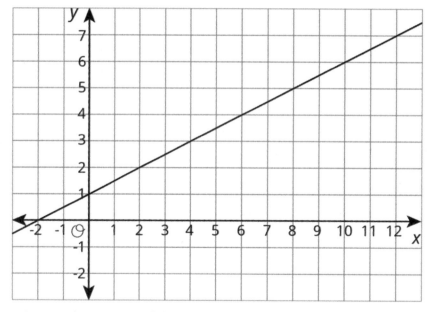

a. When x is 4, is the output of the equation or the graph greater?

b. What value for x produces the same output in both the graph and the equation?

iM KH

(From Unit 6, Lesson 7.)

3. This graph shows a trip on a bike trail. The trail has markers every 0.5 km showing the distance from the beginning of the trail.

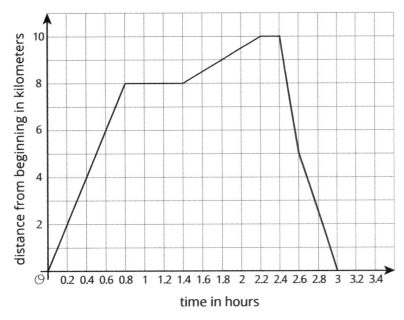

a. When was the bike rider going the fastest?

b. When was the bike rider going the slowest?

c. During what times was the rider going away from the beginning of the trail?

d. During what times was the rider going back towards the beginning of the trail?

e. During what times did the rider stop?

4. The expression $-25t + 1250$ represents the volume of liquid of a container after t seconds. The expression $50t + 250$ represents the volume of liquid of another container after t seconds. What does the equation $-25t + 1250 = 50t + 250$ mean in this situation?

(From Unit 4, Lesson 17.)

Lesson 11: Slicing Solids

Let's see what shapes you get when you slice a three-dimensional object.

11.1: Prisms, Pyramids, and Polyhedra

Describe each shape as precisely as you can.

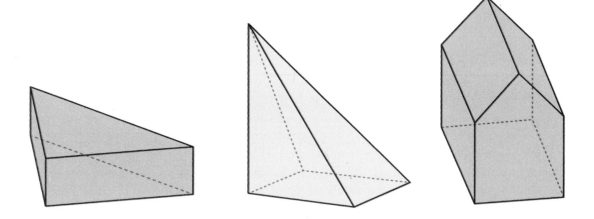

iM KH

11.2: What's the Cross Section?

Here is a rectangular **prism** and a **pyramid** with the same base and same height.

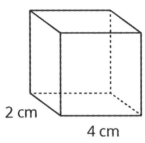 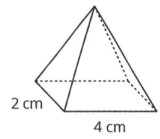

2 cm   4 cm   2 cm   4 cm

1. Think about slicing each solid parallel to its **base**, halfway up. What shape would each **cross section** be? What is the same about the two cross sections? What is different?

2. Think about slicing each solid parallel to its base, near the top. What shape would each cross section be? What is the same about the two cross sections? What is different?

Are you ready for more?

Describe the cross sections that would result from slicing each solid perpendicular to its base.

11.3: Card Sort: Cross Sections

Your teacher will give you a set of cards. Sort the images into groups that make sense to you. Be prepared to explain your reasoning.

11.4: Drawing Cross Sections

Draw and describe each cross section.

1. Here is a picture of a rectangular prism, 4 units by 2 units by 3 units.

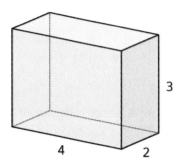

a. A plane cuts the prism parallel to the bottom and top faces.

b. The plane moves up and cuts the prism at a different height.

iM KH

c. A vertical plane cuts the prism diagonally.

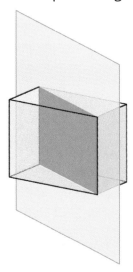

2. A square pyramid has a base that is 4 units by 4 units. Its height is also 4 units.

a. A plane cuts the pyramid parallel to the base.

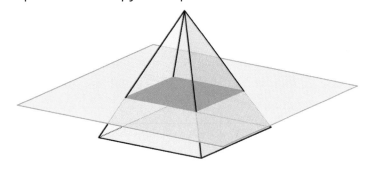

b. A vertical plane cuts the prism.

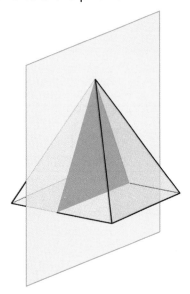

3. A cube has an edge of length 4.

a. A plane cuts off the corner of the cube.

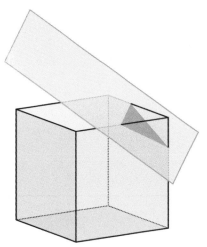

b. The plane moves farther from the corner and makes a cut through the middle of the cube.

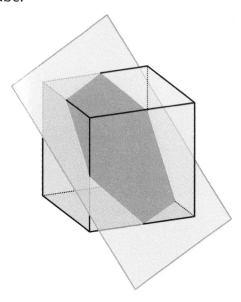

Lesson 11 Summary

When we slice a three-dimensional object, we expose new faces that are two dimensional. The two-dimensional face is a **cross section**. Many different cross sections are possible when slicing the same three-dimensional object.

Here are two peppers. One is sliced horizontally, and the other is sliced vertically, producing different cross sections.

  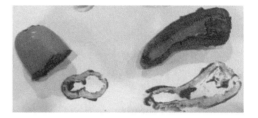

The imprints of the slices represent the two-dimensional faces created by each slice.

It takes practice imagining what the cross section of a three-dimensional object will be for different slices. It helps to experiment and see for yourself what happens!

Glossary

- base (of a prism or pyramid)
- cross section
- prism
- pyramid

Lesson 11 Practice Problems

1. A cube is cut into two pieces by a single slice that passes through points A, B, and C. What shape is the cross section?

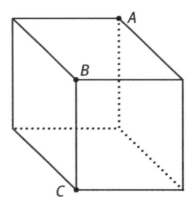

2. Describe how to slice the three-dimensional figure to result in each cross section.

Three-dimensional figure: Cross sections:

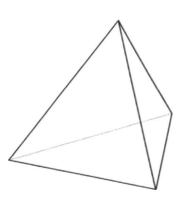

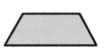

3. Here are two three-dimensional figures.

A   B

Describe a way to slice one of the figures so that the cross section is a rectangle.

4. Each row contains the degree measures of two supplementary angles. Complete the table.

measure of an angle	measure of its supplement
80°	
25°	
119°	
x	

(From Unit 1, Lesson 12.)

Lesson 12: Filling Containers

Let's fill containers with water.

12.1: Which One Doesn't Belong: Solids

These are drawings of three-dimensional objects. Which one doesn't belong? Explain your reasoning.

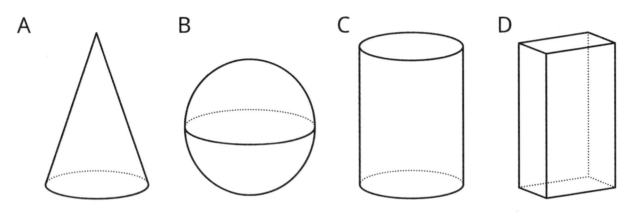

12.2: Height and Volume

Your teacher will give you a graduated cylinder, water, and some other supplies. Your group will use these supplies to investigate the height of water in the cylinder as a function of the water volume.

    1. Before you get started, make a prediction about the shape of the graph.

2. Fill the cylinder with different amounts of water and record the data in the table.

volume (ml)			
height (cm)			

3. Create a graph that shows the height of the water in the cylinder as a function of the water volume.

4. Choose a point on the graph and explain its meaning in the context of the situation.

12.3: What Is the Shape?

1. The graph shows the height vs. volume function of an unknown container. What shape could this container have? Explain how you know and draw a possible container.

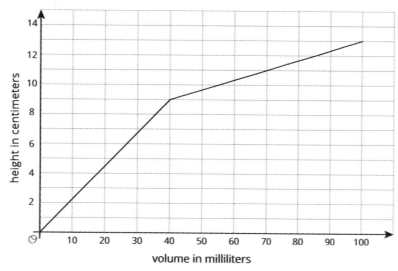

2. The graph shows the height vs. volume function of a different unknown container. What shape could this container have? Explain how you know and draw a possible container.

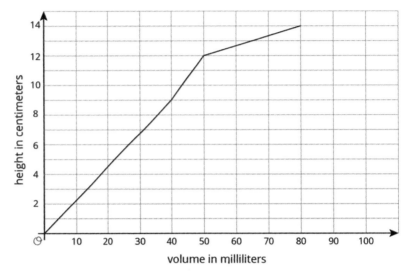

3. How are the two containers similar? How are they different?

Are you ready for more?

The graph shows the height vs. volume function of an unknown container. What shape could this container have? Explain how you know and draw a possible container.

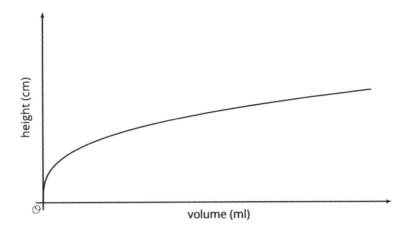

Lesson 12 Summary

When filling a shape like a cylinder with water, we can see how the dimensions of the cylinder affect things like the changing height of the water. For example, let's say we have two cylinders, D and E, with the same height, but D has a radius of 3 cm and E has a radius of 6 cm.

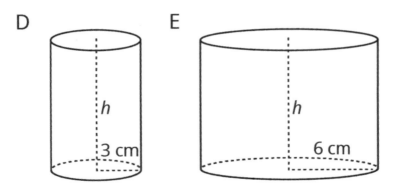

If we pour water into both cylinders at the same rate, the height of water in D will increase faster than the height of water in E due to its smaller radius. This means that if we made graphs of the height of water as a function of the volume of water for each cylinder, we would have two lines and the slope of the line for cylinder D would be greater than the slope of the line for cylinder E.

Glossary

- cylinder

Lesson 12 Practice Problems

1. Cylinder A, B, and C have the same radius but different heights. Put the cylinders in order of their volume from least to greatest.

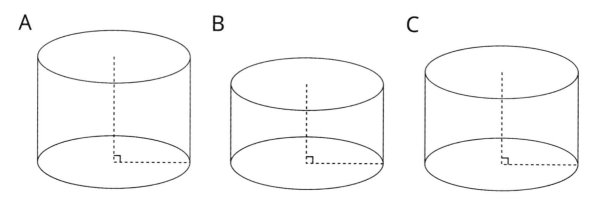

A   B   C

2. Two cylinders, a and b, each started with different amounts of water. The graph shows how the height of the water changed as the volume of water increased in each cylinder. Match the graphs of a and b to Cylinders P and Q. Explain your reasoning.

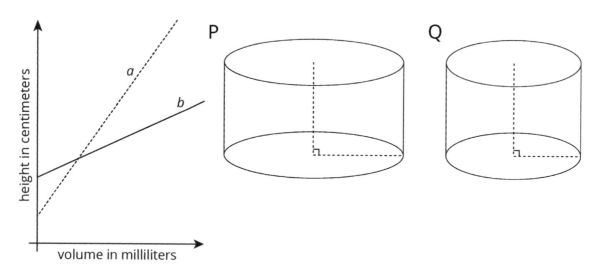

iM KH

3. Which of the following graphs could represent the volume of water in a cylinder as a function of its height? Explain your reasoning.

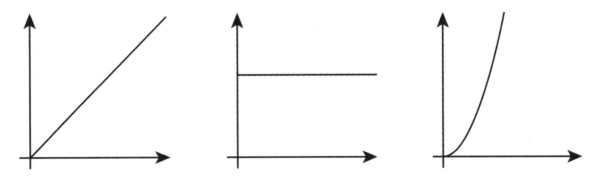

4. Together, the areas of the rectangles sum to 30 square centimeters.

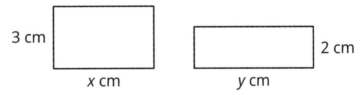

a. Write an equation showing the relationship between x and y.

b. Fill in the table with the missing values.

x	3		8		12
y		5		10	

(From Unit 6, Lesson 3.)

Lesson 13: How Much Will Fit?

Let's reason about the volume of different shapes.

13.1: Two Containers

Your teacher will show you some containers. The small container holds 200 beans. Estimate how many beans the large jar holds.

13.2: What's Your Estimate?

Your teacher will show you some containers.

1. If the pasta box holds 8 cups of rice, how much rice would you need for the other rectangular prisms?

2. If the pumpkin can holds 15 fluid ounces of rice, how much do the other cylinders hold?

3. If the small **cone** holds 2 fluid ounces of rice, how much does the large cone hold?

4. If the golf ball were hollow, it would hold about 0.2 cups of water. If the baseball were hollow, how much would the **sphere** hold?

13.3: Do You Know These Figures?

- What shapes are the faces of each type of object shown here? For example, all six faces of a cube are squares.

1. Which faces could be referred to as a "base" of the object?

2. Here is a method for quickly sketching a cylinder:

- Draw two ovals.

- Connect the edges.

- Which parts of your drawing would be hidden behind the cylinder? Make these parts dashed lines.

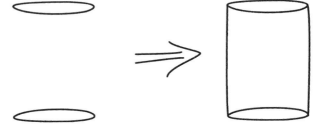

- Practice sketching some cylinders. Sketch a few different sizes, including short, tall, narrow, wide, and sideways. Label the radius r and height h on each cylinder.

Are you ready for more?

A soccer ball is a polyhedron with 12 black pentagonal faces and 20 white hexagonal faces. How many edges in total are on this polyhedron?

Lesson 13 Summary

The volume of a three-dimensional figure, like a jar or a room, is the amount of space the shape encloses. We can measure volume by finding the number of equal-sized volume units that fill the figure without gaps or overlaps. For example, we might say that a room has a volume of 1,000 cubic feet, or that a pitcher can carry 5 gallons of water. We could even measure volume of a jar by the number of beans it could hold, though a bean count is not really a measure of the volume in the same way that a cubic centimeter is because there is space between the beans. (The number of beans that fit in the jar do depend on the volume of the jar, so it is an okay estimate when judging the relative sizes of containers.)

In earlier grades, we studied three-dimensional figures with flat faces that are polygons. We learned how to calculate the volumes of rectangular prisms. Now we will study three-dimensional figures with circular faces and curved surfaces: cones, cylinders, and spheres.

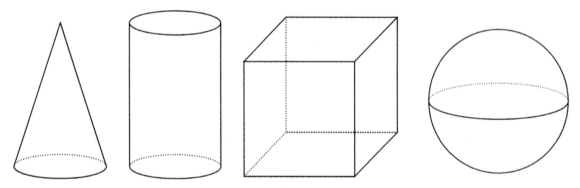

To help us see the shapes better, we can use dotted lines to represent parts that we wouldn't be able to see if a solid physical object were in front of us. For example, if we think of the cylinder in this picture as representing a tin can, the dotted arc in the bottom half of that cylinder represents the back half of the circular base of the can. What objects could the other figures in the picture represent?

Glossary

- cone
- sphere

Lesson 13 Practice Problems

1. a. Sketch a cube and label its side length as 4 cm (this will be Cube A).

   b. Sketch a cube with sides that are twice as long as Cube A and label its side length (this will be Cube B).

   c. Find the volumes of Cube A and Cube B.

2. Two paper drink cups are shaped like cones. The small cone can hold 6 oz of water. The large cone is $\frac{4}{3}$ the height and $\frac{4}{3}$ the diameter of the small cone. Which of these could be the amount of water the large cone holds?

   A. 8 cm

   B. 14 oz

   C. 4.5 oz

   D. 14 cm

3. The graph represents the volume of a cylinder with a height equal to its radius.

a. When the diameter is 2 cm, what is the radius of the cylinder?

b. Express the volume of a cube of side length s as an equation.

c. Make a table for volume of the cube at $s = 0$ cm, $s = 1$ cm, $s = 2$ cm, and $s = 3$ cm.

d. Which volume is greater: the volume of the cube when $s = 3$ cm, or the volume of the cylinder when its diameter is 3 cm?

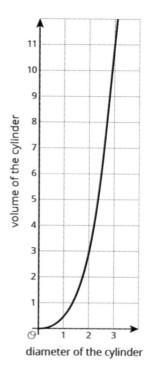

volume of the cylinder

diameter of the cylinder

(From Unit 6, Lesson 7.)

4. Select **all** the points that are on a line with slope 2 that also contains the point $(2, -1)$.

A. $(3, 1)$

B. $(1, 1)$

C. $(1, -3)$

D. $(4, 0)$

E. $(6, 7)$

(From Unit 5, Lesson 9.)

iM KH

5. Several glass aquariums of various sizes are for sale at a pet shop. They are all shaped like rectangular prisms. A 15-gallon tank is 24 inches long, 12 inches wide, and 12 inches tall. Match the dimensions of the other tanks with the volume of water they can each hold.

A. Tank 1: 36 inches long, 18 inches wide, and 12 inches tall

B. Tank 2: 16 inches long, 8 inches wide, and 10 inches tall

C. Tank 3: 30 inches long, 12 inches wide, and 12 inches tall

D. Tank 4: 20 inches long, 10 inches wide, and 12 inches tall

1. 5 gallons

2. 10 gallons

3. 20 gallons

4. 30 gallons

6. Solve: $\begin{cases} y = \text{-}2x - 20 \\ y = x + 4 \end{cases}$

(From Unit 5, Lesson 15.)

Lesson 14: Volume of Right Prisms

Let's look at volumes of prisms.

14.1: Three Prisms with the Same Volume

Rectangles A, B, and C represent bases of three prisms.

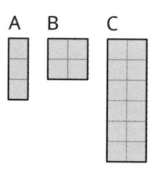

1. If each prism has the same height, which one will have the greatest **volume**, and which will have the least? Explain your reasoning.

2. If each prism has the same volume, which one will have the tallest height, and which will have the shortest? Explain your reasoning.

14.2: Finding Volume with Cubes

Your teacher will give you a paper with a shape on it and some snap cubes.

1. Using the face of a snap cube as your area unit, what is the area of the shape? Explain or show your reasoning.

2. Use snap cubes to build the shape from the paper. Add another layer of cubes on top of the shape you have built. Describe this three-dimensional object.

3. What is the volume of your object? Explain your reasoning.

4. Right now, your object has a height of 2. What would the volume be:

   a. if it had a height of 5?

   b. if it had a height of 8.5?

14.3: Can You Find the Volume?

Your teacher will give you a set of three-dimensional figures.

1. For each figure, determine whether the shape is a prism.

2. For each prism:
   a. Find the area of the base of the prism.
   b. Find the height of the prism.
   c. Calculate the volume of the prism.

	Is it a prism?	area of prism base (cm^2)	height (cm)	volume (cm^3)
figure A				
figure B				
figure C				
figure D				
figure E				
figure F				

Are you ready for more?

Imagine a large, solid cube made out of 64 white snap cubes. Someone spray paints all 6 faces of the large cube blue. After the paint dries, they disassemble the large cube into a pile of 64 snap cubes.

1. How many of those 64 snap cubes have exactly 2 faces that are blue?

2. What are the other possible numbers of blue faces the cubes can have? How many of each are there?

3. Try this problem again with some larger-sized cubes that use more than 64 snap cubes to build. What patterns do you notice?

14.4: What's the Prism's Height?

There are 4 different prisms that all have the same volume. Here is what the base of each prism looks like.

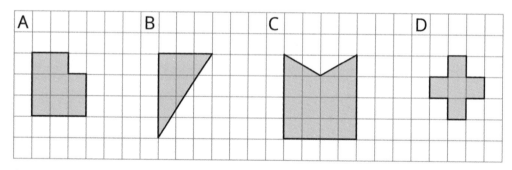

1. Order the prisms from shortest to tallest. Explain your reasoning.

2. If the volume of each prism is 60 units^3, what would be the height of each prism?

iM KH

3. For a volume other than 60 units^3, what could be the height of each prism?

4. Discuss your thinking with your partner. If you disagree, work to reach an agreement.

Lesson 14 Summary

Any cross section of a prism that is parallel to the base will be identical to the base. This means we can slice prisms up to help find their volume. For example, if we have a rectangular prism that is 3 units tall and has a base that is 4 units by 5 units, we can think of this as 3 layers, where each layer has 4 · 5 cubic units.

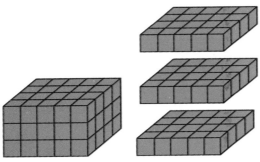

That means the volume of the original rectangular prism is 3(4 · 5) cubic units.

This works with any prism! If we have a prism with height 3 cm that has a base of area 20 cm^2, then the volume is 3 · 20 cm^3 regardless of the shape of the base. In general, the volume of a prism with height h and area B is

$$V = B \cdot h$$

For example, these two prisms both have a volume of 100 cm^3.

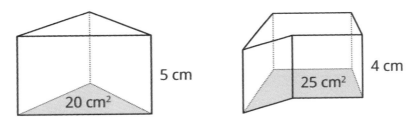

Glossary

* volume

Lesson 14 Practice Problems

1. a. Select **all** the prisms.

    b. For each prism, shade one of its bases.

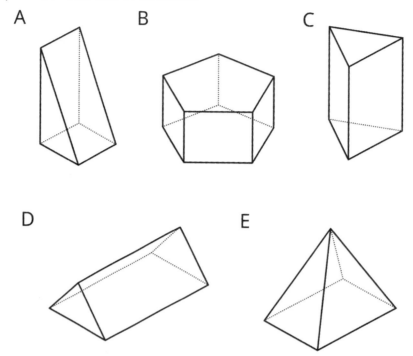

A   B   C

D   E

2. The volume of both of these trapezoidal prisms is 24 cubic units. Their heights are 6 and 8 units, as labeled. What is the area of a trapezoidal base of each prism?

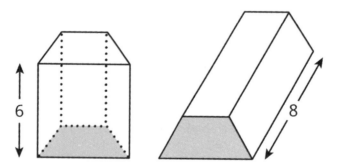

3. Two angles are complementary. One has a measure of 19 degrees. What is the measure of the other?

(From Unit 1, Lesson 12.)

4. Two angles are supplementary. One has a measure that is twice as large as the other. Find the two angle measures.

(From Unit 1, Lesson 12.)

5. Match each expression in the first list with an equivalent expression from the second list.

A. $7(x + 2) - x + 3$

B. $6x + 3 + 4x + 5$

C. $\frac{-2}{5}x - 7 + \frac{3}{5}x - 3$

D. $8x - 5 + 4 - 9$

E. $24x + 36$

1. $\frac{1}{5}x - 10$

2. $6x + 17$

3. $2(5x + 4)$

4. $12(2x + 3)$

5. $8x + (-5) + 4 + (-9)$

(From Unit 4, Lesson 11.)

Lesson 15: Decomposing Bases for Area

Let's look at how some people use volume.

15.1: Are These Prisms?

1. Which of these solids are prisms? Explain how you know.

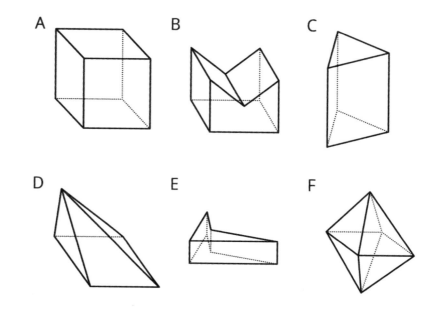

2. For each of the prisms, what does the base look like?

   a. Shade one base in the picture.

   b. Draw a cross section of the prism parallel to the base.

15.2: A Box of Chocolates

A box of chocolates is a prism with a base in the shape of a heart and a height of 2 inches. Here are the measurements of the base.

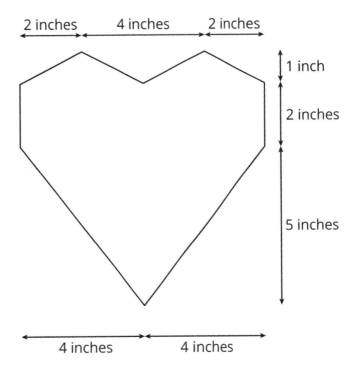

To calculate the volume of the box, three different students have each drawn line segments showing how they plan on finding the area of the heart-shaped base.

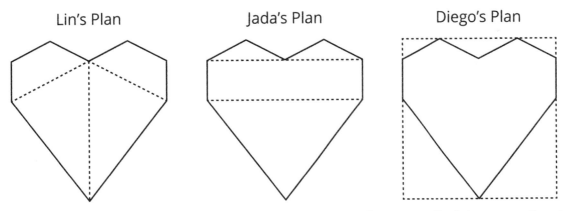

Lin's Plan   Jada's Plan   Diego's Plan

1. For each student's plan, describe the shapes the student must find the area of and the operations they must use to calculate the total area.

2. Although all three methods could work, one of them requires measurements that are not provided. Which one is it?

3. Between you and your partner, decide which of you will use which of the remaining two methods.

4. Using the quadrilaterals and triangles drawn in your selected plan, find the area of the base.

5. Trade with a partner and check each other's work. If you disagree, work to reach an agreement.

6. Return their work. Calculate the volume of the box of chocolates.

Are you ready for more?

The box has 30 pieces of chocolate in it, each with a volume of 1 in^3. If all the chocolates melt into a solid layer across the bottom of the box, what will be the height of the layer?

15.3: Another Prism

A house-shaped prism is created by attaching a triangular prism on top of a rectangular prism.

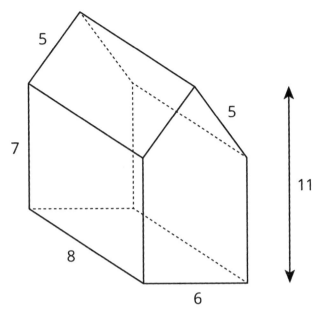

1. Draw the base of this prism and label its dimensions.

2. What is the area of the base? Explain or show your reasoning.

3. What is the volume of the prism?

Lesson 15 Summary

To find the area of any polygon, you can decompose it into rectangles and triangles. There are always many ways to decompose a polygon.

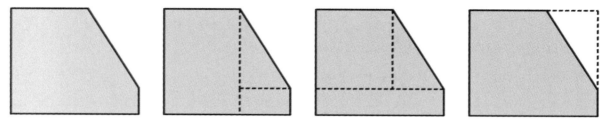

Sometimes it is easier to enclose a polygon in a rectangle and subtract the area of the extra pieces.

To find the volume of a prism with a polygon for a base, you find the area of the base, B, and multiply by the height, h.

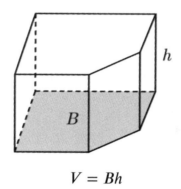

$$V = Bh$$

Lesson 15 Practice Problems

1. You find a crystal in the shape of a prism. Find the volume of the crystal.

   The point B is directly underneath point E, and the following lengths are known:

   - From A to B: 2 mm
   - From B to C: 3 mm
   - From A to F: 6 mm
   - From B to E: 10 mm
   - From C to D: 7 mm
   - From A to G: 4 mm

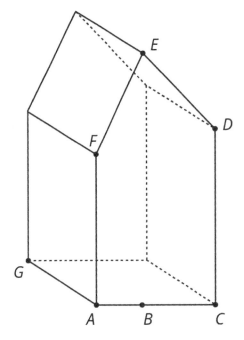

2. A rectangular prism with dimensions 5 inches by 13 inches by 10 inches was cut to leave a piece as shown in the image. What is the volume of this piece? What is the volume of the other piece not pictured?

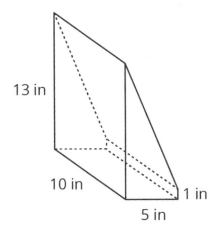

3. A triangle has one side that is 7 cm long and another side that is 3 cm long.

a. Sketch this triangle and label your sketch with the given measures. (If you are stuck, try using a compass or cutting some straws to these two lengths.)

b. Draw one more triangle with these measures that is not identical to your first triangle.

c. Explain how you can tell they are not identical.

(From Unit 1, Lesson 17.)

4. Select **all** equations that represent a relationship between angles in the figure.

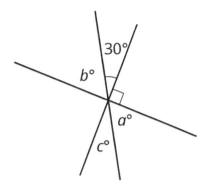

A. $90 - 30 = b$

B. $30 + b = a + c$

C. $a + c + 30 + b = 180$

D. $a = 30$

E. $a = c = 30$

F. $90 + a + c = 180$

(From Unit 1, Lesson 12.)

Lesson 16: Surface Area of Right Prisms

Let's look at the surface area of prisms.

16.1: Multifaceted

Your teacher will show you a prism.

1. What are some things you could measure about the object?

2. What units would you use for these measurements?

iM KH

16.2: So Many Faces

Here is a picture of your teacher's prism:

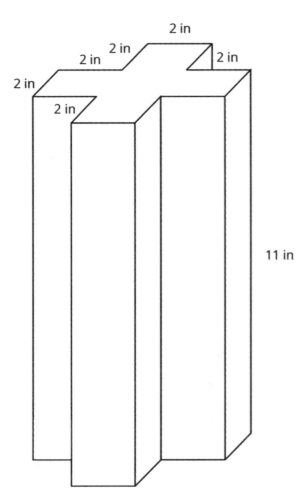

Three students are trying to calculate the **surface area** of this prism.

- Noah says, "This is going to be a lot of work. We have to find the areas of 14 different faces and add them up."

- Elena says, "It's not so bad. All 12 rectangles are identical copies, so we can find the area for one of them, multiply that by 12 and then add on the areas of the 2 bases."

- Andre says, "Wait, I see another way! Imagine unfolding the prism into a net. We can use 1 large rectangle instead of 12 smaller ones."

1. Do you agree with any of them? Explain your reasoning.

2. How big is the "1 large rectangle" Andre is talking about? Explain or show your reasoning. If you get stuck, consider drawing a net for the prism.

3. Will Noah's method always work for finding the surface area of any prism? Elena's method? Andre's method? Be prepared to explain your reasoning.

4. Which method do you prefer? Why?

16.3: Revisiting the Box of Chocolates

The other day, you calculated the volume of this heart-shaped box of chocolates.

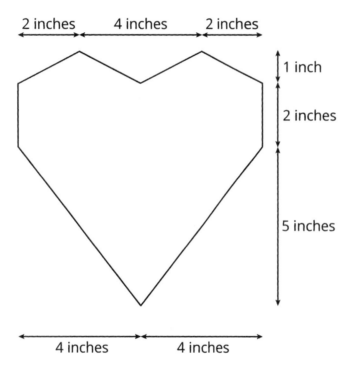

2 inches   4 inches   2 inches

1 inch

2 inches

5 inches

4 inches   4 inches

The depth of the box is 2 inches. How much cardboard is needed to create the box?

16.4: A Wheelbarrow of Concrete

A wheelbarrow is being used to carry wet concrete. Here are its dimensions.

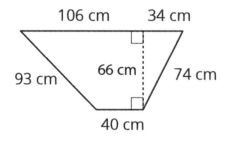 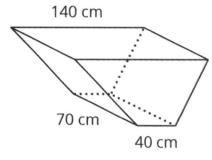

1. What volume of concrete would it take to fill the tray?

2. After dumping the wet concrete, you notice that a thin film is left on the inside of the tray. What is the area of the concrete coating the tray? (Remember, there is no top.)

Lesson 16 Summary

To find the surface area of a three-dimensional figure whose faces are made up of polygons, we can find the area of each face, and add them up!

Sometimes there are ways to simplify our work. For example, all the faces of a cube with side length s are the same. We can find the area of one face, and multiply by 6. Since the area of one face of a cube is s^2, the surface area of a cube is $6s^2$.

We can use this technique to make it faster to find the surface area of any figure that has faces that are the same.

For prisms, there is another way. We can treat the prism as having three parts: two identical bases, and one long rectangle that has been taped along the edges of the bases. The rectangle has the same height as the prism, and its width is the perimeter of the base. To find the surface area, add the area of this rectangle to the areas of the two bases.

When working with prisms, sometimes we need to find the volume and sometimes we need to find the surface area.

Here are some examples of quantities related to volume:

- How much water a container can hold

- How much material it took to build a solid object

Volume is measured in cubic units, like in^3 or m^3.

Here are some examples of quantities related to surface area:

- How much fabric is needed to cover a surface

- How much of an object needs to be painted

Surface area is measured in square units, like in^2 or m^2.

Glossary

- surface area

Lesson 16 Practice Problems

1. Edge lengths are given in units. Find the surface area of each prism in square units.

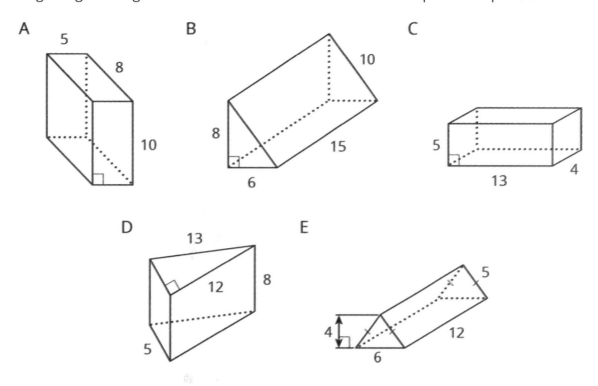

2. Here is the base of a prism.

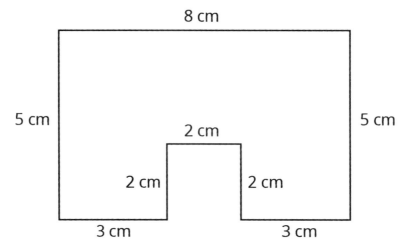

a. If the height of the prism is 5 cm, what is its surface area? What is its volume?

b. If the height of the prism is 10 cm, what is its surface area? What is its volume?

c. When the height doubled, what was the percent increase for the surface area? For the volume?

3. Select **all** the situations where knowing the volume of an object would be more useful than knowing its surface area.

   A. Determining the amount of paint needed to paint a barn.

   B. Determining the monetary value of a piece of gold jewelry.

   C. Filling an aquarium with buckets of water.

   D. Deciding how much wrapping paper a gift will need.

   E. Packing a box with watermelons for shipping.

   F. Charging a company for ad space on your race car.

   G. Measuring the amount of gasoline left in the tank of a tractor.

iM KH

4. Priya says, "No matter which way you slice this rectangular prism, the cross section will be a rectangle." Mai says, "I'm not so sure." Describe a slice that Mai might be thinking of.

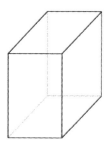

(From Unit 6, Lesson 11.)

5. B is the intersection of line AC and line ED. Find the measure of each of the angles.

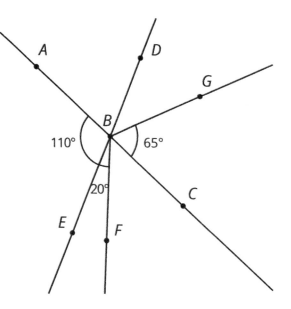

   a. Angle ABF

   b. Angle ABD

   c. Angle EBC

   d. Angle FBC

   e. Angle DBG

(From Unit 3, Lesson 13.)

6. Write each expression with fewer terms.

   a. $12m - 4m$

   b. $12m - 5k + m$

   c. $9m + k - (3m - 2k)$

(From Unit 4, Lesson 9.)

Lesson 17: Applying Volume and Surface Area

Let's explore things that are proportional to volume or surface area.

17.1: You Decide

For each situation, decide if it requires Noah to calculate surface area or volume. Explain your reasoning.

1. Noah is planning to paint the bird house he built. He is unsure if he has enough paint.

2. Noah is planning to use a box with a trapezoid base to hold modeling clay. He is unsure if the clay will all fit in the box.

17.2: Foam Play Structure

At a daycare, Kiran sees children climbing on this foam play structure.

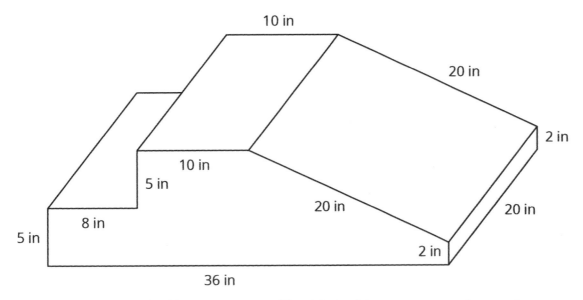

Kiran is thinking about building a structure like this for his younger cousins to play on.

1. The entire structure is made out of soft foam so the children don't hurt themselves. How much foam would Kiran need to build this play structure?

2. The entire structure is covered with vinyl so it is easy to wipe clean. How much vinyl would Kiran need to build this play structure?

3. The foam costs 0.8¢ per in^3. Here is a table that lists the costs for different amounts of vinyl. What is the total cost for all the foam and vinyl needed to build this play structure?

vinyl (in^2)	cost ($)
75	0.45
125	0.75

Are you ready for more?

When he examines the play structure more closely, Kiran realizes it is really two separate pieces that are next to each other.

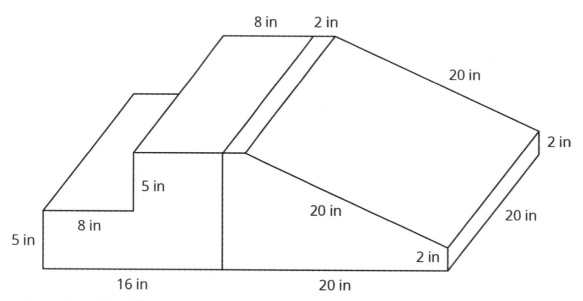

1. How does this affect the amount of foam in the play structure?

2. How does this affect the amount of vinyl covering the play structure?

iM KH

17.3: Filling the Sandbox

The daycare has two sandboxes that are both prisms with regular hexagons as their bases. The smaller sandbox has a base area of 1,146 in^2 and is filled 10 inches deep with sand.

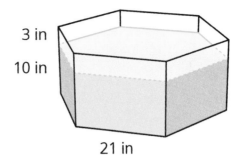

3 in
10 in
21 in

1. It took 14 bags of sand to fill the small sandbox to this depth. What volume of sand comes in one bag? (Round to the nearest whole cubic inch.)

2. The daycare manager wants to add 3 more inches to the depth of the sand in the small sandbox. How many bags of sand will they need to buy?

3. The daycare manager also wants to add 3 more inches to the depth of the sand in the large sandbox. The base of the large sandbox is a scaled copy of the base of the small sandbox, with a scale factor of 1.5. How many bags of sand will they need to buy for the large sandbox?

4. A lawn and garden store is selling 6 bags of sand for $19.50. How much will they spend to buy all the new sand for both sandboxes?

Lesson 17 Summary

Suppose we wanted to make a concrete bench like the one shown in this picture. If we know that the finished bench has a volume of 10 ft^3 and a surface area of 44 ft^2 we can use this information to solve problems about the bench.

For example,

- How much does the bench weigh?

- How long does it take to wipe the whole bench clean?

- How much will the materials cost to build the bench and to paint it?

To figure out how much the bench weighs, we can use its volume, 10 ft^3. Concrete weighs about 150 pounds per cubic foot, so this bench weighs about 1,500 pounds, because $10 \cdot 150 = 1,500$.

To figure out how long it takes to wipe the bench clean, we can use its surface area, 44 ft^2. If it takes a person about 2 seconds per square foot to wipe a surface clean, then it would take about 88 seconds to clean this bench, because $44 \cdot 2 = 88$. It may take a little less than 88 seconds, since the surfaces where the bench is touching the ground do not need to be wiped.

Would you use the volume or the surface area of the bench to calculate the cost of the concrete needed to build this bench? And for the cost of the paint?

iM KH

Lesson 17 Practice Problems

1. A landscape architect is designing a pool that has this top view:

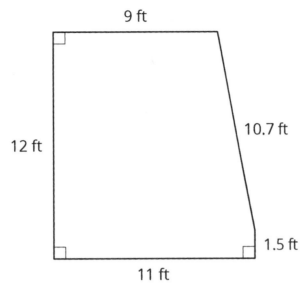

a. How much water will be needed to fill this pool 4 feet deep?

b. Before filling up the pool, it gets lined with a plastic liner. How much liner is needed for this pool?

c. Here are the prices for different amounts of plastic liner. How much will all the plastic liner for the pool cost?

plastic liner (ft^2)	cost ($)
25	3.75
50	7.50
75	11.25

2. Shade in a base of the trapezoidal prism. (The base is not the same as the bottom.)

    a. Find the area of the base you shaded.

    b. Find the volume of this trapezoidal prism.

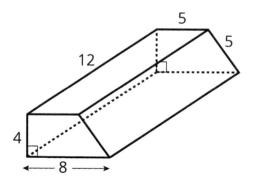

(From Unit 6, Lesson 15.)

3. Han draws a triangle with a 50° angle, a 40° angle, and a side of length 4 cm as shown. Can you draw a different triangle with the same conditions?

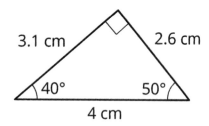

(From Unit 1, Lesson 17.)

iM KH

Lesson 18: The Volume and Dimensions of a Cylinder

Let's explore cylinder volumes and dimensions.

18.1: A Circle's Dimensions

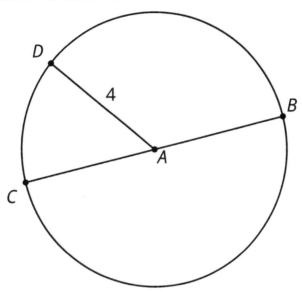

Here is a circle. Points A, B, C, and D are drawn, as well as Segments AD and BC.

1. What is the area of the circle, in square units? Select all that apply.

    a. 4π

    b. $\pi 8$

    c. 16π

    d. $\pi 4^2$

    e. approximately 25

    f. approximately 50

2. If the area of a circle is 49π square units, what is its radius? Explain your reasoning.

18.2: Circular Volumes

What is the volume of each figure, in cubic units? Even if you aren't sure, make a reasonable guess.

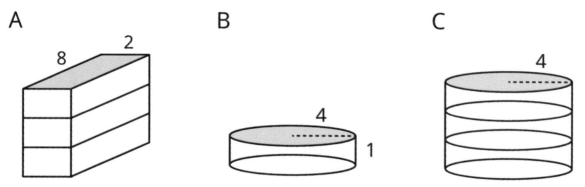

A   B   C

1. Figure A: A rectangular prism whose base has an area of 16 square units and whose height is 3 units.

2. Figure B: A cylinder whose base has an area of 16π square units and whose height is 1 unit.

3. Figure C: A cylinder whose base has an area of 16π square units and whose height is 3 units.

Are you ready for more?

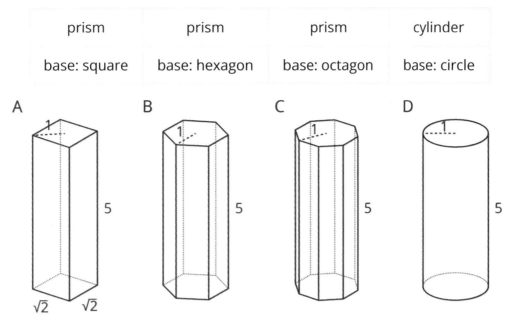

prism	prism	prism	cylinder
base: square	base: hexagon	base: octagon	base: circle

Here are solids that are related by a common measurement. In each of these solids, the distance from the center of the base to the furthest edge of the base is 1 unit, and the height of the solid is 5 units. Use 3.14 as an approximation for π to solve these problems.

1. Find the area of the square base and the circular base.

2. Use these areas to compute the volumes of the rectangular prism and the cylinder. How do they compare?

3. Without doing any calculations, list the figures from smallest to largest by volume. Use the images and your knowledge of polygons to explain your reasoning.

4. The area of the hexagon is approximately 2.6 square units, and the area of the octagon is approximately 2.83 square units. Use these areas to compute the volumes of the prisms with the hexagon and octagon bases. How does this match your explanation to the previous question?

18.3: What's the Dimension?

The volume V of a cylinder with radius r is given by the formula $V = \pi r^2 h$.

1. The volume of this cylinder with radius 5 units is 50π cubic units. This statement is true: $50\pi = 5^2 \pi h$

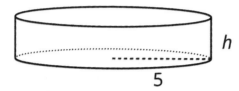

What does the height of this cylinder have to be? Explain how you know.

2. The volume of this cylinder with height 4 units is 36π cubic units. This statement is true: $36\pi = r^2 \pi 4$

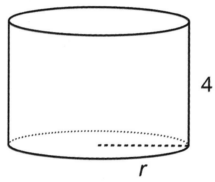

What does the radius of this cylinder have to be? Explain how you know.

Are you ready for more?

Suppose a cylinder has a volume of 36π cubic inches, but it is not the same cylinder as the one you found earlier in this activity.

1. What are some possibilities for the dimensions of the cylinder?

2. How many different cylinders can you find that have a volume of 36π cubic inches?

iM KH

18.4: Cylinders with Unknown Dimensions

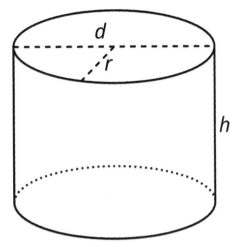

Each row of the table has information about a particular cylinder. Complete the table with the missing dimensions.

diameter (units)	radius (units)	area of the base (square units)	height (units)	volume (cubic units)
	3		5	
12				108π
			11	99π
8				16π
			100	16π
	10			20π
20				314
			b	$\pi \cdot b \cdot a^2$

Lesson 18 Summary

We can find the volume of a cylinder with radius r and height h using two ideas we've seen before:

- The volume of a rectangular prism is a result of multiplying the area of its base by its height.

- The base of the cylinder is a circle with radius r, so the base area is πr^2.

Remember that π is the number we get when we divide the circumference of any circle by its diameter. The value of π is approximately 3.14.

Just like a rectangular prism, the volume of a cylinder is the area of the base times the height. For example, take a cylinder whose radius is 2 cm and whose height is 5 cm.

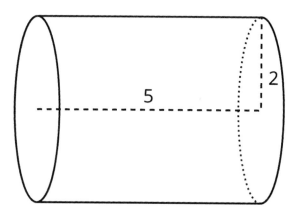

The base has an area of 4π cm^2 (since $\pi \cdot 2^2 = 4\pi$), so the volume is 20π cm^3 (since $4\pi \cdot 5 = 20\pi$). Using 3.14 as an approximation for π, we can say that the volume of the cylinder is approximately 62.8 cm^3.

In general, the base of a cylinder with radius r units has area πr^2 square units. If the height is h units, then the volume V in cubic units is

$$V = \pi r^2 h$$

It is also true that if we know the volume and one dimension (either radius or height), we can find the other dimension.

For example, imagine a cylinder that has a volume of 500π cm^3 and a radius of 5 cm, but the height is unknown. From the volume formula we know that

$$500\pi = \pi \cdot 25 \cdot h$$

must be true. Looking at the structure of the equation, we can see that $500 = 25h$. That means that the height has to be 20 cm, since $500 \div 25 = 20$.

Now imagine another cylinder that also has a volume of 500π cm^3 with an unknown radius and a height of 5 cm. Then we know that

$$500\pi = \pi \cdot r^2 \cdot 5$$

must be true. Looking at the structure of this equation, we can see that $r^2 = 100$. So the radius must be 10 cm.

Lesson 18 Practice Problems

1. ○ Sketch a cylinder.

   ○ Label its radius 3 and its height 10.

   ○ Shade in one of its bases.

2. At a farm, animals are fed bales of hay and buckets of grain. Each bale of hay is in the shape a rectangular prism. The base has side lengths 2 feet and 3 feet, and the height is 5 feet. Each bucket of grain is a cylinder with a diameter of 3 feet. The height of the bucket is 5 feet, the same as the height of the bale.

   a. Which is larger in area, the rectangular base of the bale or the circular base of the bucket? Explain how you know.

   b. Which is larger in volume, the bale or the bucket? Explain how you know.

3. Match each set of information about a circle with the area of that circle.

   A. Circle A has a radius of 4 units.   1. 4π square units

   B. Circle B has a radius of 10 units.   2. approximately 314 square units

   C. Circle C has a diameter of 16 units.   3. 64π square units

   D. Circle D has a circumference of 4π 4. 16π square units
      units.

iM KH

4. Complete the table with all of the missing information about three different cylinders.

diameter of base (units)	area of base (square units)	height (units)	volume (cubic units)
4		10	
6			63π
	25π	6	

5. A cylinder has volume 45π and radius 3. What is its height?

6. Three cylinders have a volume of 2826 cm^3. Cylinder A has a height of 900 cm. Cylinder B has a height of 225 cm. Cylinder C has a height of 100 cm. Find the radius of each cylinder. Use 3.14 as an approximation for π.

Lesson 19: The Volume of a Cone

Let's explore cones and their volumes.

19.1: Which Has a Larger Volume?

The cone and cylinder have the same height, and the radii of their bases are equal.

1. Which figure has a larger volume?

2. Do you think the volume of the smaller one is more or less than $\frac{1}{2}$ the volume of the larger one? Explain your reasoning.

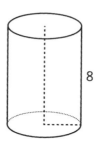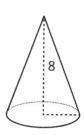

3. Sketch two different sized cones. The oval doesn't have to be on the bottom! For each drawing, label the cone's radius with r and height with h.

Here is a method for quickly sketching a cone:

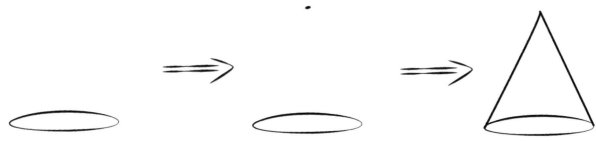

- Draw an oval.

- Draw a point centered above the oval.

- Connect the edges of the oval to the point.

- Which parts of your drawing would be hidden behind the object? Make these parts dashed lines.

19.2: From Cylinders to Cones

A cone and cylinder have the same height and their bases are congruent circles.

1. If the volume of the cylinder is 90 cm^3, what is the volume of the cone?

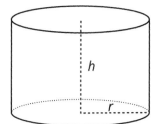 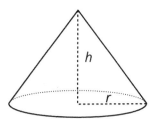

2. If the volume of the cone is 120 cm^3, what is the volume of the cylinder?

3. If the volume of the cylinder is $V = \pi r^2 h$, what is the volume of the cone? Either write an expression for the cone or explain the relationship in words.

19.3: Calculate That Cone

1. Here is a cylinder and cone that have the same height and the same base area. What is the volume of each figure? Express your answers in terms of π.

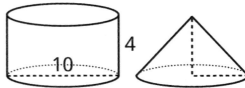

2. Here is a cone.
    a. What is the area of the base? Express your answer in terms of π.

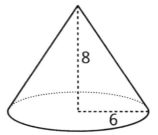

    b. What is the volume of the cone? Express your answer in terms of π.

3. A cone-shaped popcorn cup has a radius of 5 centimeters and a height of 9 centimeters. How many cubic centimeters of popcorn can the cup hold? Use 3.14 as an approximation for π, and give a numerical answer.

iM KH

Are you ready for more?

A grain silo has a cone shaped spout on the bottom in order to regulate the flow of grain out of the silo. The diameter of the silo is 8 feet. The height of the cylindrical part of the silo above the cone spout is 12 feet while the height of the entire silo is 16 feet.

How many cubic feet of grain are held in the cone spout of the silo? How many cubic feet of grain can the entire silo hold?

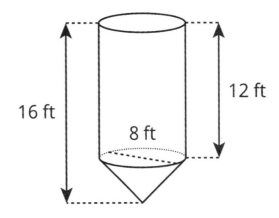

Lesson 19 Summary

If a cone and a cylinder have the same base and the same height, then the volume of the cone is $\frac{1}{3}$ of the volume of the cylinder. For example, the cylinder and cone shown here both have a base with radius 3 feet and a height of 7 feet.

The cylinder has a volume of 63π cubic feet since $\pi \cdot 3^2 \cdot 7 = 63\pi$. The cone has a volume that is $\frac{1}{3}$ of that, or 21π cubic feet.

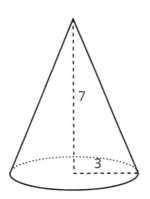
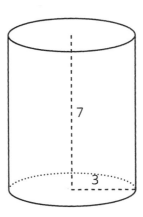

If the radius for both is r and the height for both is h, then the volume of the cylinder is $\pi r^2 h$. That means that the volume, V, of the cone is

$$V = \frac{1}{3}\pi r^2 h$$

Lesson 19 Practice Problems

1. A cylinder and cone have the same height and radius. The height of each is 5 cm, and the radius is 2 cm. Calculate the volume of the cylinder and the cone.

2. The volume of this cone is 36π cubic units.

   What is the volume of a cylinder that has the same base area and the same height?

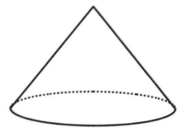

3. A cylinder has a diameter of 6 cm and a volume of 36π cm^3.

   a. Sketch the cylinder.

   b. Find its height and radius in centimeters.

   c. Label your sketch with the cylinder's height and radius.

   (From Unit 6, Lesson 18.)

iM KH

4. Lin wants to get some custom T-shirts printed for her basketball team. Shirts cost $10 each if you order 10 or fewer shirts and $9 each if you order 11 or more shirts.

   a. Make a graph that shows the total cost of buying shirts, for 0 through 15 shirts.

   b. There are 10 people on the team. Do they save money if they buy an extra shirt? Explain your reasoning.

   c. What is the slope of the graph between 0 and 10? What does it mean in the story?

   d. What is the slope of the graph between 11 and 15? What does it mean in the story?

   (From Unit 6, Lesson 10.)

5. In the following graphs, the horizontal axis represents time and the vertical axis represents distance from school. Write a possible story for each graph.

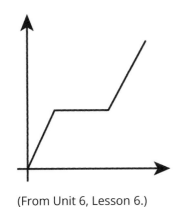 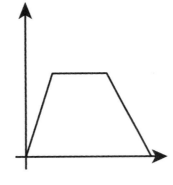 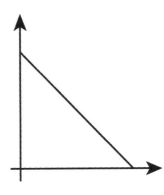

   (From Unit 6, Lesson 6.)

Lesson 20: Finding Cone Dimensions

Let's figure out the dimensions of cones.

20.1: Number Talk: Thirds

For each equation, decide what value, if any, would make it true.

$27 = \frac{1}{3}h$

$27 = \frac{1}{3}r^2$

$12\pi = \frac{1}{3}\pi a$

$12\pi = \frac{1}{3}\pi b^2$

20.2: An Unknown Radius

The volume V of a cone with radius r is given by the formula $V = \frac{1}{3}\pi r^2 h$.

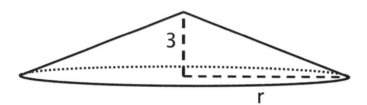

The volume of this cone with height 3 units and radius r is $V = 64\pi$ cubic units. This statement is true:

$$64\pi = \frac{1}{3}\pi r^2 \cdot 3$$

What does the radius of this cone have to be? Explain how you know.

iM KH

20.3: Cones with Unknown Dimensions

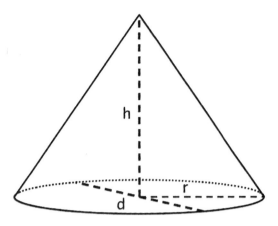

Each row of the table has some information about a particular cone. Complete the table with the missing dimensions.

diameter (units)	radius (units)	area of the base (square units)	height (units)	volume of cone (cubic units)
	4		3	
	$\frac{1}{3}$		6	
		144π	$\frac{1}{4}$	
20				200π
			12	64π
			3	3.14

Are you ready for more?

A *frustum* is the result of taking a cone and slicing off a smaller cone using a cut parallel to the base.

Find a formula for the volume of a frustum, including deciding which quantities you are going to include in your formula.

20.4: Popcorn Deals

A movie theater offers two containers:

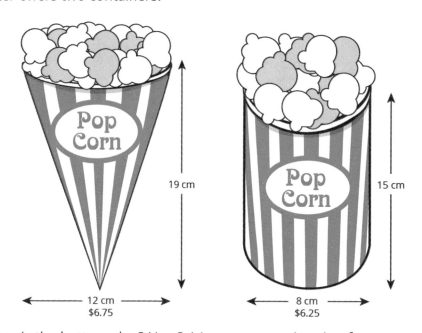

Which container is the better value? Use 3.14 as an approximation for π.

iM KH

Lesson 20 Summary

As we saw with cylinders, the volume V of a cone depends on the radius r of the base and the height h:

$$V = \frac{1}{3}\pi r^2 h$$

If we know the radius and height, we can find the volume. If we know the volume and one of the dimensions (either radius or height), we can find the other dimension.

For example, imagine a cone with a volume of 64π cm^3, a height of 3 cm, and an unknown radius r. From the volume formula, we know that

$$64\pi = \frac{1}{3}\pi r^2 \cdot 3$$

Looking at the structure of the equation, we can see that $r^2 = 64$, so the radius must be 8 cm.

Now imagine a different cone with a volume of 18π cm^3, a radius of 3 cm, and an unknown height h. Using the formula for the volume of the cone, we know that

$$18\pi = \frac{1}{3}\pi 3^2 h$$

so the height must be 6 cm. Can you see why?

Lesson 20 Practice Problems

1. The volume of this cylinder is 175π cubic units.

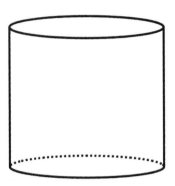

   What is the volume of a cone that has the same base area and the same height?

   (From Unit 6, Lesson 19.)

2. A cone has volume 12π cubic inches. Its height is 4 inches. What is its radius?

3. A cone has volume 3π.

   a. If the cone's radius is 1, what is its height?

   b. If the cone's radius is 2, what is its height?

   c. If the cone's radius is 5, what is its height?

   d. If the cone's radius is $\frac{1}{2}$, what is its height?

   e. If the cone's radius in r, then what is the height?

iM KH

4. Three cylinders have a height of 8 cm. Cylinder 1 has a radius of 1 cm. Cylinder 2 has a radius of 2 cm. Cylinder 3 has a radius of 3 cm. Find the volume of each cylinder.

(From Unit 6, Lesson 18.)

5. A gas company's delivery truck has a cylindrical tank that is 14 feet in diameter and 40 feet long.

    a. Sketch the tank, and mark the radius and the height.

    b. How much gas can fit in the tank?

(From Unit 6, Lesson 18.)

6. Three people are playing near the water. Person A stands on the dock. Person B starts at the top of a pole and ziplines into the water, then climbs out of the water. Person C climbs out of the water and up the zipline pole. Match the people to the graphs where the horizontal axis represents time in seconds and the vertical axis represents height above the water level in feet.

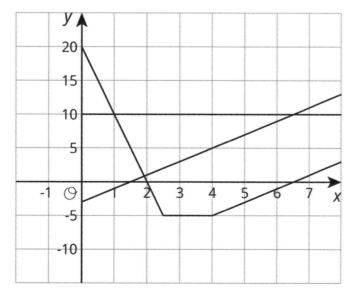

(From Unit 6, Lesson 6.)

7. A room is 15 feet tall. An architect wants to include a window that is 6 feet tall. The distance between the floor and the bottom of the window is b feet. The distance between the ceiling and the top of the window is a feet. This relationship can be described by the equation

$$a = 15 - (b + 6)$$

a. Which variable is independent based on the equation given?

b. If the architect wants b to be 3, what does this mean? What value of a would work with the given value for b?

c. The customer wants the window to have 5 feet of space above it. Is the customer describing a or b? What is the value of the other variable?

(From Unit 6, Lesson 3.)

8. Select **all** of the given points in the coordinate plane that lie on the graph of the linear equation $4x - y = 3$.

A. $(-1, -7)$

B. $(0, 3)$

C. $(\frac{3}{4}, 0)$

D. $(1, 1)$

E. $(2, 5)$

F. $(4, -1)$

(From Unit 5, Lesson 10.)

iM KH

Lesson 21: Scaling One Dimension

Let's see how changing one dimension changes the volume of a shape.

21.1: Driving the Distance

Here is a graph of the amount of gas burned during a trip by a tractor-trailer truck as it drives at a constant speed down a highway:

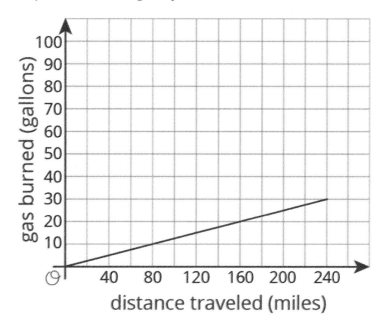

1. At the end of the trip, how far did the truck drive, and how much gas did it use?

2. If a truck traveled half this distance at the same rate, how much gas would it use?

3. If a truck traveled double this distance at the same rate, how much gas would it use?

4. Complete the sentence: _____ is a function of _____.

21.2: Double the Edge

There are many right rectangular prisms with one edge of length 5 units and another edge of length 3 units. Let s represent the length of the third edge and V represent the volume of these prisms.

1. Write an equation that represents the relationship between V and s.

2. Graph this equation and label the axes.

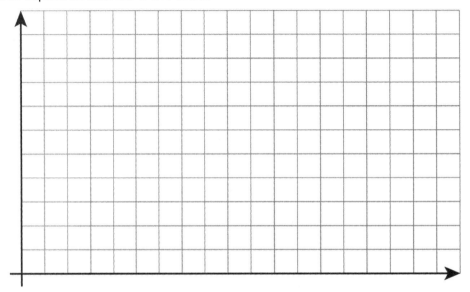

3. What happens to the volume if you double the edge length s? Where do you see this in the graph? Where do you see it algebraically?

21.3: Halve the Height

There are many cylinders with radius 5 units. Let h represent the height and V represent the volume of these cylinders.

1. Write an equation that represents the relationship between V and h. Use 3.14 as an approximation of π.

2. Graph this equation and label the axes.

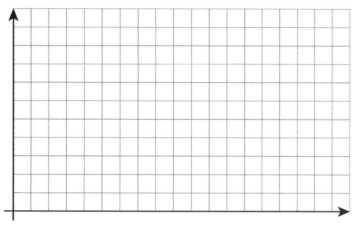

3. What happens to the volume if you halve the height, h? Where can you see this in the graph? How can you see it algebraically?

Are you ready for more?

Suppose we have a rectangular prism with dimensions 2 units by 3 units by 6 units, and we would like to make a rectangular prism of volume 216 cubic units by stretching *one* of the three dimensions.

- What are the three ways of doing this? Of these, which gives the prism with the smallest surface area?

- Repeat this process for a starting rectangular prism with dimensions 2 units by 6 units by 6 units.

- Can you give some general tips to someone who wants to make a box with a certain volume, but wants to save cost on material by having as small a surface area as possible?

21.4: Figuring Out Cone Dimensions

Here is a graph of the relationship between the height and the volume of some cones that all have the same radius:

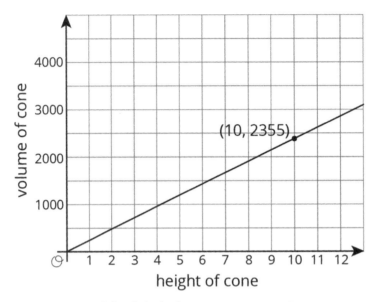

1. What do the coordinates of the labeled point represent?

2. What is the volume of the cone with height 5? With height 30?

3. Use the labeled point to find the radius of these cones. Use 3.14 as an approximation for π.

4. Write an equation that relates the volume V and height h.

iM KH

Lesson 21 Summary

Imagine a cylinder with a radius of 5 cm that is being filled with water. As the height of the water increases, the volume of water increases.

We say that the volume of the water in the cylinder, V, depends on the height of the water h. We can represent this relationship with an equation: $V = \pi \cdot 5^2 h$ or just

$$V = 25\pi h$$

This equation represents a *proportional relationship* between the height and the volume. We can use this equation to understand how the volume changes when the height is tripled.

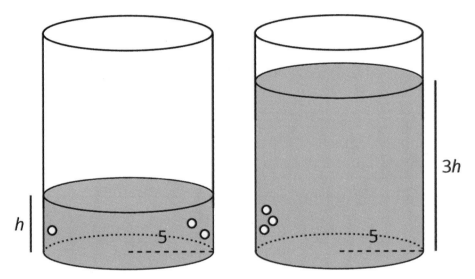

The new volume would be $V = 25\pi(3h) = 75\pi h$, which is precisely 3 times as much as the old volume of $25\pi h$. In general, when one quantity in a proportional relationship changes by a given factor, the other quantity changes by the same factor.

Remember that proportional relationships are examples of linear relationships, which can also be thought of as functions. So in this example V, the volume of water in the cylinder, is a function of the height h of the water.

Lesson 21 Practice Problems

1. A cylinder has a volume of 48π cm^3 and height h. Complete this table for volume of cylinders with the same radius but different heights.

height (cm)	volume (cm^3)
h	48π
$2h$	
$5h$	
$\frac{h}{2}$	
$\frac{h}{5}$	

2. A cylinder has a radius of 3 cm and a height of 5 cm.

   a. What is the volume of the cylinder?

   b. What is the volume of the cylinder when its height is tripled?

   c. What is the volume of the cylinder when its height is halved?

3. A graduated cylinder that is 24 cm tall can hold 1 L of water. What is the radius of the cylinder? What is the height of the 500 ml mark? The 250 ml mark? Recall that 1 liter (L) is equal to 1000 milliliters (ml), and that 1 liter (L) is equal to 1,000 cm^3.

4. An ice cream shop offers two ice cream cones. The waffle cone holds 12 ounces and is 5 inches tall. The sugar cone also holds 12 ounces and is 8 inches tall. Which cone has a larger radius?

(From Unit 6, Lesson 20.)

5. A 6 oz paper cup is shaped like a cone with a diameter of 4 inches. How many ounces of water will a plastic cylindrical cup with a diameter of 4 inches hold if it is the same height as the paper cup?

(From Unit 6, Lesson 19.)

6. Lin's smart phone was fully charged when she started school at 8:00 a.m. At 9:20 a.m., it was 90% charged, and at noon, it was 72% charged.

   a. When do you think her battery will die?

   b. Is battery life a function of time? If yes, is it a linear function? Explain your reasoning.

(From Unit 6, Lesson 9.)

Lesson 22: Scaling Two Dimensions

Let's change more dimensions of shapes.

22.1: Tripling Statements

m, n, a, b, and c all represent positive integers. Consider these two equations:

$$m = a + b + c$$
$$n = abc$$

1. Which of these statements are true? Select **all** that apply.
    a. If a is tripled, m is tripled.

    b. If a, b, and c are all tripled, then m is tripled.

    c. If a is tripled, n is tripled.

    d. If a, b, and c are all tripled, then n is tripled.

2. Create a true statement of your own about one of the equations.

22.2: A Square Base

Clare sketches a rectangular prism with a height of 11 and a square base and labels the edges of the base s. She asks Han what he thinks will happen to the volume of the rectangular prism if she triples s.

Han says the volume will be 9 times bigger. Is he right? Explain or show your reasoning.

Are you ready for more?

A cylinder can be constructed from a piece of paper by curling it so that you can glue together two opposite edges (the dashed edges in the figure).

1. If you wanted to increase the volume inside the resulting cylinder, would it make more sense to double x, y, or does it not matter?

2. If you wanted to increase the surface area of the resulting cylinder, would it make more sense to double x, y, or does it not matter?

3. How would your answers to these questions change if we made a cylinder by gluing together the solid lines instead of the dashed lines?

22.3: Playing with Cones

There are many cones with a height of 7 units. Let *r* represent the radius and *V* represent the volume of these cones.

1. Write an equation that expresses the relationship between *V* and *r*. Use 3.14 as an approximation for π.

2. Predict what happens to the volume if you triple the value of *r*.

3. Graph this equation.

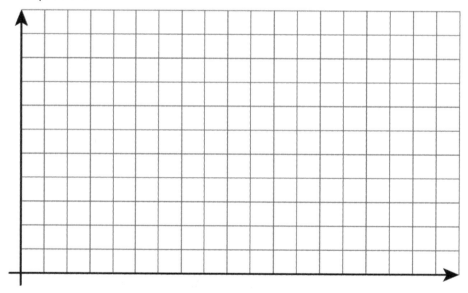

4. What happens to the volume if you triple *r*? Where do you see this in the graph? How can you see it algebraically?

Lesson 22 Summary

There are many rectangular prisms that have a length of 4 units and width of 5 units but differing heights. If h represents the height, then the volume V of such a prism is

$$V = 20h$$

The equation shows us that the volume of a prism with a base area of 20 square units is a linear function of the height. Because this is a proportional relationship, if the height gets multiplied by a factor of a, then the volume is also multiplied by a factor of a:

$$V = 20(ah)$$

What happens if we scale *two* dimensions of a prism by a factor of a? In this case, the volume gets multiplied by a factor of a twice, or a^2.

For example, think about a prism with a length of 4 units, width of 5 units, and height of 6 units. Its volume is 120 cubic units since $4 \cdot 5 \cdot 6 = 120$. Now imagine the length and width each get scaled by a factor of a, meaning the new prism has a length of $4a$, width of $5a$, and a height of 6. The new volume is $120a^2$ cubic units since $4a \cdot 5a \cdot 6 = 120a^2$.

A similar relationship holds for cylinders. Think of a cylinder with a height of 6 and a radius of 5. The volume would be 150π cubic units since $\pi \cdot 5^2 \cdot 6 = 150\pi$. Now, imagine the radius is scaled by a factor of a. Then the new volume is $\pi \cdot (5a)^2 \cdot 6 = \pi \cdot 25a^2 \cdot 6$ or $150a^2\pi$ cubic units. So scaling the radius by a factor of a has the effect of multiplying the volume by a^2!

Why does the volume multiply by a^2 when only the radius changes? This makes sense if we imagine how scaling the radius changes the base area of the cylinder. As the radius increases, the base area gets larger in two dimensions (the circle gets wider and also taller), while the third dimension of the cylinder, height, stays the same.

Lesson 22 Practice Problems

1. There are many cylinders with a height of 18 meters. Let r represent the radius in meters and V represent the volume in cubic meters.

   a. Write an equation that represents the volume V as a function of the radius r.

   b. Complete this table, giving three possible examples.

   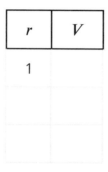

r	V
1	

   c. If the radius of a cylinder is doubled, does the volume double? Explain how you know.

   d. Is the graph of this function a line? Explain how you know.

2. As part of a competition, Diego must spin around in a circle 6 times and then run to a tree. The time he spends on each spin is represented by s and the time he spends running is r. He gets to the tree 21 seconds after he starts spinning.

   a. Write an equation showing the relationship between s and r.

   b. Rearrange the equation so that it shows r as a function of s.

   c. If it takes Diego 1.2 seconds to spin around each time, how many seconds did he spend running?

   (From Unit 6, Lesson 3.)

iM KH

3. The table and graph represent two functions. Use the table and graph to answer the questions.

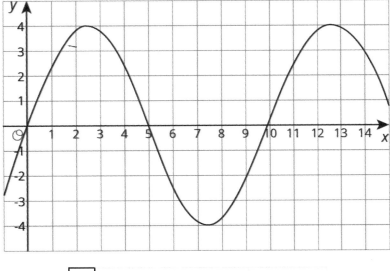

x	1	2	3	4	5	6
y	3	-1	0	4	5	-1

a. For which values of x is the output from the table less than the output from the graph?

b. In the graphed function, which values of x give an output of 0?

(From Unit 6, Lesson 7.)

4. A cone has a radius of 3 units and a height of 4 units.

a. What is this volume of this cone?

b. Another cone has quadruple the radius, and the same height. How many times larger is the new cone's volume?

Lesson 23: Estimating a Hemisphere

Let's estimate volume of hemispheres with figures we know.

23.1: Notice and Wonder: Two Shapes

Here are two shapes.

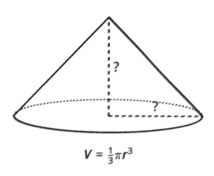 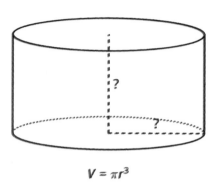

$$V = \frac{1}{3}\pi r^3$$

$$V = \pi r^3$$

What do you notice? What do you wonder?

23.2: Hemispheres in Boxes

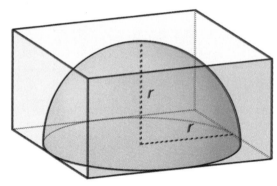

1. Mai has a dome paperweight that she can use as a magnifier. The paperweight is shaped like a hemisphere made of solid glass, so she wants to design a box to keep it in so it won't get broken. Her paperweight has a radius of 3 cm.

    a. What should the dimensions of the inside of box be so the box is as small as possible?

    b. What is the volume of the box?

    c. What is a reasonable estimate for the volume of the paperweight?

2. Tyler has a different box with side lengths that are twice as long as the sides of Mai's box. Tyler's box is just large enough to hold a different glass paperweight.

    a. What is the volume of the new box?

    b. What is a reasonable estimate for the volume of this glass paperweight?

    c. How many times bigger do you think the volume of the paperweight in this box is than the volume of Mai's paperweight? Explain your thinking.

23.3: Estimating Hemispheres

1. A hemisphere with radius 5 units fits snugly into a cylinder of the same radius and height.

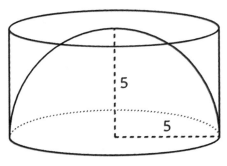

    a. Calculate the volume of the cylinder.

    b. Estimate the volume of the hemisphere. Explain your reasoning.

2. A cone fits snugly inside a hemisphere, and they share a radius of 5.

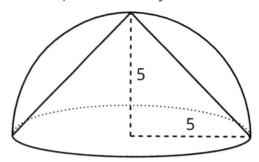

    a. What is the volume of the cone?

    b. Estimate the volume of the hemisphere. Explain your reasoning.

3. Compare your estimate for the hemisphere with the cone inside to your estimate of the hemisphere inside the cylinder. How do they compare to the volumes of the cylinder and the cone?

Are you ready for more?

Estimate what fraction of the volume of the cube is occupied by the pyramid that shares the base and a top vertex with the cube, as in the figure.

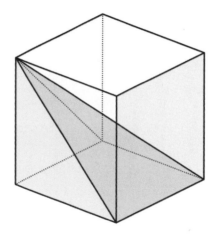

iM KH

Lesson 23 Summary

We can estimate the volume of a hemisphere by comparing it to other shapes for which we know the volume. For example, a hemisphere of radius 1 unit fits inside a cylinder with a radius of 1 unit and height of 1 unit.

Since the hemisphere is *inside* the cylinder, it must have a smaller volume than the cylinder making the cylinder's volume a reasonable over-estimate for the volume of the hemisphere.

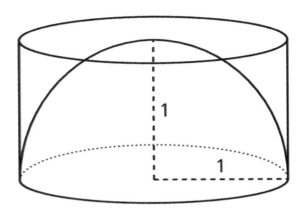

The volume of this particular cylinder is about 3.14 units^3 since $\pi(1)^2(1) = \pi$, so we know the volume of the hemisphere is less than 3.14 cubic units.

Using similar logic, a cone of radius 1 unit and height 1 unit fits inside of the hemisphere of radius 1 unit.

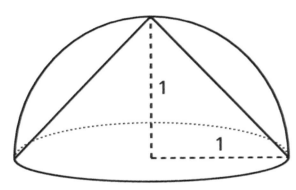

Since the cone is *inside* the hemisphere, the cone must have a smaller volume than the hemisphere making the cone's volume a reasonable under-estimate for the volume of the hemisphere.

The volume of this particular cone is about 1.05 units^3 since $\frac{1}{3}\pi(1)^2(1) = \frac{1}{3}\pi \approx 1.05$, so we know the volume of the hemisphere is more than 1.05 cubic units.

Averaging the volumes of the cylinder and the cone, we can estimate the volume of the hemisphere to be about 2.10 units^3 since $\frac{3.14+1.05}{2} \approx 2.10$. And, since a hemisphere is half of a sphere, we can also estimate that a sphere with radius of 1 would be double this volume, or about 4.20 units^3.

Lesson 23 Practice Problems

1. A baseball fits snugly inside a transparent display cube. The length of an edge of the cube is 2.9 inches.

   Is the baseball's volume greater than, less than, or equal to 2.9^3 cubic inches? Explain how you know.

2. There are many possible cones with a height of 18 meters. Let r represent the radius in meters and V represent the volume in cubic meters.

   a. Write an equation that represents the volume V as a function of the radius r.

   b. Complete this table for the function, giving three possible examples.

   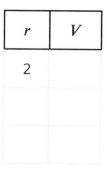

r	V
2	

   c. If you double the radius of a cone, does the volume double? Explain how you know.

   d. Is the graph of this function a line? Explain how you know.

(From Unit 6, Lesson 22.)

iM KH

3. A hemisphere fits snugly inside a cylinder with a radius of 6 cm. A cone fits snugly inside the same hemisphere.

   a. What is the volume of the cylinder?

   b. What is the volume of the cone?

   c. Estimate the volume of the hemisphere by calculating the average of the volumes of the cylinder and cone.

4. a. Find the hemisphere's diameter if its radius is 6 cm.

   b. Find the hemisphere's diameter if its radius is $\frac{1000}{3}$ m.

   c. Find the hemisphere's diameter if its radius is 9.008 ft.

   d. Find the hemisphere's radius if its diameter is 6 cm.

   e. Find the hemisphere's radius if its diameter is $\frac{1000}{3}$ m.

   f. Find the hemisphere's radius if its diameter is 9.008 ft.

5. After almost running out of space on her phone, Elena checks with a couple of friends who have the same phone to see how many pictures they have on their phones and how much memory they take up. The results are shown in the table.

number of photos	2,523	3,148	1,875
memory used in MB	8,072	10,106	6,037

a. Could this information be reasonably modeled with a linear function? Explain your reasoning.

b. Elena needs to delete photos to create 1,200 MB of space. Estimate the number of photos should she delete.

(From Unit 6, Lesson 9.)

6. Clare was solving an equation, but when she checked her answer she saw her solution was incorrect. She knows she made a mistake, but she can't find it. Where is Clare's mistake and what is the solution to the equation?

$$12(5 + 2y) = 4y - (5 - 9y)$$
$$72 + 24y = 4y - 5 - 9y$$
$$72 + 24y = \text{-}5y - 5$$
$$24y = \text{-}5y - 77$$
$$29y = \text{-}77$$
$$y = \frac{\text{-}77}{29}$$

(From Unit 4, Lesson 13.)

iM KH

Lesson 24: The Volume of a Sphere

Let's explore spheres and their volumes.

24.1: Sketch a Sphere

Here is a method for quickly sketching a sphere:

- Draw a circle.

- Draw an oval in the middle whose edges touch the sphere.

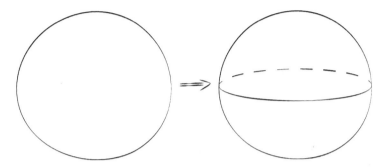

1. Practice sketching some spheres. Sketch a few different sizes.

2. For each sketch, draw a radius and label it *r*.

24.2: A Sphere in a Cylinder

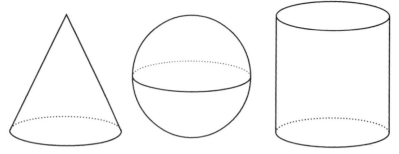

Here are a cone, a sphere, and a cylinder that all have the same radii and heights. The radius of the cylinder is 5 units. When necessary, express all answers in terms of π.

1. What is the height of the cylinder?

2. What is the volume of the cylinder?

3. What is the volume of the cone?

4. What is the volume of the sphere? Explain your reasoning.

24.3: Spheres in Cylinders

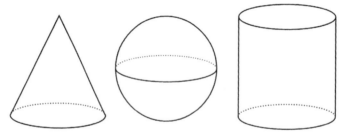

Here are a cone, a sphere, and a cylinder that all have the same radii and heights. Let the radius of the cylinder be r units. When necessary, express answers in terms of π.

1. What is the height of the cylinder in terms of r?

2. What is the volume of the cylinder in terms of r?

3. What is the volume of the cone in terms of r?

4. What is the volume of the sphere in terms of r?

5. A volume of the cone is $\frac{1}{3}$ the volume of a cylinder. The volume of the sphere is what fraction of the volume of the cylinder?

iM KH

Lesson 24 Summary

Think about a sphere with radius r units that fits snugly inside a cylinder. The cylinder must then also have a radius of r units and a height of $2r$ units. Using what we have learned about volume, the cylinder has a volume of $\pi r^2 h = \pi r^2 \cdot (2r)$, which is equal to $2\pi r^3$ cubic units.

We know from an earlier lesson that the volume of a cone with the same base and height as a cylinder has $\frac{1}{3}$ of the volume. In this example, such a cone has a volume of $\frac{1}{3} \cdot \pi r^2 \cdot 2r$ or just $\frac{2}{3}\pi r^3$ cubic units.

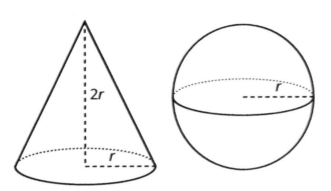 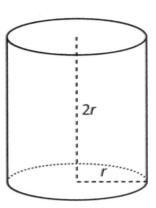

If we filled the cone and sphere with water, and then poured that water into the cylinder, the cylinder would be completely filled. That means the volume of the sphere and the volume of the cone add up to the volume of the cylinder. In other words, if V is the volume of the sphere, then

$$V + \frac{2}{3}\pi r^3 = 2\pi r^3$$

This leads to the formula for the volume of the sphere,

$$V = \frac{4}{3}\pi r^3$$

Lesson 24 Practice Problems

1. a. A cube's volume is 512 cubic units. What is the length of its edge?

   b. If a sphere fits snugly inside this cube, what is its volume?

   c. What fraction of the cube is taken up by the sphere? What percentage is this? Explain or show your reasoning.

2. Sphere A has radius 2 cm. Sphere B has radius 4 cm.

   a. Calculate the volume of each sphere.

   b. The radius of Sphere B is double that of Sphere A. How many times greater is the volume of B?

3. Three cones have a volume of 192π cm^3. Cone A has a radius of 2 cm. Cone B has a radius of 3 cm. Cone C has a radius of 4 cm. Find the height of each cone.

(From Unit 6, Lesson 20.)

iM KH

4. The graph represents the average price of regular gasoline in the United States in dollars as a function of the number of months after January 2014.

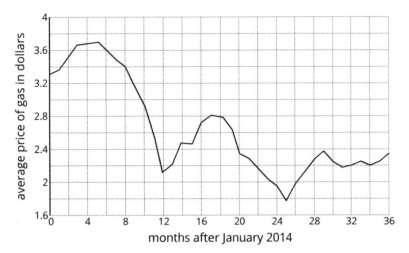

a. How many months after January 2014 was the price of gas the greatest?

b. Did the average price of gas ever get below $2?

c. Describe what happened to the average price of gas in 2014.

(From Unit 6, Lesson 5.)

5. Match the description of each sphere to its correct volume.

A. Sphere A: radius of 4 cm

B. Sphere B: diameter of 6 cm

C. Sphere C: radius of 8 cm

D. Sphere D: radius of 6 cm

1. 288π cm^3

2. $\frac{256}{3}\pi$ cm^3

3. 36π cm^3

4. $\frac{2048}{3}\pi$ cm3

6. While conducting an inventory in their bicycle shop, the owner noticed the number of bicycles is 2 fewer than 10 times the number of tricycles. They also know there are 410 wheels on all the bicycles and tricycles in the store. Write and solve a system of equations to find the number of bicycles in the store.

(From Unit 5, Lesson 16.)

Lesson 25: Cylinders, Cones, and Spheres

Let's find the volume of shapes.

25.1: Sphere Arguments

Four students each calculated the volume of a sphere with a radius of 9 centimeters and they got four different answers.

- Han thinks it is 108 cubic centimeters.

- Jada got 108π cubic centimeters.

- Tyler calculated 972 cubic centimeters.

- Mai says it is 972π cubic centimeters.

Do you agree with any of them? Explain your reasoning.

25.2: Sphere's Radius

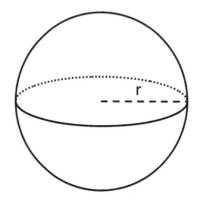

The volume of this sphere with radius r is $V = 288\pi$. This statement is true:

$$288\pi = \frac{4}{3}r^3\pi.$$

What is the value of r for this sphere? Explain how you know.

25.3: Info Gap: Unknown Dimensions

Your teacher will give you either a *problem card* or a *data card*. Do not show or read your card to your partner.

If your teacher gives you the *problem card*:

1. Silently read your card and think about what information you need to be able to answer the question.

2. Ask your partner for the specific information that you need.

3. Explain how you are using the information to solve the problem.

   Continue to ask questions until you have enough information to solve the problem.

4. Share the *problem card* and solve the problem independently.

5. Read the *data card* and discuss your reasoning.

If your teacher gives you the *data card*:

1. Silently read your card.

2. Ask your partner *"What specific information do you need?"* and wait for them to *ask* for information.

   If your partner asks for information that is not on the card, do not do the calculations for them. Tell them you don't have that information.

3. Before sharing the information, ask *"Why do you need that information?"* Listen to your partner's reasoning and ask clarifying questions.

4. Read the *problem card* and solve the problem independently.

5. Share the *data card* and discuss your reasoning.

Pause here so your teacher can review your work. Ask your teacher for a new set of cards and repeat the activity, trading roles with your partner.

25.4: The Right Fit

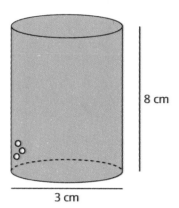

8 cm

3 cm

A cylinder with diameter 3 centimeters and height 8 centimeters is filled with water. Decide which figures described here, if any, could hold all of the water from the cylinder. Explain your reasoning.

1. Cone with a height of 8 centimeters and a radius of 3 centimeters.

2. Cylinder with a diameter of 6 centimeters and height of 2 centimeters.

3. Rectangular prism with a length of 3 centimeters, width of 4 centimeters, and height of 8 centimeters.

4. Sphere with a radius of 2 centimeters.

Are you ready for more?

A thirsty crow wants to raise the level of water in a cylindrical container so that it can reach the water with its beak.

- The container has diameter of 2 inches and a height of 9 inches.

- The water level is currently at 6 inches.

- The crow can reach the water if it is 1 inch from the top of the container.

In order to raise the water level, the crow puts spherical pebbles in the container. If the pebbles are approximately $\frac{1}{2}$ inch in diameter, what is the fewest number of pebbles the crow needs to drop into the container in order to reach the water?

Lesson 25 Summary

The formula

$$V = \frac{4}{3}\pi r^3$$

gives the volume of a sphere with radius r. We can use the formula to find the volume of a sphere with a known radius. For example, if the radius of a sphere is 6 units, then the volume would be

$$\frac{4}{3}\pi(6)^3 = 288\pi$$

or approximately 904 cubic units. We can also use the formula to find the radius of a sphere if we only know its volume. For example, if we know the volume of a sphere is 36π cubic units but we don't know the radius, then this equation is true:

$$36\pi = \frac{4}{3}\pi r^3$$

That means that $r^3 = 27$, so the radius r has to be 3 units in order for both sides of the equation to have the same value.

Many common objects, from water bottles to buildings to balloons, are similar in shape to rectangular prisms, cylinders, cones, and spheres—or even combinations of these shapes! Using the volume formulas for these shapes allows us to compare the volume of different types of objects, sometimes with surprising results.

For example, a cube-shaped box with side length 3 centimeters holds less than a sphere with radius 2 centimeters because the volume of the cube is 27 cubic centimeters ($3^3 = 27$), and the volume of the sphere is around 33.51 cubic centimeters ($\frac{4}{3}\pi \cdot 2^3 \approx 33.51$).

Lesson 25 Practice Problems

1. A scoop of ice cream has a 3-inch diameter. How tall should the ice cream cone of the same diameter be in order to contain all of the ice cream inside the cone?

2. Calculate the volume of the following shapes with the given information. For the first three questions, give each answer both in terms of π and by using 3.14 to approximate π. Make sure to include units.

   a. Sphere with a diameter of 6 inches

   b. Cylinder with a height of 6 inches and a diameter of 6 inches

   c. Cone with a height of 6 inches and a radius of 3 inches

   d. How are these three volumes related?

3. A coin-operated bouncy ball dispenser has a large glass sphere that holds many spherical balls. The large glass sphere has a radius of 9 inches. Each bouncy ball has radius of 1 inch and sits inside the dispenser.

   If there are 243 bouncy balls in the large glass sphere, what proportion of the large glass sphere's volume is taken up by bouncy balls? Explain how you know.

4. A farmer has a water tank for cows in the shape of a cylinder with radius of 7 ft and a height of 3 ft. The tank comes equipped with a sensor to alert the farmer to fill it up when the water falls to 20% capacity. What is the volume of the tank be when the sensor turns on?

   (From Unit 6, Lesson 18.)

Lesson 26: Building Prisms

Let's build a triangular prism from scratch.

26.1: Nets

Here are some nets for various prisms.

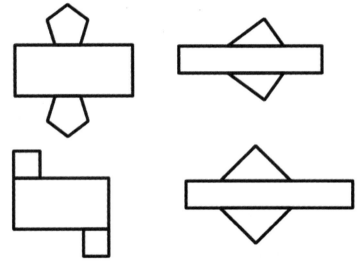

1. What would each net look like when folded?

2. What do you notice about the nets?

iM KH

26.2: Making the Base

The base of a triangular prism has one side that is 7 cm long, one side that is 5.5 cm long, and one angle that measures 45°.

 1. Draw as many different triangles as you can with these given measurements.

 2. Select one of the triangles you have drawn. Measure and calculate to approximate its area. Explain or show your reasoning.

26.3: Making the Prism

Your teacher will give you an incomplete net. Follow these instructions to complete the net and assemble the triangular prism:

1. Draw an identical copy of the triangle you selected in the previous activity along the top of the rectangle, with one vertex on point A.

2. Draw another copy of your triangle, flipped upside down, along the bottom of the rectangle, with one vertex on point C.

3. Determine how long the rectangle needs to be to wrap all the way around your triangular bases. Pause here so your teacher can review your work.

4. Cut out and assemble your net.

After you finish assembling your triangular prism, answer these questions. Explain or show your reasoning.

1. What is the volume of your prism?

2. What is the surface area of your prism?

3. Stand your prism up so it is sitting on its triangular base.

   a. If you were to cut your prism in half horizontally, what shape would the cross section be?

   b. If you were to cut your prism in half vertically, what shape would the cross section be?

26.4: Combining Prisms

1. Compare your prism with your partner's prism. What is the same? What is different?

2. Find a way you can put your prism and your partner's prism together to make one new, larger prism. Describe your new prism.

3. Draw the base of your new prism and label the lengths of the sides.

4. As you answer these questions about your new prism, look for ways you can use your calculations from the previous activity to help you. Explain or show your reasoning.

   a. What is the area of its base?

   b. What is its height?

   c. What is its volume?

   d. What is its surface area?

Are you ready for more?

How many identical copies of your prism would it take you to put together a new larger prism in which every dimension was twice as long?

Lesson 27: Volume As a Function of . . .

Let's compare water heights in different containers.

27.1: Missing Information?

A cylinder and sphere have the same height.

1. If the sphere has a volume of 36π cubic units, what is the height of the cylinder?

2. What is a possible volume for the cylinder? Be prepared to explain your reasoning.

27.2: Scaling Volume of a Sphere

1. Fill in the missing volumes in terms of π. Add two more radius and volume pairs of your choosing.

radius	1	2	3	$\frac{1}{2}$	$\frac{1}{3}$	100			r
volume	$\frac{4}{3}\pi$								

a. How does the volume of a sphere with radius 2 cm compare to the volume of a sphere with radius 1 cm?

b. How does the volume of a sphere with radius $\frac{1}{2}$ cm compare to the volume of a sphere with radius 1 cm?

2. A sphere has a radius of length r.
   a. What happens to the volume of this sphere if its radius is doubled?

   b. What happens to the volume of this sphere if its radius is halved?

3. Sphere Q has a volume of 500 cm^3. Sphere S has a radius $\frac{1}{5}$ as large as Sphere Q. What is the volume of Sphere S?

27.3: A Cylinder, a Cone, and a Sphere

Three containers of the same height were filled with water at the same rate. One container is a cylinder, one is a cone, and one is a sphere. As they were filled, the relationship between the volume of water and the height of the water was recorded in different ways, shown here:

- Cylinder: $h = \frac{V}{4\pi}$

- Cone:

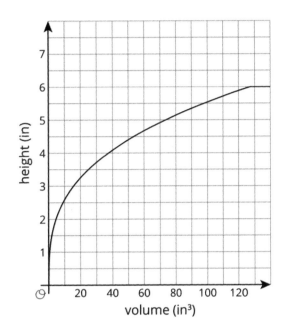

- Sphere:

volume (in³)	height (in)
0	0
8.38	1
29.32	2
56.55	3
83.76	4
104.72	5
113.04	6
120	6
200	6

1. The maximum volume of water the cylinder can hold is 24π. What is the radius of the cylinder?

2. Graph the relationship between the volume of water poured into the cylinder and the height of water in the cylinder on the same axes as the cone. What does the slope of this line represent?

iM KH

3. Which container can fit the largest volume of water? The smallest?

4. About how much water does it take for the cylinder and the sphere to have the same height? The cylinder and the cone? Explain how you know.

5. For what approximate range of volumes is the height of the water in the cylinder greater than the height of the water in the cone? Explain how you know.

6. For what approximate range of volumes is the height of the water in the sphere less than the height of the water in the cylinder? Explain how you know.

Learning Targets

Lesson 1: Inputs and Outputs

- I can write rules when I know input-output pairs.

- I know how an input-output diagram represents a rule.

Lesson 2: Introduction to Functions

- I know that a function is a rule with exactly one output for each allowable input.

- I know that if a rule has exactly one output for each allowable input, then the output depends on the input.

Lesson 3: Equations for Functions

- I can find the output of a function when I know the input.

- I can name the independent and dependent variables for a given function and represent the function with an equation.

Lesson 4: Tables, Equations, and Graphs of Functions

- I can identify graphs that do, and do not, represent functions.

- I can use a graph of a function to find the output for a given input and to find the input(s) for a given output.

Lesson 5: More Graphs of Functions

- I can explain the story told by the graph of a function.

Lesson 6: Even More Graphs of Functions

- I can draw the graph of a function that represents a real-world situation.

Lesson 7: Connecting Representations of Functions

- I can compare inputs and outputs of functions that are represented in different ways.

Lesson 8: Linear Functions

- I can determine whether a function is increasing or decreasing based on whether its rate of change is positive or negative.

- I can explain in my own words how the graph of a linear function relates to its rate of change and initial value.

Lesson 9: Linear Models

- I can decide when a linear function is a good model for data and when it is not.

- I can use data points to model a linear function.

Lesson 10: Piecewise Linear Functions

- I can create graphs of non-linear functions with pieces of linear functions.

Lesson 11: Slicing Solids

- I can explain that when a three dimensional figure is sliced it creates a face that is two dimensional.

- I can picture different cross sections of prisms and pyramids.

Lesson 12: Filling Containers

- I can collect data about a function and represent it as a graph.

- I can describe the graph of a function in words.

Lesson 13: How Much Will Fit?

- I know that volume is the amount of space contained inside a three-dimensional figure.

- I recognize the 3D shapes cylinder, cone, rectangular prism, and sphere.

Lesson 14: Volume of Right Prisms

- I can explain why the volume of a prism can be found by multiplying the area of the base and the height of the prism.

Lesson 15: Decomposing Bases for Area

- I can calculate the the volume of a prism with a complicated base by decomposing the base into quadrilaterals or triangles.

Lesson 16: Surface Area of Right Prisms

- I can find and use shortcuts when calculating the surface area of a prism.

- I can picture the net of a prism to help me calculate its surface area.

Lesson 17: Applying Volume and Surface Area

- I can solve problems involving the volume and surface area of children's play structures.

Lesson 18: The Volume and Dimensions of a Cylinder

- I can find missing information about a cylinder if I know its volume and some other information.

- I know the formula for volume of a cylinder.

Lesson 19: The Volume of a Cone

- I can find the volume of a cone in mathematical and real-world situations.

- I know the formula for the volume of a cone.

Lesson 20: Finding Cone Dimensions

- I can find missing information of about a cone if I know its volume and some other information.

Lesson 21: Scaling One Dimension

- I can create a graph the relationship between volume and height for all cylinders (or cones) with a fixed radius.

- I can explain in my own words why changing the height by a scale factor changes the volume by the same scale factor.

Lesson 22: Scaling Two Dimensions

- I can create a graph representing the relationship between volume and radius for all cylinders (or cones) with a fixed height.

- I can explain in my own words why changing the radius by a scale factor changes the volume by the scale factor squared.

Lesson 23: Estimating a Hemisphere

- I can estimate the volume of a hemisphere by calculating the volume of shape I know is larger and the volume of a shape I know is smaller.

Lesson 24: The Volume of a Sphere

- I can find the volume of a sphere when I know the radius.

Lesson 25: Cylinders, Cones, and Spheres

- I can find the radius of a sphere if I know its volume.

- I can solve mathematical and real-world problems about the volume of cylinders, cones, and spheres.

Lesson 26: Building Prisms

- I can build a triangular prism from scratch.

Lesson 27: Volume As a Function of . . .

- I can compare functions about volume represented in different ways.

Glossary

alternate interior angles

Interior angles are angles that are made by a transversal crossing two parallel lines. They are the angles that lie between the parallel lines, not outside them.

If two interior angles lie on opposite sides of the transversal they are called alternate interior angles.

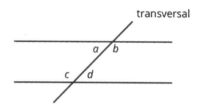

In the figure, *a* and *d* are alternate interior angles, and *b* and *c* are also alternate interior angles.

base (of a prism or pyramid)

The word *base* can also refer to a face of a polyhedron.

A prism has two identical bases that are parallel. A pyramid has one base.

A prism or pyramid is named for the shape of its base.

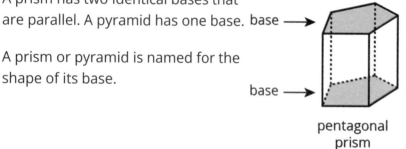

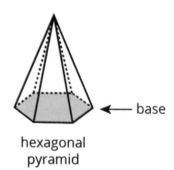

pentagonal prism   hexagonal pyramid

center of a dilation

The center of a dilation is a fixed point on a plane. It is the starting point from which we measure distances in a dilation.

In this diagram, point *P* is the center of the dilation.

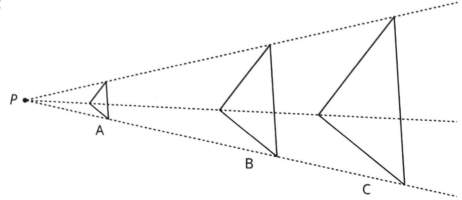

iM KH

clockwise

Clockwise means to turn in the same direction as the hands of a clock. The top turns to the right. This diagram shows Figure A turned clockwise to make Figure B.

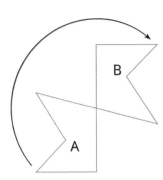

coefficient

A coefficient is a number that is multiplied by a variable.

For example, in the expression $3x + 5$, the coefficient of x is 3. In the expression $y + 5$, the coefficient of y is 1, because $y = 1 \cdot y$.

complementary

Complementary angles have measures that add up to 90 degrees.

For example, a $15°$ angle and a $75°$ angle are complementary.

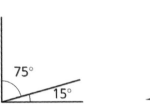 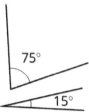

cone

A cone is a three-dimensional figure like a pyramid, but the base is a circle.

congruent

One figure is congruent to another if it can be moved with translations, rotations, and reflections to fit exactly over the other.

In the figure, Triangle A is congruent to Triangles B, C, and D. A translation takes Triangle A to Triangle B, a rotation takes Triangle B to Triangle C, and a reflection takes Triangle C to Triangle D.

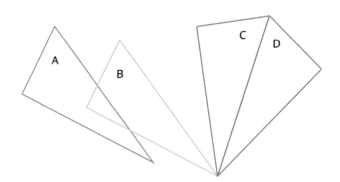

constant of proportionality

In a proportional relationship, the values for one quantity are each multiplied by the same number to get the values for the other quantity. This number is called the constant of proportionality.

In this example, the constant of proportionality is 3, because $2 \cdot 3 = 6$, $3 \cdot 3 = 9$, and $5 \cdot 3 = 15$. This means that there are 3 apples for every 1 orange in the fruit salad.

number of oranges	number of apples
2	6
3	9
5	15

constant term

In an expression like $5x + 2$, the number 2 is called the constant term because it doesn't change when x changes.

In the expression $7x + 9$, 9 is the constant term.
In the expression $5x + (-8)$, -8 is the constant term.
In the expression $12 - 4x$, 12 is the constant term.

iM KH

coordinate plane

The coordinate plane is a system for telling where points are. For example. point R is located at $(3, 2)$ on the coordinate plane, because it is three units to the right and two units up.

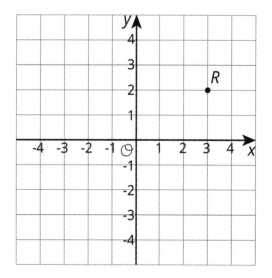

corresponding

When part of an original figure matches up with part of a copy, we call them corresponding parts. These could be points, segments, angles, or distances.

For example, point B in the first triangle corresponds to point E in the second triangle. Segment AC corresponds to segment DF.

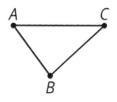
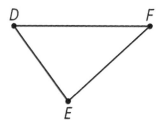

counterclockwise

Counterclockwise means to turn opposite of the way the hands of a clock turn. The top turns to the left.

This diagram shows Figure A turned counterclockwise to make Figure B.

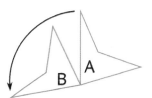

cross section

A cross section is the new face you see when you slice through a three-dimensional figure.

For example, if you slice a rectangular pyramid parallel to the base, you get a smaller rectangle as the cross section.

cylinder

A cylinder is a three-dimensional figure like a prism, but with bases that are circles.

dependent variable

A dependent variable represents the output of a function.

For example, suppose we need to buy 20 pieces of fruit and decide to buy apples and bananas. If we select the number of apples first, the equation $b = 20 - a$ shows the number of bananas we can buy. The number of bananas is the dependent variable because it depends on the number of apples.

dilation

A dilation with center O and positive scale factor r takes a point P along the line OP to another point whose distance is r times further away from O than P is. If $r < 1$ then the new point is really closer to O, not further away.

The triangle DEF is a dilation of the triangle ABC with center O and with scale factor 3. So D is 3 times further away from O than A is, E is 3 times further away from O than B is, and F is 3 times further away from O than C is.

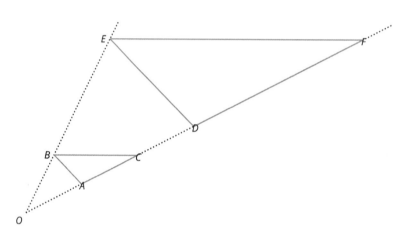

equivalent expressions

Equivalent expressions are always equal to each other. If the expressions have variables, they are equal whenever the same value is used for the variable in each expression.

For example, $3x + 4x$ is equivalent to $5x + 2x$. No matter what value we use for x, these expressions are always equal. When x is 3, both expressions equal 21. When x is 10, both expressions equal 70.

expand

To expand an expression, we use the distributive property to rewrite a product as a sum. The new expression is equivalent to the original expression.

For example, we can expand the expression $5(4x + 7)$ to get the equivalent expression $20x + 35$.

factor (an expression)

To factor an expression, we use the distributive property to rewrite a sum as a product. The new expression is equivalent to the original expression.

For example, we can factor the expression $20x + 35$ to get the equivalent expression $5(4x + 7)$.

function

A function is a rule that assigns exactly one output to each possible input.

The function $y = 6x + 4$ assigns one value of the output, y, to each value of the input, x. For example, when x is 5, then $y = 6(5) + 4$ or 34.

image

An image is the result of translations, rotations, and reflections on an object. Every part of the original object moves in the same way to match up with a part of the image.

In this diagram, triangle ABC has been translated up and to the right to make triangle DEF. Triangle DEF is the image of the original triangle ABC.

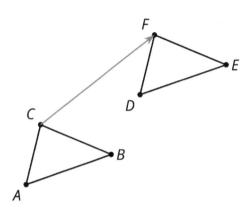

independent variable

An independent variable represents the input of a function.

For example, suppose we need to buy 20 pieces of fruit and decide to buy some apples and bananas. If we select the number of apples first, the equation $b = 20 - a$ shows the number of bananas we can buy. The number of apples is the independent variable because we can choose any number for it.

linear relationship

A linear relationship between two quantities means they are related like this: When one quantity changes by a certain amount, the other quantity always changes by a set amount. In a linear relationship, one quantity has a constant rate of change with respect to the other.

The relationship is called linear because its graph is a line.

The graph shows a relationship between number of days and number of pages read.

When the number of days increases by 2, the number of pages read always increases by 60. The rate of change is constant, 30 pages per day, so the relationship is linear.

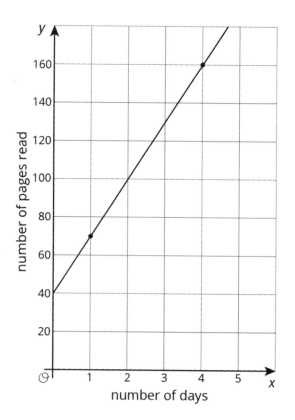

negative association

A negative association is a relationship between two quantities where one tends to decrease as the other increases. In a scatter plot, the data points tend to cluster around a line with negative slope.

Different stores across the country sell a book for different prices.

The scatter plot shows that there is a negative association between the the price of the book in dollars and the number of books sold at that price.

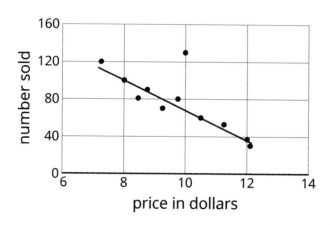

outlier

An outlier is a data value that is far from the other values in the data set.

iM KH

Here is a scatter plot that shows lengths and widths of 20 different left feet. The foot whose length is 24.5 cm and width is 7.8 cm is an outlier.

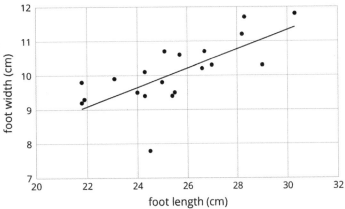

positive association

A positive association is a relationship between two quantities where one tends to increase as the other increases. In a scatter plot, the data points tend to cluster around a line with positive slope.

The relationship between height and weight for 25 dogs is shown in the scatter plot. There is a positive association between dog height and dog weight.

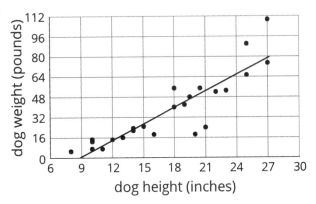

prism

A prism is a type of polyhedron that has two bases that are identical copies of each other. The bases are connected by rectangles or parallelograms.

Here are some drawings of prisms.

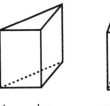
triangular
prism

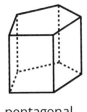
pentagonal
prism

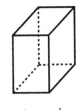
rectangular
prism

pyramid

A pyramid is a type of polyhedron that has one base. All the other faces are triangles, and they all meet at a single vertex.

Here are some drawings of pyramids.

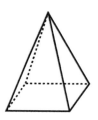 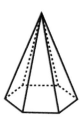 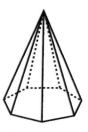

rectangular   hexagonal   heptagonal
pyramid   pyramid   pyramid

radius

A radius is a line segment that goes from the center to the edge of a circle. A radius can go in any direction. Every radius of the circle is the same length. We also use the word *radius* to mean the length of this segment.

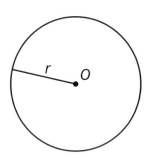

For example, r is the radius of this circle with center O.

rate of change

The rate of change in a linear relationship is the amount y changes when x increases by 1. The rate of change in a linear relationship is also the slope of its graph.

In this graph, y increases by 15 dollars when x increases by 1 hour. The rate of change is 15 dollars per hour.

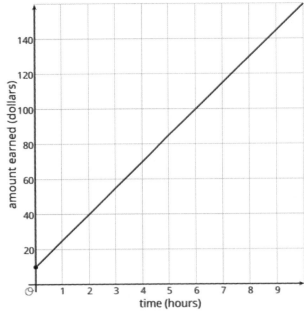

reflection

A reflection across a line moves every point on a figure to a point directly on the opposite side of the line. The new point is the same distance from the line as it was in the original figure.

This diagram shows a reflection of A over line ℓ that makes the mirror image B.

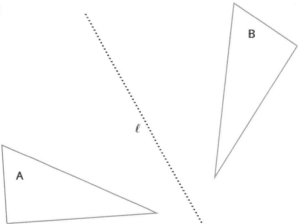

relative frequency

The relative frequency of a category tells us the proportion at which the category occurs in the data set. It is expressed as a fraction, a decimal, or a percentage of the total number.

For example, suppose there were 21 dogs in the park, some white, some brown, some black, and some multi-color. The table shows the frequency and the relative frequency of each color.

color	frequency	relative frequency
white	5	$\frac{5}{21}$
brown	7	$\frac{7}{21}$
black	3	$\frac{3}{21}$
multi-color	6	$\frac{6}{21}$

right angle

A right angle is half of a straight angle. It measures 90 degrees.

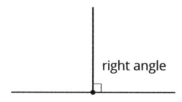

right angle

rigid transformation

A rigid transformation is a move that does not change any measurements of a figure. Translations, rotations, and reflections are rigid transformations, as is any sequence of these.

rotation

A rotation moves every point on a figure around a center by a given angle in a specific direction.

This diagram shows Triangle A rotated around center O by 55 degrees clockwise to get Triangle B.

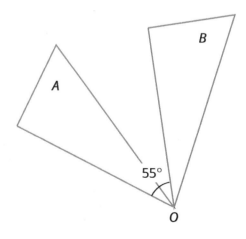

iM KH

scale

A scale tells how the measurements in a scale drawing represent the actual measurements of the object.

For example, the scale on this floor plan tells us that 1 inch on the drawing represents 8 feet in the actual room. This means that 2 inches would represent 16 feet, and $\frac{1}{2}$ inch would represent 4 feet.

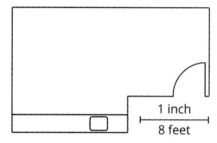

1 inch
8 feet

scale drawing

A scale drawing represents an actual place or object. All the measurements in the drawing correspond to the measurements of the actual object by the same scale.

scale factor

To create a scaled copy, we multiply all the lengths in the original figure by the same number. This number is called the scale factor.

In this example, the scale factor is 1.5, because $4 \cdot (1.5) = 6$, $5 \cdot (1.5) = 7.5$, and $6 \cdot (1.5) = 9$.

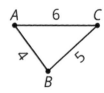
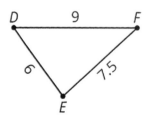

scaled copy

A scaled copy is a copy of a figure where every length in the original figure is multiplied by the same number.

For example, triangle DEF is a scaled copy of triangle ABC. Each side length on triangle ABC was multiplied by 1.5 to get the corresponding side length on triangle DEF.

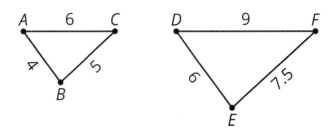

scatter plot

A scatter plot is a graph that shows the values of two variables on a coordinate plane. It allows us to investigate connections between the two variables.

Each plotted point corresponds to one dog. The coordinates of each point tell us the height and weight of that dog.

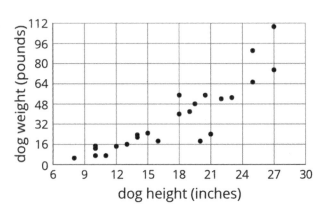

segmented bar graph

A segmented bar graph compares two categories within a data set. The whole bar represents all the data within one category. Then, each bar is separated into parts (segments) that show the percentage of each part in the second category.

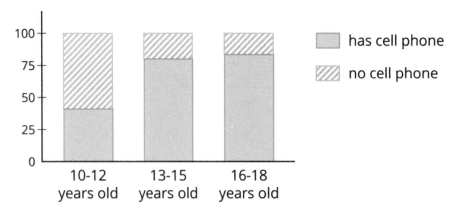

This segmented bar graph shows the percentage of people in different age groups that do and do not have a cell phone. For example, among people ages 10 to 12, about 40% have a cell phone and 60% do not have a cell phone.

sequence of transformations

A sequence of transformations is a set of translations, rotations, reflections, and dilations on a figure. The transformations are performed in a given order.

This diagram shows a sequence of transformations to move Figure A to Figure C.

First, A is translated to the right to make B. Next, B is reflected across line ℓ to make C.

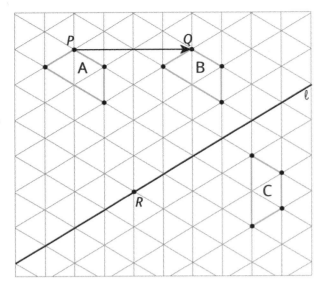

similar

Two figures are similar if one can fit exactly over the other after rigid transformations and dilations.

In this figure, triangle ABC is similar to triangle DEF.

If ABC is rotated around point B and then dilated with center point O, then it will fit exactly over DEF. This means that they are similar.

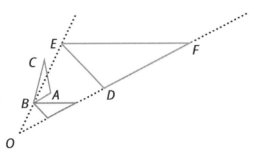

slope

The slope of a line is a number we can calculate using any two points on the line. To find the slope, divide the vertical distance between the points by the horizontal distance.

The slope of this line is 2 divided by 3 or $\frac{2}{3}$.

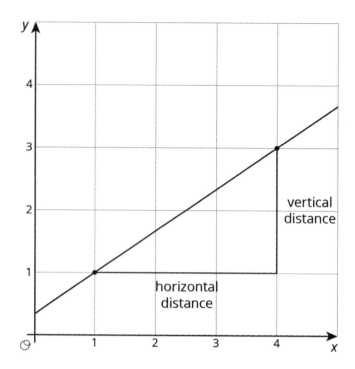

solution to an equation with two variables

A solution to an equation with two variables is a pair of values of the variables that make the equation true.

For example, one possible solution to the equation $4x + 3y = 24$ is $(6, 0)$. Substituting 6 for x and 0 for y makes this equation true because $4(6) + 3(0) = 24$.

solution to an inequality

A solution to an inequality is a number that can be used in place of the variable to make the inequality true.

For example, 5 is a solution to the inequality $c < 10$, because it is true that $5 < 10$. Some other solutions to this inequality are 9.9, 0, and -4.

sphere

A sphere is a three-dimensional figure in which all cross-sections in every direction are circles.

straight angle

A straight angle is an angle that forms a straight line. It measures 180 degrees.

straight angle

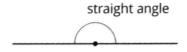

supplementary

Supplementary angles have measures that add up to 180 degrees.

For example, a 15° angle and a 165° angle are supplementary.

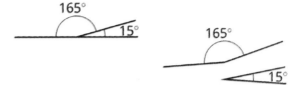

surface area

The surface area of a polyhedron is the number of square units that covers all the faces of the polyhedron, without any gaps or overlaps.

For example, if the faces of a cube each have an area of 9 cm^2, then the surface area of the cube is $6 \cdot 9$, or 54 cm^2.

system of equations

A system of equations is a set of two or more equations. Each equation contains two or more variables. We want to find values for the variables that make all the equations true.

These equations make up a system of equations:

$$\begin{cases} x + y = \text{-}2 \\ x - y = 12 \end{cases}$$

The solution to this system is $x = 5$ and $y = \text{-}7$ because when these values are substituted for x and y, each equation is true: $5 + (\text{-}7) = \text{-}2$ and $5 - (\text{-}7) = 12$.

term

A term is a part of an expression. It can be a single number, a variable, or a number and a variable that are multiplied together. For example, the expression $5x + 18$ has two terms. The first term is $5x$ and the second term is 18.

tessellation

A tessellation is a repeating pattern of one or more shapes. The sides of the shapes fit together perfectly and do not overlap. The pattern goes on forever in all directions.

This diagram shows part of a tessellation.

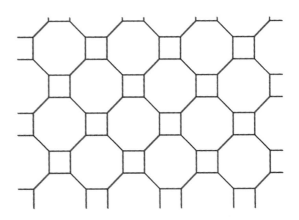

transformation

A transformation is a translation, rotation, reflection, or dilation, or a combination of these.

translation

A translation moves every point in a figure a given distance in a given direction.

This diagram shows a translation of Figure A to Figure B using the direction and distance given by the arrow.

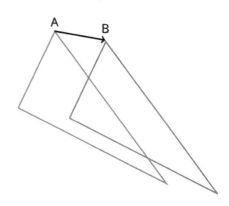

transversal

A transversal is a line that crosses parallel lines.

iM KH

This diagram shows a transversal line k intersecting parallel lines m and ℓ.

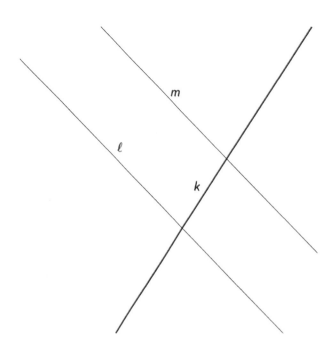

two-way table

A two-way table provides a way to compare two categorical variables.

It shows one of the variables across the top and the other down one side. Each entry in the table is the frequency or relative frequency of the category shown by the column and row headings.

A study investigates the connection between meditation and the state of mind of athletes before a track meet. This two-way table shows the results of the study.

	meditated	did not meditate	total
calm	45	8	53
agitated	23	21	44
total	68	29	97

vertex

A vertex is a point where two or more edges meet. When we have more than one vertex, we call them vertices.

The vertices in this polygon are labeled A, B, C, D, and E.

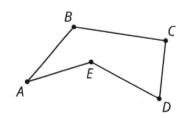

vertical angles

Vertical angles are opposite angles that share the same vertex. They are formed by a pair of intersecting lines. Their angle measures are equal.

For example, angles AEC and DEB are vertical angles. If angle AEC measures 120°, then angle DEB must also measure 120°.

Angles AED and BEC are another pair of vertical angles.

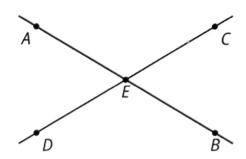

vertical intercept

The vertical intercept is the point where the graph of a line crosses the vertical axis.

The vertical intercept of this line is (0, -6) or just -6.

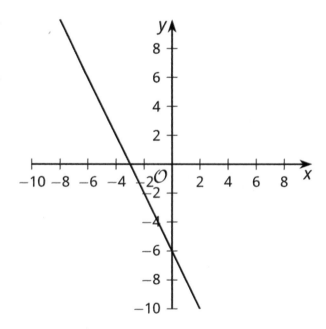

volume

Volume is the number of cubic units that fill a three-dimensional region, without any gaps or overlaps.

For example, the volume of this rectangular prism is 60 units^3, because it is composed of 3 layers that are each 20 units^3.

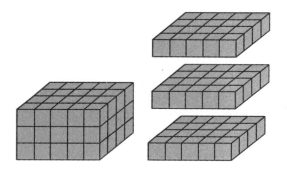

Attributions

"Notice and Wonder" and "I Notice/I Wonder" are trademarks of the National Council of Teachers of Mathematics, reflecting approaches developed by the Math Forum (http://www.nctm.org/mathforum/), and used here with permission.

Images that are not the original work of Illustrative Mathematics are in the public domain or released under a Creative Commons Attribution (CC-BY) license, and include an appropriate citation. Images that are the original work of Illustrative Mathematics do not include such a citation.

Image Attributions

"Giant Panda 2", by Sheila Lau (Own work) . Public Domain. Wikimedia Commons. https://commons.wikimedia.org/wiki/File:Giant_Panda_2.JPG.

By Couleur. Public Domain. Pixabay. https://pixabay.com/en/peacock-butterfly-butterfly-insect-1655724/.

By PublicDomainPictures. Public Domain. Pixabay. https://pixabay.com/en/scrapyard-recycling-dump-garbage-70908/.

By Shirley810. Public Domain. Pixabay. https://pixabay.com/en/recycling-bins-recycle-environment-373156/.

"football / soccer ball", by Tobbi. Public Domain. OpenClipArt. https://openclipart.org/detail/196123/football-soccer-ball.

"Concrete seats, Balfour Street pocket park", by Didiunsw (Own work). CC BY-SA 4.0. Wikimedia Commons. https://commons.wikimedia.org/wiki/File:Concrete_seats,_balfour_street_pocket_park.JPG.

Notes

Notes